INDEPENDENT AND UNOFFICIAL GUIDE

MINECRAFT EPIC BUILDS

W9-CBJ-068

SCHOLASTIC INC.

WELCOME

You don't need us to tell you that Minecraft is one of the best video games on the planet right now. We're guessing, too, that you don't need to be told that it's wonderful for coming up with brilliant, imaginative build projects.

Instead, in the pages of this jam-packed book, we're going to show you some of the amazing Minecraft builds out there. From incredible spaceships and *Frozen* castles, to vibrant cities, locations based on video games, and even a trip inside the TARDIS. We've included links to some of the projects and names of the people behind them if you want to seek out more details.

If you're anything like us, though, we bet you'll be inspired to tackle a build project or two of your own by the end of this book. As such, we've also got some tips on making your own epic builds!

Have fun!
We did!

Just one of the builds that awaits...

ADAMANTIS

8

31

IMPERIAL CITY

48

DOCTOR WHO

ORIGINAL BUILDS

REAL-WORLD BUILDS

MOVIES & TV SHOWS

VIDEO GAME BUILDS

TECHNICAL BUILDS

ADVENTURE MAP BUILDS

PIXEL ART

MAKING YOUR OWN EPIC BUILD

Inspired to try your own epic build? We finish off with some tips to help you do just that on page 132!

ORIGINAL BUILDS

ORIGINAL BUILDS

Often, the best Minecraft builds aren't based on a TV show or video game; they're simply the result of a player's creativity

ADAMANTIS

What a place to start! Sometimes, a build just takes your breath away, and this simply sublime creation from jamdelaney1 is a perfect example. This incredible creation took around three months to build using—wait for it—60 million blocks! Yes, that's 60,000,000! This immense city of the gods is an ornate and grand urban sprawl with heavy hints of Rome and Atlantis, and more than a sprinkling of fantasy. With its massive aqueducts, towering palaces, and stunning central dome, this is one of the most attractive cities you'll ever see in Mojang's sandbox world. You can download the map from *www.planetminecraft.com/project/the-city-of-adamantis*

So many columns! This is one build that requires immense dedication

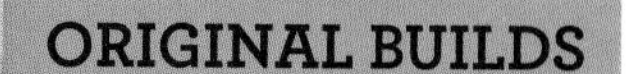

ADAMANTIS
CITY OF THE GODS

Surely one of the most complex builds we've ever seen—the city of Adamantis

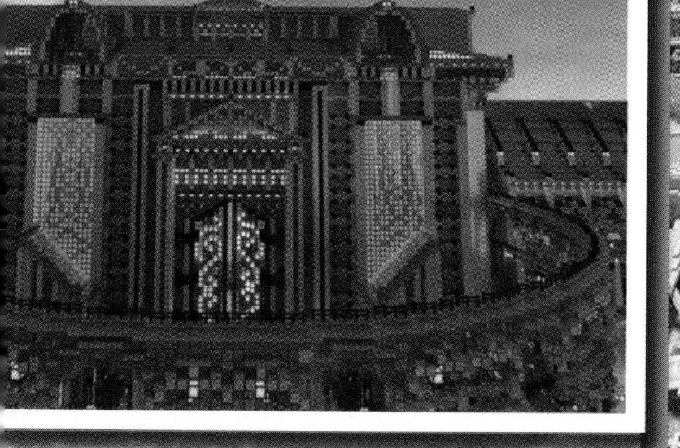

You'd usually see this kind of detail in prerendered scenes, not within the world of Minecraft

It's hard to know where to start when a build is as detailed as this

A wide shot showing just how impressive this build is

At night, the city takes on a whole different aesthetic

TOWER OF BABEL

Based on the biblical structure of the same name, this is a very impressive creation by user Hyta. The design is great on its own, being a cylindrical tower with simple, striking architecture topped by a glass dome, but it's the scale of the build that's the high point, if you'll forgive the pun. The tower is 100 floors high, consists of over seven million blocks, and has around 90,000 lights. Seen from a distance, such as in the isometric render here, it's a genuine wonder.

The tower is 100 floors high, consists of over seven million blocks, and has around 90,000 lights

Now that's what you call a tower, ready to be smote

It's so high that without mods you'll be unable to see all the way to the top

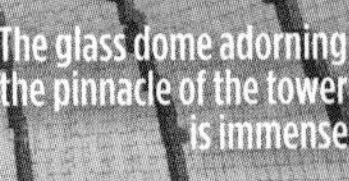

The glass dome adorning the pinnacle of the tower is immense

The topmost floors of the Tower of Babel

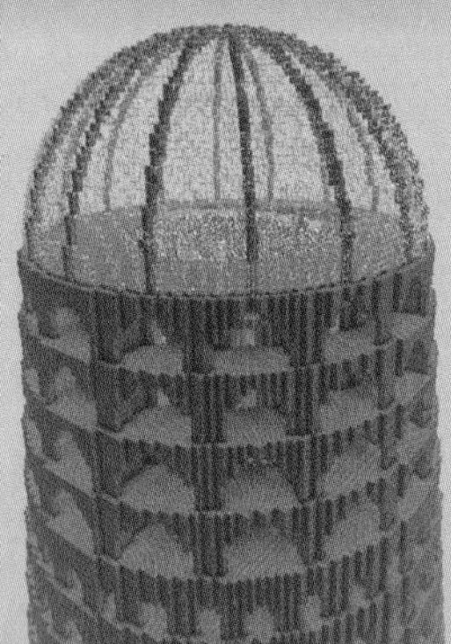

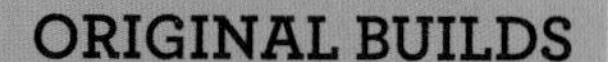

This city reproduces the height of a civilization

This build shows what you can do with simple structures and a limited color scheme

From above, you can see the whole layout in all its glory

Sandstone and wool are used to create this striking build

Find this one at www.tinyurl.com/EpicBuildsBabylonian

BABYLONIAN CITY

It's another city, this time based on Babylonian architecture, which means plenty of sandstone, columns, rivers, and palaces. The city is multilevel, with complex pathways and stairs winding their way through the sprawl, and the color scheme, although simple, makes the whole build pop. Compared to other builds, the structure here may be simple, but that's the point. The architecture is more straightforward, but it looks authentic and succeeds in reproducing the feel of the city's main influence in design.

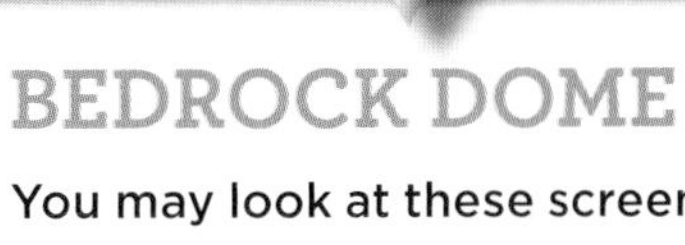

BEDROCK DOME

You may look at these screens and think, “Yeah, the glass dome looks good, but the whole thing isn’t exactly pretty.” You’d be right, but the amazing thing about this build is the fact that the two creators, Geef and JiFish, created this on their own, one block at a time, in Survival mode. The aim was to mine to the game’s lowest point (bedrock), to create a huge hole and top it off with a mammoth glass dome. This goal was achieved, and the result is something very impressive indeed. Nice work, guys. You can find out about the duo’s journey at *jifish.co.uk/jifish/fishcraft/bedrock/#completed*

The early mining in progress. That’s one big hole

Any player of Minecraft can appreciate just how much work went into the excavation, which was all done in Survival mode

Once the pit was excavated, an elaborate wooden staircase and scaffold were built

The dome eventually grew to encapsulate the entire pit

The final build, fully covered by the huge dome

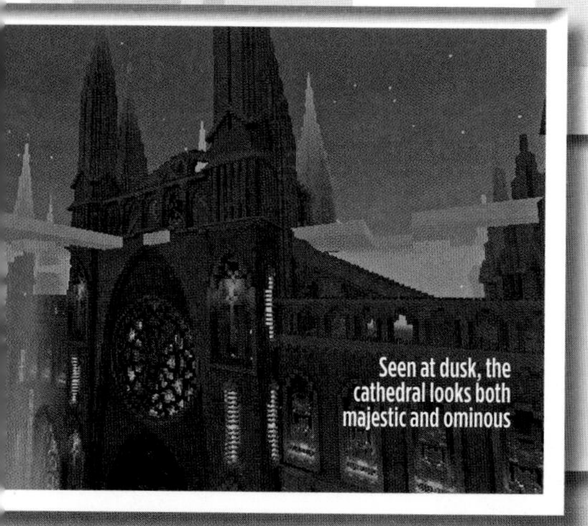
Seen at dusk, the cathedral looks both majestic and ominous

The massive structure is so tall that clouds even build up in the vaulted ceilings

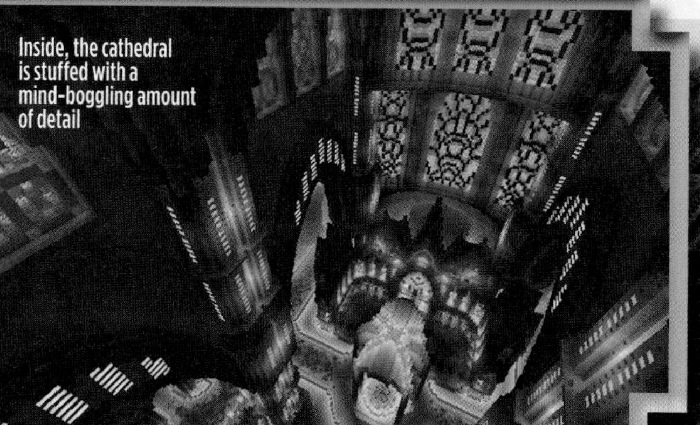
Inside, the cathedral is stuffed with a mind-boggling amount of detail

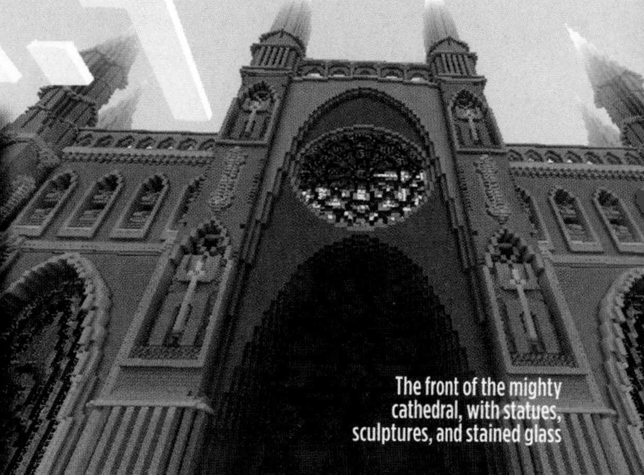
The front of the mighty cathedral, with statues, sculptures, and stained glass

The mosaics on the floor look great

CATHEDRAL

Built by user GNRfrancis, this is an absolutely stunning and enormous cathedral that consists of over two million blocks. The massive structure is so tall that clouds even build up in the vaulted ceilings. It has row after row of pews, confessional booths, altars, intricate floor designs, and architecture straight out of the Renaissance. You'll need to ramp up your draw distance, or even use third-party mods, to be able to render all of this behemoth at once. You can download the save file from *bit.ly/1GHYaqN*

CITY BUILDING PROJECT

The title of this build is pretty self-explanatory, being a project that's, uh, building a city. This is a city that's extremely realistic and, unlike a lot of builds, this attempt isn't a fantasy or historical creation, but one that's crafting a modern-day metropolis. The buildings aren't unlike any structures you'd find in a large real-world city, and it's got roads, traffic lights, pathways, and various interiors. There's even a large airport, complete with parked aircraft.

Roads, street lights, and realistic buildings are the order of the day here

The docks look like a cool place to relax

Find out more at www.projectcitybuild.com

A tribute to the Twin Towers

This isometric render shows how well the city has been designed

The mammoth stone structures of this dwarven city wouldn't be out of place in Middle-earth

A mega-build city that's packed with locations and a heap of intricate construction

So much work has gone into each and every building, and it clearly shows

Immense halls and Gothic/Nordic architecture dot the city

Find out more at www.tinyurl.com/EpicBuildsConsilium

DWARVEN CITY OF CONSILIUM

Built by Creolucis, this is a mega-build city that's packed with locations and a heap of intricate construction. The city is inspired by Nordic architecture, with a heavy dose of fantasy, like that seen in *The Lord of the Rings*, but it's a wholly original and unique place. The huge stone buildings, with some perched atop cliffs, make for a daunting citadel that could well be the home to a race of warrior dwarves bent on repelling any invaders to their kingdom.

THE GOLDEN CITY

An ongoing server build that's already moved servers due to biome changes, this is actually the second incarnation of this mega build, and it's fantastic. It's a sprawling, classic city that has all sorts of different areas, including a port, farms, upper and lower city districts, a university, and even ornate flying airships. The architecture is all uniform, so the city really does fit together as a believable place, and its complexity and top-notch design make it a build that's among the best server projects around. Just look at some of these screens.

The port to the city, with a ship dropping off its goods

The city is littered with great little touches, such as this Atlas statue

You can find the full project at www.tinyurl.com/EpicBuildsGoldenCity

There are some very detailed and impressive structures within the city

The architecture is all uniform, so the city fits together as a believable place

This giant wall separates the upper and lower districts

The layout isn't too crowded, allowing for greenery and a more realistic look

Influences from a wide variety of cultures make up the city

The flying airships look great

THE TEMPLE OF KREDIK SHAW

It's got an odd name, but this huge temple is nothing short of spectacular. The builder Lynchyinc took inspiration from the Hagia Sophia in Istanbul, and has created a fantasy temple that sits within a dense jungle. The towering spires are filled with intricate patterns and detail, and the temple has numerous glass domes, grand archways, and curious architectural elements. The interior is also impressive.

Huge archways lead to the main entrance to the temple

The greenery growing on the temple adds a really unique twist to the build

It's a secluded temple, surrounded by dense foliage

Find more at www.tinyurl.com/EpicBuildsKredikShaw

Lit up at night, the temple certainly looks divine

Many parts of New Port Notch resemble real places, such as the famous Flatiron Building

The whole city hangs together with a believable style and planning

The river between the two islands has multiple bridges

The city even has a TV studio

Find this project at www.tinyurl.com/EpicBuildsNewPortNotch

NEW PORT NOTCH

The team behind this mega build, headed up by ThatDutchLad, have crafted an entire city bearing the Minecraft creator's name, complete with its own subway system. Spanning Persson and Bergenlyn Isles (again, named after Notch and another Mojang developer, Jens Bergensten), the city has various districts. There are office buildings, diners, TV studios, a General Assembly, and a Seattle-style Space Needle. The whole city fits together with a believable style and planning, and it's a great map to explore.

NETHER CATHEDRAL

Most builds are built in Minecraft's Overworld, but this build by user UltramarineXIII is different. Obviously, as given away by the name, this mighty cathedral is built within the confines of Minecraft's nightmarish dimension of the Nether. It's a huge evil structure that goes above and beyond normal Nether fortresses, and looks like a powerful and nasty creature calls it home. It features a daunting entryway, and is surrounded by lava pools for that extra super-villain aesthetic.

You seriously need some diamond gear and some potions before even thinking of entering here

The classic ship-in-a-bottle ornament, only in blocky Minecraft form

SHIP IN A BOTTLE

The skilled art of making ships in bottles is one of those tricks that bemuses people, and it's also found its way into Minecraft. There are several examples, with this creation by stefarent008 among the best. The ship within the bottle is very detailed, complete with sails, flags, on-deck detail, and portholes. The ship sits on some water, also contained in the bottle, which is corked and perched on a mount. The bottle itself is well made out of glass blocks, and the whole thing looks authentic.

This ship is large inside, and has plenty of detail

STATELY CASTLE

Castles are a very, very popular structure with Minecraft users, and they come in all shapes and sizes, from classic medieval stone-walled forts to more elaborate fantasy-themed citadels. This example, from user TofoNoodles, is a unique part-mansion, part-castle that uses an asymmetric design and heavy fantasy influence to deliver a striking build. It uses fairly clean lines and design, but manages to produce a solid, attractive dwelling that any baron would wage war for.

Worlds collide in this walled mega City

Towers? Check. Grand doorways? Check. More bedrooms than are feasibly necessary? Double check

WALLED MEGA CITY

This circular walled city by user Rfextra is an ongoing project that began life as a small village, then grew outward, with each ring of the city adding to the size. The image you see here is around two weeks' worth of work, and the builder intends to keep expanding on it. The city is made up of a range of small, red-roofed buildings, with large walls dividing the various districts, much like TES: Oblivion's Imperial City. It also has Japanese-style pagoda towers, which rise above the rest of the city. Very nice.

REAL-WORLD BUILDS

REAL-WORLD BUILDS

Fictional and fantasy builds may be out of this world, but to create an amazing work of Minecraft art, you can stick closer to reality

APPLE STORE

A lot of great builds have featured on *minecraft.worth1000.com*, some of which we've featured on these very pages. The site pits creators against one another to create the best themed builds, often with interesting subjects. One example is an Apple Store, the best of which has to be this realistic recreation by Sofokal. Its clean lines, neutral tones, and simplicity perfectly mirror both the real-world stores and Apple's own design aesthetic.

A properly dressed sales member is on hand to help you peruse Apple's gadgets

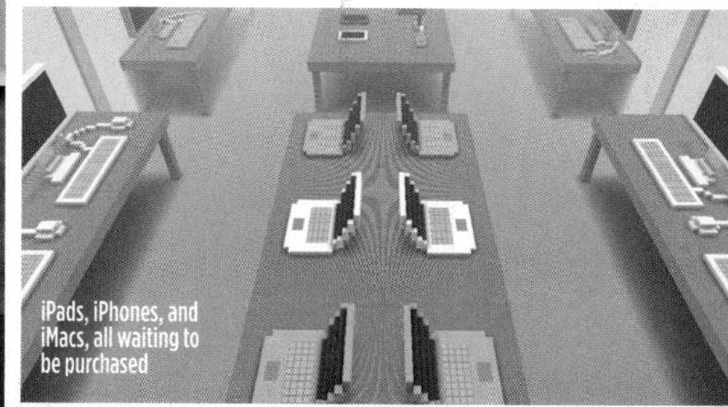

iPads, iPhones, and iMacs, all waiting to be purchased

A side view of the room

It's a huge build that bears an uncanny resemblance to the real thing

The detail on the PC and desk is great

It's a room with a view, at least in its digital form

And here's the desk for real

1:1 BEDROOM

Although this isn't exactly a famous location, this 1:1 replica of the creator's bedroom is nonetheless eye-catching, especially when it's compared to photos of the real thing. Creator CGMiller spent a long time applying meticulous detail to this recreation, right down to the trackball, keyboard, even cables of the PC, and shelves full of Minecraft statues. It's a huge build that bears an uncanny resemblance to the real thing. You can find out more and download the map at ***imgur.com/a/KzReq***

BUCKINGHAM PALACE

Alongside the Houses of Parliament, Buckingham Palace stands as another world-famous London sight and is the home of the queen and the rest of the royal family. The huge palace has been recreated in Minecraft by user bss1950, and it's a stunningly complex and realistic build featuring the entire palace, with a suitably plush interior. The entire grounds are modeled, right down to the entrance gates that many sightseers line up at to get that special photo opportunity.

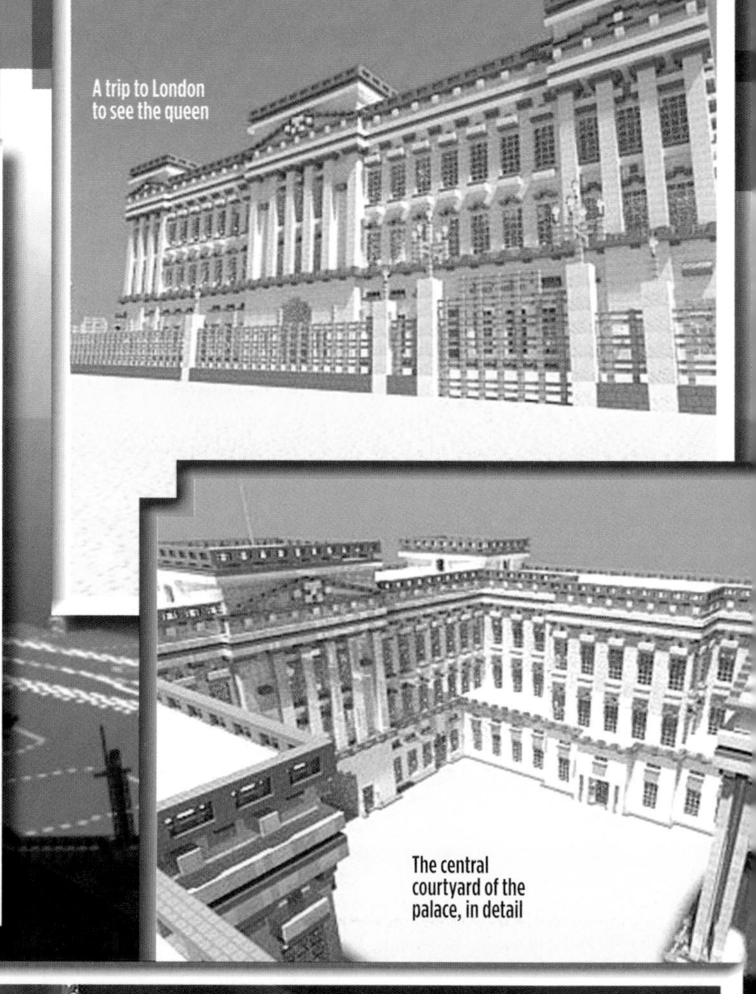

A trip to London to see the queen

The central courtyard of the palace, in detail

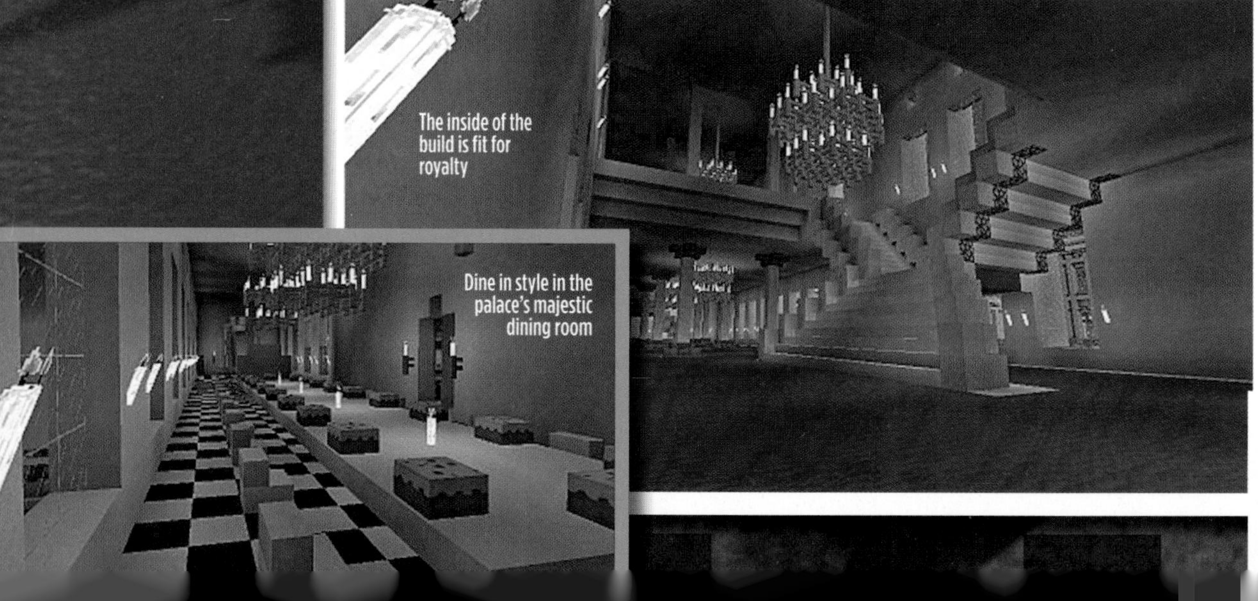

The inside of the build is fit for royalty

Dine in style in the palace's majestic dining room

BUND CENTER

The Bund Center is a striking office building in Shanghai, China, and this Minecraft version is so close to the real thing that you could be forgiven for mistaking the two if you don't take a longer look. The detail on the build is simply stunning, and user B35chty has put a ton of effort into replicating each and every window, column, and design featured on the skyscraper. There are even elaborate neighboring buildings and roads running next to it.

Seen side by side, the Bund Center in Minecraft is truly impressive

The famous home of Congress recreated in the world of Minecraft

Inside, the building is an elaborate and grand venue

CAPITOL BUILDING

Based upon the Capitol Building, also known as Capitol Hill and the United States Capitol, in Washington DC, this complex structure is a stately masterpiece that captures the details and layout of the real-world location well. It's the home of Congress, and you'll find all of the important elements here, including the famous rotunda, the east and west wings, and the grand interior. This was built by user CalypsoDave.

CHRIST THE REDEEMER

The huge tribute to Jesus Christ in Rio de Janeiro, Brazil, is one of the most visually striking statues in the world, perched as it is high above the city. It's more like something out of *The Lord of the Rings* or *Game of Thrones* than a real-world statue, but real it very much is. The Minecraft version is also impressive and, despite being relatively simple in terms of design, it's accurate and detailed enough to match its real-world counterpart. All it needs now is the city below. This project has been put together by Minecraft user SunnyCraft25, and you can download it from Planet Minecraft at ***www.tinyurl.com/EpicBuildsRedeemer***

Just like a visit to Rio, only without the luggage

Seen during sunset, the statue certainly looks holy

THE EARTH

A lot of places have been recreated in Minecraft, but did you know there's a project to recreate the entire world? Well, there is, and it's suitably massive in scale. Moderated by Lentebriesje, this server build is trying to create a 1:1,500 replica of the Earth, and is around 16,200x32,400 blocks. The entire world is reproduced, with the goal of people using the base map to recreate the world as they see fit, be it in Creative or Survival mode. It's an impressive sight, and having an accurate map of the world to build upon makes for a rather unique adventure for any server community. Get ready for a large download, however, as the save, should you want to try it, is around 2GB compacted and unpacks to around 7GB.

Builds don't come any bigger than the whole world, even at 1:1,500 scale

An epic building that boggles the mind when you consider how long ago it was built

Few structures in the world are as imposing as the Colosseum

The Colosseum from above, showing just how large this build is

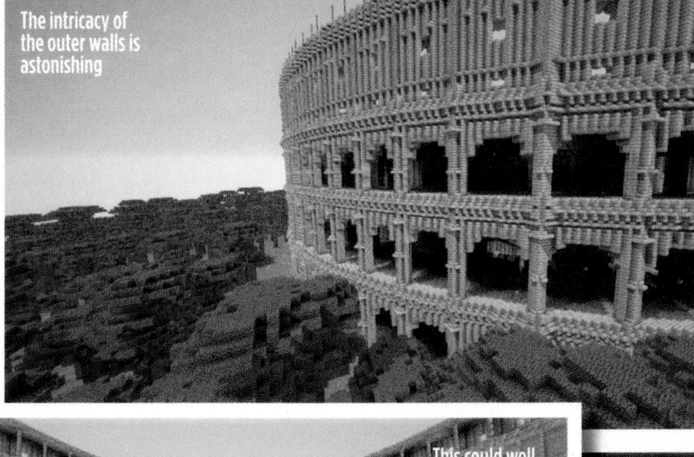

The intricacy of the outer walls is astonishing

This could well be the last view many gladiators saw before their untimely demises

THE COLOSSEUM

One of the world's most wondrous structures, the Colosseum, also known as the Flavian Amphitheater, is an epic building that boggles the mind when you consider how long ago it was built. This arena has been recreated in Minecraft by user AndItsOllie, albeit in a much more complete state than the ancient ruin is today. The great, arched walls form the outside of the structure, while the inside holds the famous arena where many a gladiator met his end. It even has the various tunnels and chambers, and when seen from above it is truly spectacular.

EIFFEL TOWER

This complex and downright amazing build comes courtesy of Seyone1, and is a mammoth build of the Eiffel Tower. It's over 210 blocks high, covers an area of 60,000 blocks, and consists of over 100,000 blocks in all. It took around 50 hours over the course of a month to build this epic landmark, and we think you'll agree that the results certainly show the hard work that was put into it.

This build dominates the landscape, much like the real-world structure

The complex metal sculpture isn't easy to reproduce

From a distance, the build really shines

It took around 50 hours over the course of a month to build this epic landmark

The tower at night. Very nice, indeed

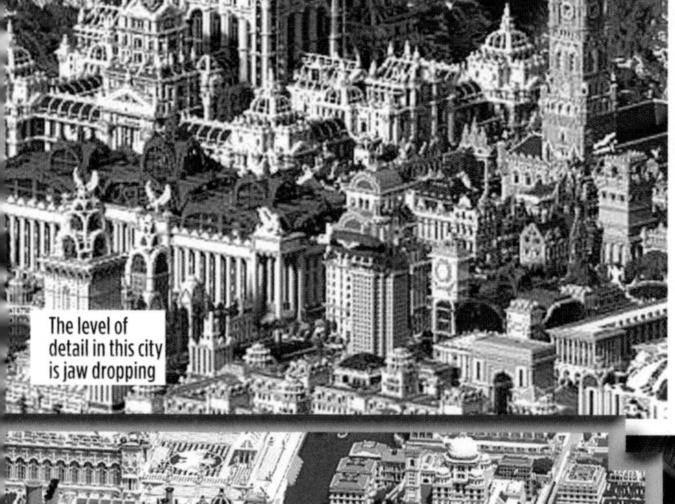

The level of detail in this city is jaw dropping

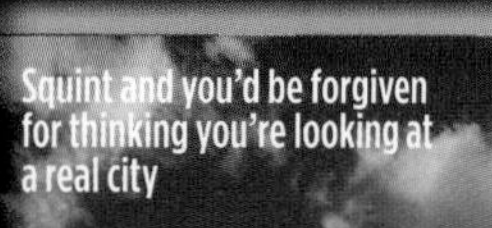

Squint and you'd be forgiven for thinking you're looking at a real city

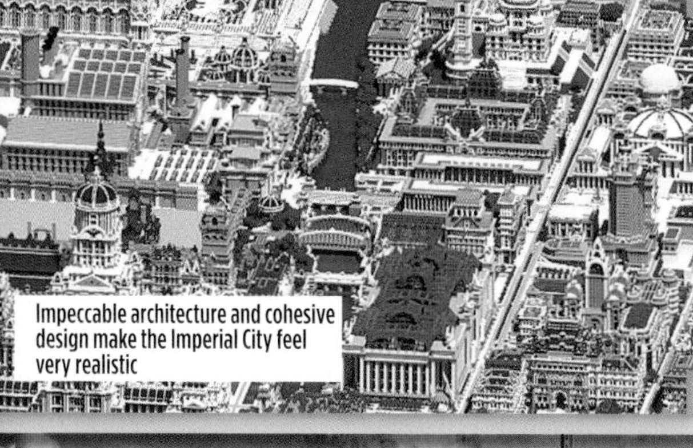

Impeccable architecture and cohesive design make the Imperial City feel very realistic

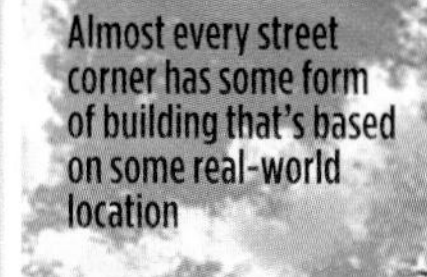

Almost every street corner has some form of building that's based on some real-world location

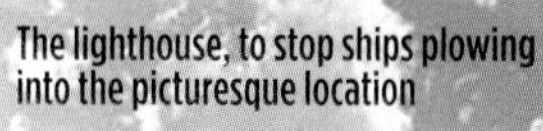

The lighthouse, to stop ships plowing into the picturesque location

IMPERIAL CITY

Although not based specifically on an actual building or location, this server-sized project takes inspiration from real-world architecture from the 19th and 20th centuries. The result is a stunning city populated by all sorts of realistic and grandiose buildings. There are hints of Paris, Rome, Venice, and more contained within this palatial urban sprawl, which is divided by a river and has docks, a huge, stunning palace, and rotundas aplenty. Run by admins Comeon and Rigolo, this project is, as with many server builds, ongoing. Sadly, due to some griefing, visitors to the official server are no longer accepted. You can grab a texture pack, though, and find out more about the build at *bit.ly/1eHNL5d*

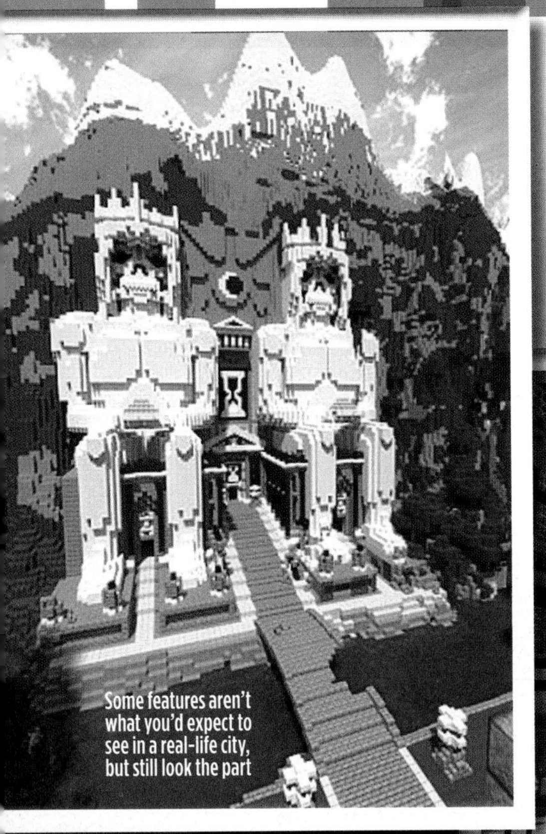

Some features aren't what you'd expect to see in a real-life city, but still look the part

"Wow" is just about all you can say

The city even has a market district

Chariot races are still very popular in this city

A stunning city populated by all sorts of realistic and grandiose buildings

Just imagine how long it took to place each and every column and window...

STATUE OF LIBERTY

Without a doubt one of the most iconic and instantly recognizable landmarks in the world, New York's Statue of Liberty is popular inspiration for Minecraft builds, and this one by Avalanche_All is great, even including an impressive build of the Empire State Building to boot. The statue itself is very highly detailed, with the sculpted shape of Lady Liberty looking the part, and there's even the interior, which you can explore if you wish. The dimensions of the statue itself are 52Wx52Lx126H, and it took around 18,095 blocks. You can just feel the freedom. You can download it for yourself at ***bit.ly/3bBBRKm***

Seen next to builds of other New York landmarks, Lady Liberty in all her glory

The build is suitably tall, piercing the cloud layer

The base of the statue can be entered and explored

The view from below on a misty day in New York

LONDON

One of the oldest and most storied cities in the world, London has its fair share of iconic buildings, and it's no surprise that it's been recreated in part, or in full, within Minecraft many times. This build by user KnownTheRanger is an attempt to map a 1:8 recreation of London, and it's very good, indeed. It may not be as detailed or complex as some builds, but it includes a large area of London, packing in plenty of familiar landmarks, such as the London Eye, Houses of Parliament, the Gherkin, and even the MI6 HQ. There are plenty of classic red buses spread around for that extra London feel. Nice work.

A postcard from London, Minecraft style

The London Eye on the banks of the Thames

There are plenty of classic red buses spread around for that extra London feel

James Bond was here

The financial district, complete with the Gherkin

New York, as mapped by computer in Minecraft

Yankee Stadium. Detail is a little basic, but the modeling is still accurate

The New York Public Library, extruded from the Minecraft sandbox

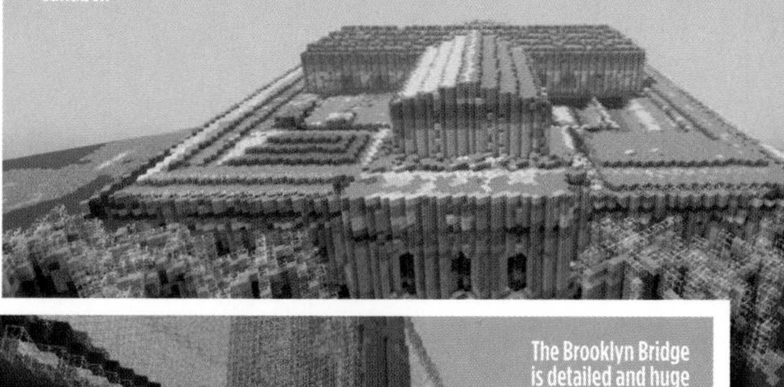

The Brooklyn Bridge is detailed and huge

The detail isn't as good as other builds due to the AI creation, but it's a promising experiment

NEW YORK

There are impressive builds, and there are builds that are simply stunning. This is clearly the latter, although there's a large caveat that keeps this from being as impressive as many other builds in terms of skill and dedication. This in-progress recreation of New York, stunning as it is, hasn't been created by a person per se, but a computer AI algorithm. The Sparse World project is an intriguing project designed to use AI to build worlds using the Minecraft engine. This model of New York is one of the first attempts, and as you can see it's very impressive already, with such landmarks as the Brooklyn Bridge, Yankee Stadium, the New York Public Library, and the New York Life Insurance Building. The actual detail isn't quite as good as other builds due to the AI creation, but it's great nonetheless, and is a promising experiment.

BABYLON – NEW YORK CITY 1949

It's the Big Apple again, but this time it's an older, human-built one. The Babylon Project is a large-scale effort to recreate New York of yesteryear within Minecraft, the year being 1949. New York of 1949 was a very different place from what it is today, and this build aims to capture that feel. It's already managed to deliver some impressive vistas, including recreations of entire areas and important buildings of the past. The project is headed up by user C_B_John, and you can download the map from *www.tinyurl.com/EpicBuildsNY1940s*

The build is very realistic, and scale is top notch

It was a very different city back in 1949

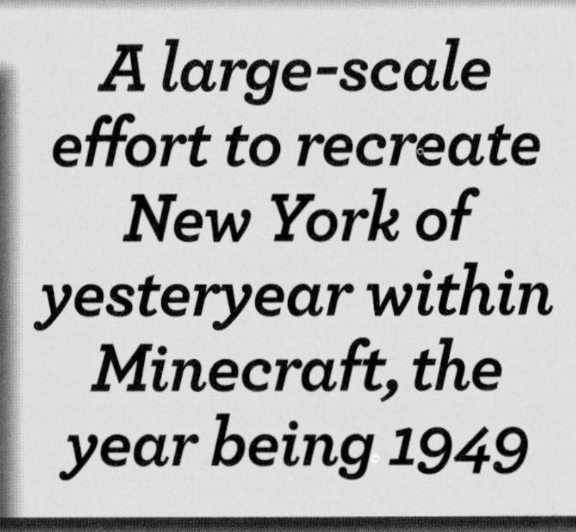

A large-scale effort to recreate New York of yesteryear within Minecraft, the year being 1949

A lot has been done, but there's still a lot of the city to go

You can clearly see the task at hand, and how impressive the final build will be

The real thing, all $70 million of it. Nice, eh?

And the Minecraft build. It's blockier, but the resemblance is there

The driveway and underground garage are featured

The view from above. It's just missing the Hollywood sign in the distance

Even the furniture has been replicated

NOTCH'S HOUSE

How could we list some of the best real-world builds without mentioning a build for the real-world house of Minecraft creator Notch? Markus "Notch" Persson famously purchased his $70 million mansion in LA, outbidding such stars as Jay-Z and Beyoncé, after selling Minecraft to Microsoft. It's a palatial abode, and one that's already been recreated in the game by many players. Perhaps one of the best is the version built by boveybrawlers. Both the exterior and interior match the real-world house, with clever use of in-game items to replicate the decoration of the house, and you can download it and look yourself at ***www.planetminecraft.com/project/notchs-la-mansion***

HOUSES OF PARLIAMENT

Love it or hate it, government needs somewhere to run a country from, and the UK has the historic and iconic Houses of Parliament. The ornate structure that contains the House of Commons and House of Lords, as well as the clock tower holding Big Ben, has been recreated in Minecraft numerous times, with this example from yesn95 being one of the best. The build includes everything, from the main buildings to the recognizable clock tower, complete with hands. The River Thames even runs alongside it. The whole building is accurate when compared to the real-world location.

Gunpowder, treason, and plot

Each wing and entrance are accurately modeled

The build includes everything, from the main buildings to the recognizable clock tower

The detail is impressive, with each famous section covered

Here be government, where decisions are made, and the public are riled

MOUNT RUSHMORE

The famous presidential landmark is one of the most impressive sculptures in the real world, and this recreation in Minecraft by user rcpongo is also quite the achievement. An older build, created around four years ago, this still holds its own for detail and accuracy, looking very close to its real-life counterpart, and it also boasts an interior to explore. The likenesses of presidents Washington, Jefferson, Roosevelt, and Lincoln are captured well, and the South Dakota landmark looks at home in the world of Minecraft.

The massive monument comes to life in Minecraft with plenty of detail

Presidents look on as the clouds rush by and creepers wander the wilds

STEVE JOBS

Although Apple's late CEO Steve Jobs wasn't actually a place, that hasn't stopped Apple fan PostColdWarKid from creating a brilliant Minecraft rendering of him, turning the billionaire into one of his stores. The detail and characterization of Mr. Jobs are great, and a clever tribute to the man who made Apple what it is today.

Inside the statue is an Apple store

SPACE SHUTTLE

The image of the space shuttle waiting for launch still captures the imagination of stargazers the world over. This build by crpeh replicates the once-mighty vehicle, complete with solid fuel boosters and access gantry. It's very detailed and accurate, except for the creator's national pride showing in the choice of wing-mounted flags.

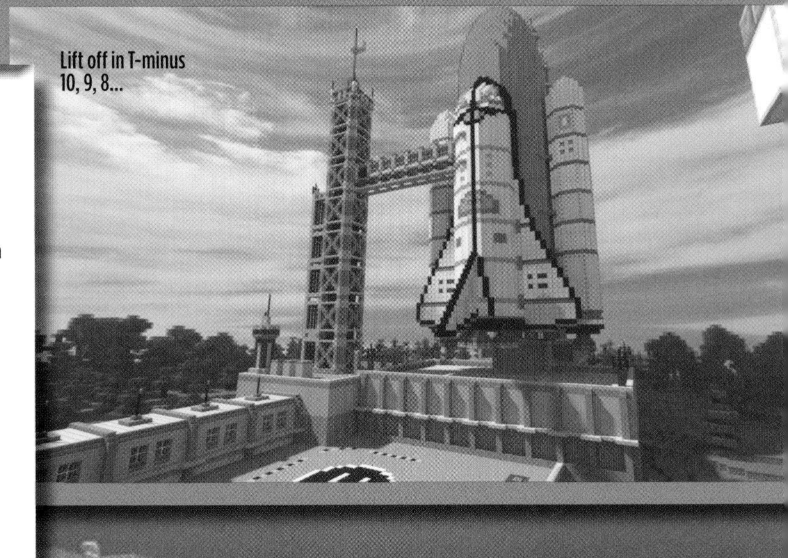

Lift off in T-minus 10, 9, 8...

This Sphinx is certainly happy, and the headdress is spot on

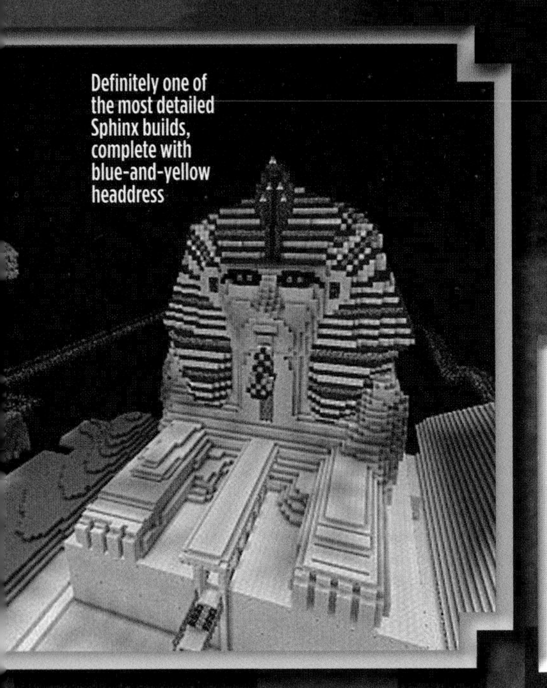

Definitely one of the most detailed Sphinx builds, complete with blue-and-yellow headdress

SPHINX

Modern landmarks are great, but few can hold a candle to the incredible Sphinx. A wonder of the world, this Egyptian structure has been built countless times in Minecraft, and here are just a couple of the best, with varying levels of detail, but both oozing quality and style.

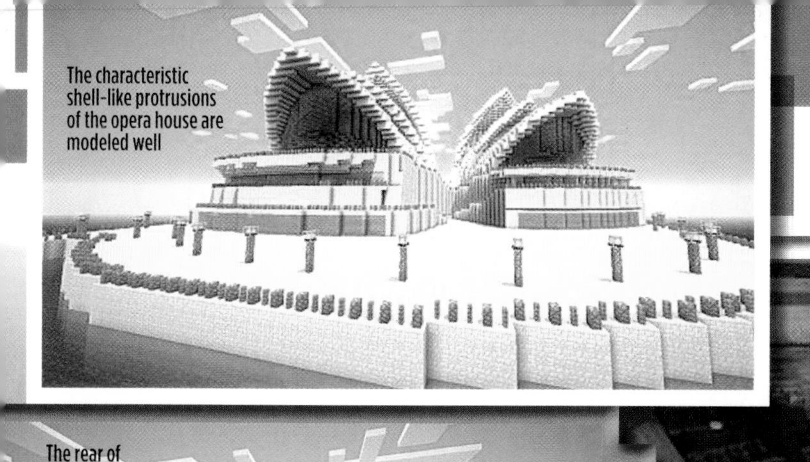

The characteristic shell-like protrusions of the opera house are modeled well

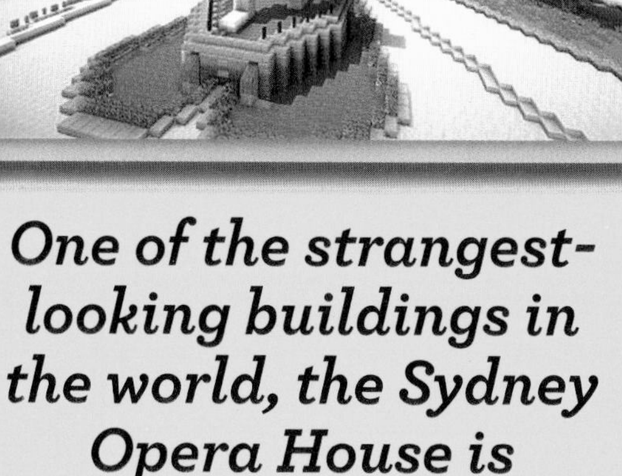

The rear of the building, complete with entrance plaza

The inside of the opera house is detailed...

One of the strangest-looking buildings in the world, the Sydney Opera House is obviously an often-built Minecraft structure

SYDNEY OPERA HOUSE

Definitely one of the strangest-looking buildings in the world, the Sydney Opera House is obviously an often-built Minecraft structure. This effort by user ole22143 is a great example. It's good not just for the build of the opera house itself, which has all of the detail of the real-world building, but also thanks to the surrounding area and the inclusion of an interior. It's got an accurate entrance and even the main stage. All it needs now are a few opera singers, and it will be time to raise the curtain.

...and features the auditorium and stage

TITANIC

This reproduction of the ill-fated cruise liner, the *Titanic*, is not only huge, but also very accurate in terms of detail, and it represents the inauguration of the ship before it sank on its first voyage, in 1912. The exterior looks the part, complete with deck settings, lifeboats, and portholes in the hull, and the whole thing was built with around 120,000 blocks, all laid by hand and using no build tools.

We definitely won't need a bigger boat

To boldly… oh, sorry. Wrong ship

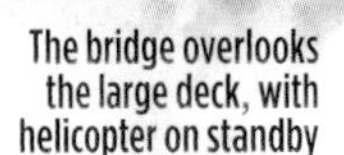

The bridge overlooks the large deck, with helicopter on standby

USS ENTERPRISE

No, not that USS *Enterprise*, but the real-world seafaring aircraft carrier. This detailed recreation of the ship by NepsterCZ and Mikes97, along with flanking vessels, is unique, being not a land-based creation, but one floating on the ocean. The markings and details of the ship are all accurate, and the scale when compared to the smaller vessels highlights the size of the carrier.

THE WHITE HOUSE

Built by bluesheep123, this recreation of the seat of power in the US government is suitably enormous, covering the White House itself, as well as a sizeable area around it, including the Washington Monument and Lafayette Square. Pennsylvania Avenue even runs along the grounds, just as in real life. It's a great build, including fine levels of detail and some superb skill to recreate the grounds with such accuracy.

Lush gardens and some fine architecture make a house fit for the most powerful person in the world

Many Minecraft builders create special renders of their work, and this is no exception

A great build, including fine levels of detail and some superb skill to recreate the grounds with such accuracy

This is the view a Minecraft president might see from the balcony of the White House

The Washington Monument

MOVIES AND TV

MOVIES AND TV

Some of the best Minecraft builds are inspired by famous fiction, and here are some of the most impressive

BATTLESTAR GALACTICA

The excellent sci-fi series *Battlestar Galactica* is prime Minecraft material for fans, and this reproduction of the titular ship from the modern remake is superb, right down to the Colonial logo adorning the craft. What's even more impressive is that this is a life-sized replica. The creator's website ***(imgur.com/a/VGERV)*** shows how the ship was built, and here you can see just how big the build is and how much time went into it. Surely one of the most accurate and impressive builds around.

The huge ship has been faithfully recreated

That's no moon...
You know the rest

A structure that can't fail to make you gaze on in admiration

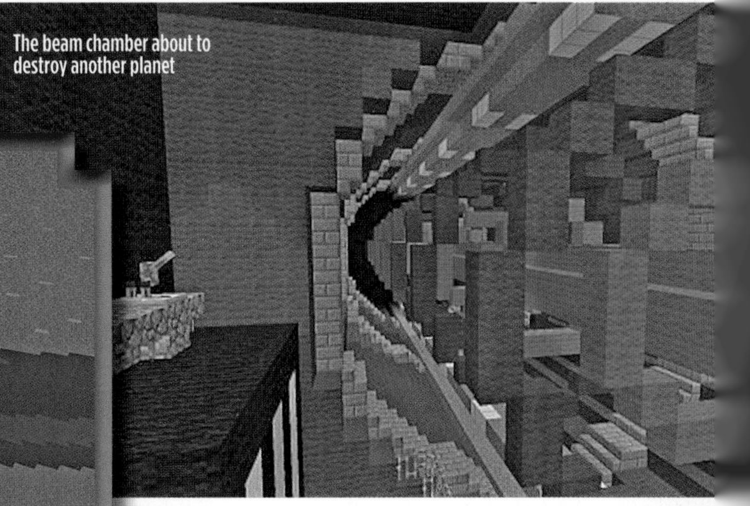

The beam chamber about to destroy another planet

cking bay,
ete with
ial shuttle

Durr, durr, durr,
duh, de, durr,
duh, de, durr

STAR WARS – DEATH STAR

Creating a sphere in Minecraft isn't easy, so creating a sphere as huge as the Death Star, complete with a large and complex interior, is very challenging, indeed. This didn't deter Flov9, who has created a Minecraft Death Star that incorporates many rooms seen in the movies. This includes the docking bay, throne room, prison, beam chamber, and trash compactor. It's a quality build, and one that's superbly detailed—a structure that can't fail to make you gaze on in admiration.

DOCTOR WHO – DALEK

As with the TARDIS (below), there are plenty of *Doctor Who* builds involving his arch enemies, the Daleks. However, this is one of the best we've seen in terms of accuracy and detail. Built on a huge scale to cram in all the detail and spherical nuance, this is a superb sculpture that stands ready to exterminate anyone who gets in its way. User The12thDoctor even made the Dalek hover, with underside hover pads visible.

Many Dalek builds are blocky and make sacrifices to accuracy. This one doesn't make that concession

DOCTOR WHO – TARDIS

As you can imagine, there's no shortage of *Doctor Who* builds, especially with the addition of the official *Doctor Who* skin pack, and many of these builds include the Doctor's blue box. Here's one of the most impressive and detailed around. Created by napalmnacey, this huge version of the time-traveling police box has all of the familiar details on the outside, such as the police box lettering, lamp, and plaque, and it even has an inside with an ornate control room. Just the place for all that wibbly wobbly, timey wimey stuff.

From the inside, you can see just how big this build is

Pair this with the official *Doctor Who* skins, and you're ready for adventure

FROZEN – ELSA'S ICE CASTLE

This Disney-themed creation is a stunning castle from *Frozen*. Created by TheVoxelBox and available to download from ***minecraftbuildinginc.com***, this build makes use of The Palceon texture pack and also requires WorldGuard and MCPatcher in order to run. This is worth it, as you get a great recreation of Elsa's ice castle, complete with frozen mountainside and a fully explorable interior as well.

Let it go! Let it go! Relive Disney's *Frozen* in Minecraft

You can enter and explore the castle's interior

Recreating the firework spectacle from the movie makes this castle look all the more impressive

Tangled's castle recreated in Minecraft form

TANGLED CASTLE

This Disney-themed castle is from the huge hit *Tangled* and was created by adybuddy_. It's situated on a lush, green island and faithfully recreates the citadel from the CG movie. The spires, rotunda, and general architectural features are all there, and it looks beautiful.

STAR TREK – USS ENTERPRISE

This simply amazing recreation of *The Next Generation*'s USS *Enterprise* NCC 1701-D is impressive for so many reasons. For one, it looks superb thanks to a custom texture pack, and its 1:6 ratio means you can explore the iconic ship in its entirety, from bridge to transporters, from crew quarters to Ten Forward. The detail here is stunning, as is the sheer scale of the build. However, that all pales in comparison to the build's true achievement. This was all done in Survival mode. Yes, creator Zinnsee built this mighty ship from scratch all while farming for materials (save for a few concessions), fending off hostile mobs, and using skill and agility to build the *Enterprise* block by block. Wow.

To boldly go where no block has gone before

Seen from the ground, Zinnsee's 1701-D is quite the spectacle

The detail here is stunning, as is the sheer scale of the build. However, the build's true achievement is that this was all done in Survival mode

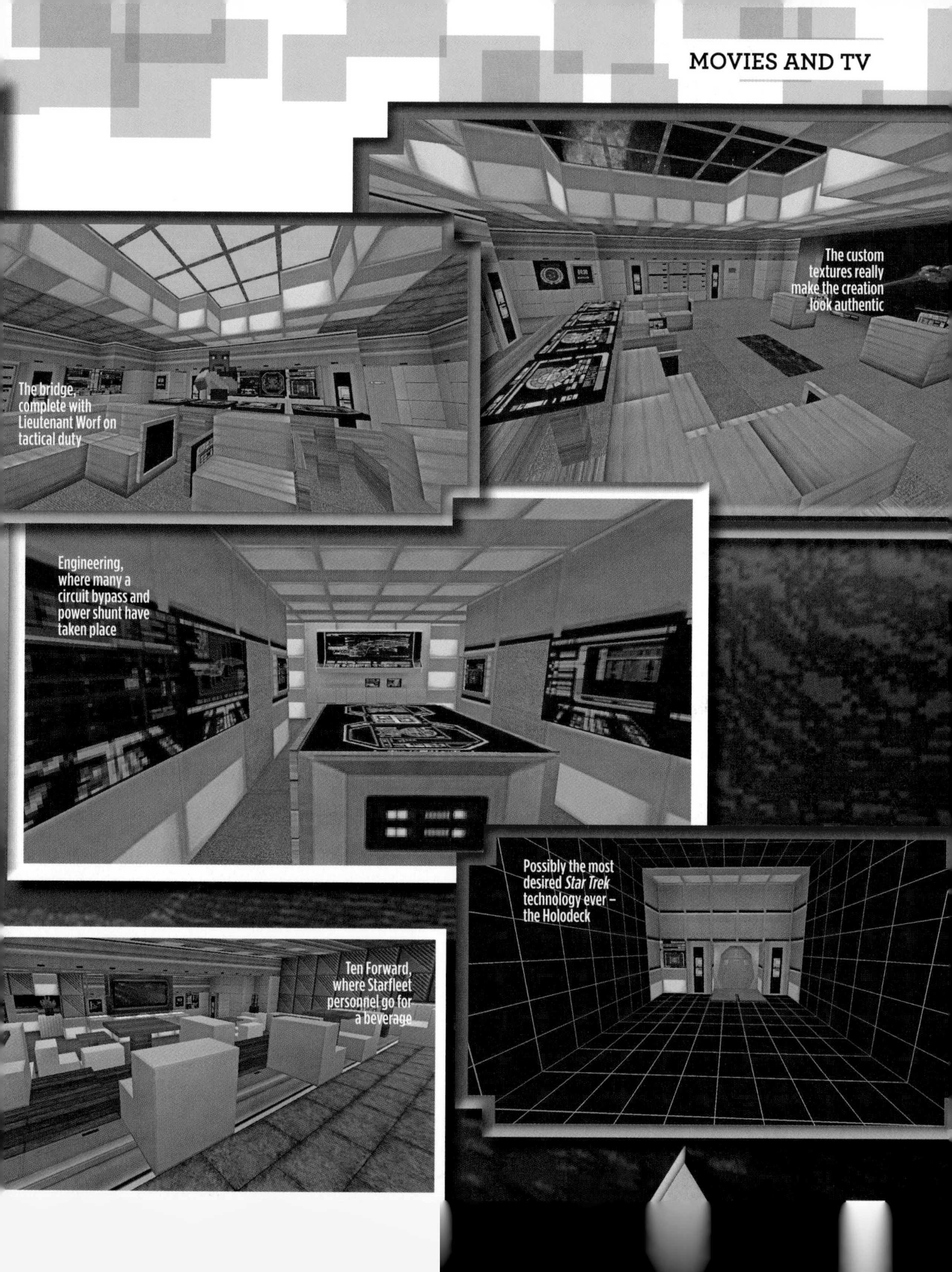

The custom textures really make the creation look authentic

The bridge, complete with Lieutenant Worf on tactical duty

Engineering, where many a circuit bypass and power shunt have taken place

Possibly the most desired *Star Trek* technology ever – the Holodeck

Ten Forward, where Starfleet personnel go for a beverage

FIREFLY – SERENITY

Despite being axed so soon, *Firefly* has a huge fan base, and many Minecraft builds are themed on it. This is one of the best, and it incorporates *Serenity*, the ship from the series and movie of the same name. The build features a recreation that's about 1:2 scale, to allow for more detail and a more playable version of the ship. Shuttles are included, and the engines make use of lava flows to depict the ship hovering above the land. It's gorram great.

The *Serenity* looking resplendent as it hovers above the Overworld

The detail on the build is great, and clever use of blocks allows for fine detail, as with the ship's main engine

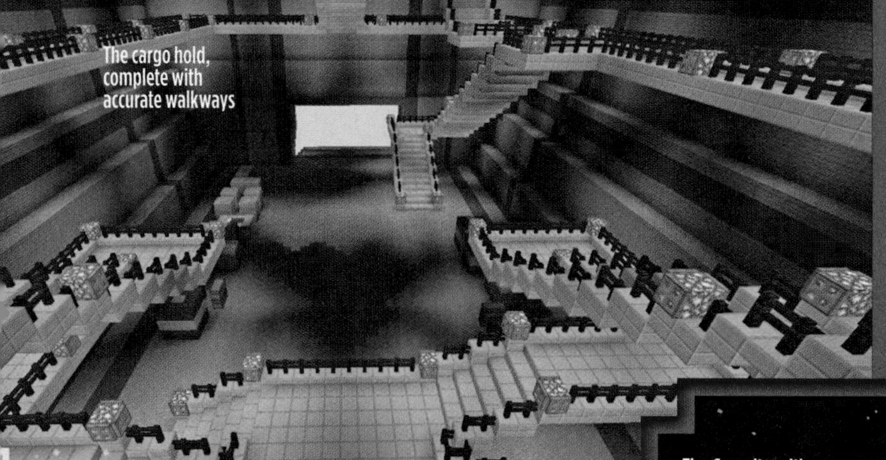

The cargo hold, complete with accurate walkways

The build features a recreation that's 1:2 scale, to allow for more detail

The *Serenity*, with launched shuttle

's likely that
ıe zombies,
‹eletons, and
'eepers are
ırrently in hiding

Long before the Power Rangers, *Gundam* was the place to be for giant robot suit battles

Now all that's needed is a mod that lets players jump in and pilot it...

Some serious landscaping was needed to build this massive mobile suit

Despite limitations, the detail of the Rx-78-2 is great, and the choice of materials is nigh-on perfect

GUNDAM – RX-78-2

The most famous mobile suit from the popular anime series, the Rx-78-2 Gundam has been recreated in all its majestic glory by user SoulSoda. The titanic battle suit stands proud with twin swords in hand, ready to take on the might of its foes. The build is around 120 blocks high and took around 30 hours to build. It uses the Voxelbox texture pack, and SoulSoda made use of WorldEdit, VoxelSnipe, and the Zombies Mod to craft it.

LAPUTA – CASTLE IN THE SKY

Inspired by the Studio Ghibli movie *Castle in the Sky*, user adybuddy_ created this floating castle, complete with the giant Eternal Tree of Life surrounded by a picturesque castle. The level of detail is impressive, especially when compared to the anime original, and it's surely going to be one of the most secure places to live, keeping you safe from creepers and other nasties. Just don't cast a spell that ends up destroying the floating metropolis.

Adding filters to your screenshots will make any build look good, but Laputa doesn't need such help

The impressive sense of scale really makes this reproduction work

Levels of detail make the uninhabited floating city come alive

The level of detail is impressive, especially when compared to the anime original

These clouds may not be real Minecraft creations, but they make this build look great

LOST – PLANE CRASH

Although this may not be totally accurate in terms of recreating the TV show (the plane didn't crash-land in one place, but was spread across the island), this is nonetheless a great build, and any fans of the show will instantly see the resemblance. The detail of the plane wreckage amidst the complex jungle setting looks great, and signs of the aircraft's age can be seen by vines dangling off the fuselage. All it needs now is a beach, mysterious hatch, and a big smoke monster.

Was it real, a dream, or were they all dead? Who knows, but *Lost* makes for good Minecraft builds

Find more on this one at bit.ly/2SE9fat

KING KONG VS. T. REX

This isn't a standard build in any way, but more a work of art. It's not really pixel art, as it's an actual 3D build, but it requires no less artistic ability. It depicts King Kong doing battle with a T. rex, all while holding Ann Darrow, keeping her safe. It's a colossal scene, and one that required a great deal of skill to build. The final result is excellent, with each character being detailed and to scale.

LORD OF THE RINGS – MINAS TIRITH

One of the most common themed builds in Minecraft involves the world of Middle-earth, and this reproduction of the city of Minas Tirith is just superb. Its huge, vertical build reproduces the city seen in Peter Jackson's film adaptations of the books, right down to the garden courtyard of the castle, and iconic jutting cliff face. The map even hides secrets and rewards around the city and its innards.

This reproduction of one of *The Lord of the Rings'* most unique locations is complex and filled with secrets

The cavernous reaches of Moria are daunting, to say the least

MINES OF MORIA

Sometimes, it's not just the scale or the actual visual aesthetic that impresses you with Minecraft builds, but also the effort to create such works of art. Eventime's Mines of Moria is one such example. It has it all: the grand scale, accuracy in reproducing the mines themselves, and the dark, foreboding atmosphere. However, the fact that this has all been sculpted within an underground cavern, successfully reproducing the subterranean vaults within a mountain, makes it even better.

Let's just hope these stairs are a little more stable than the ones from the movie

These subterranean vaults are sculpted to perfection

Mines of Moria has it all: the grand scale, accuracy in reproducing the mines themselves, and the dark, foreboding atmosphere

MINECRAFT MIDDLE EARTH PROJECT

If just one city or location from J. R. R. Tolkien's epic isn't enough for you, how about the entire world? This huge project is geared toward recreating Middle-earth in all its glory, with all the famous places included, such as Rivendell, Minas Tirith, Weathertop, Helm's Deep, Isengard, and the Mines of Moria. It's a huge project, and you can join the server at ***www.mcmiddleearth.com***. More images on the next page, too!

Helm's Deep, the supposedly impregnable fortress, is recreated

The ominous tower of Isengard, the home of the wizards

The elven homestead, Rivendell

Relive Frodo's fateful encounter with the Ringwraiths on Weathertop

This huge project is geared toward recreating Middle-earth in all its glory, with all the famous places included, such as Rivendell, Minas Tirith, Weathertop, Helm's Deep,

FUTURAMA – PLANET EXPRESS

The place of business for the hapless delivery team of Planet Express has been recreated by builder Safoo. It's a detailed replica of the odd-looking headquarters of Hubert J. Farnsworth's crew, and looks the part in its blockier guise. Welcome to the world of tomorrow!

Good news, everyone!

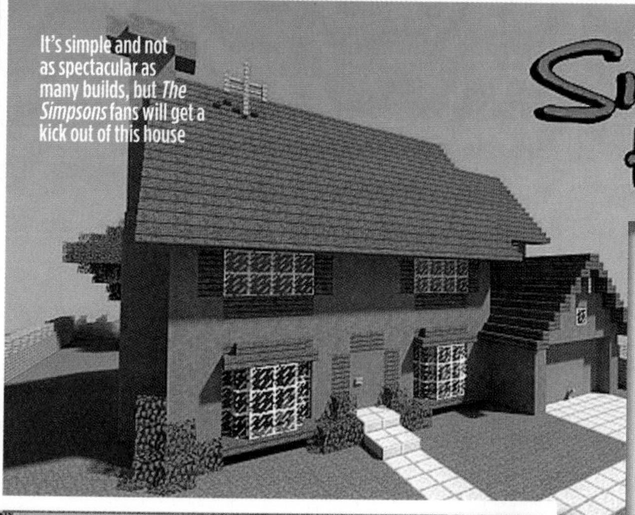

It's simple and not as spectacular as many builds, but *The Simpsons* fans will get a kick out of this house

THE SIMPSON HOUSE

Although this may not be the most complex build, it's nonetheless a great creation. User GogonGaming crafted a replica Simpson house, complete with backyard sandbox and tree house. As one of the most iconic cartoon dwellings around, it's not hard to recognize, and this version sticks closely to the original, showing complex detail isn't always needed to make a great build.

The house comes complete with the backyard and Bart's tree house

CARTOON TOWN

Created by Enderwarp, this server-based build is an ongoing project that aims to recreate all sorts of cartoon locations within Minecraft, and it already includes several familiar sights, such as the Simpson and Flanders houses, SpongeBob SquarePants's pineapple-shaped domicile, *Futurama*, and *Family Guy*'s Cleveland's and Quagmire's homes. All structures are carefully recreated, with the ultimate goal of building the greatest cartoon town ever.

Cleveland's home from *The Cleveland Show*

Quagmire's house back in good ol' Quahog

The Simpson house, alongside that of their godly neighbors

SpongeBob's house is clearly the fruit of a lot of labor

If you've watched '90s cartoons, you'll recognize Space Ghost, a cartoon hero

Space Ghost on the air and ready for a chat

Even Space Ghost's cloak and chair are modeled

His cup might be missing some coffee, but that's not going to stop the chat

Guests and other characters, like Moltar, talk to Space Ghost from across the universe

SPACE GHOST COAST TO COAST

This is an odd one, and younger readers might not recognize this. If you've watched '90s cartoons, however, you'll recognize Space Ghost, a cartoon hero who had his own talk show on Cartoon Network. This build replicates the host, along with his desk and studio, complete with TV monitor showing former super villain Moltar. Created by Featherblade.

STAR WARS – STAR DESTROYER

Even when third-party tools are used to create Minecraft builds, the results are no less incredible. Take this Star Destroyer from *Star Wars*. User arnoritter crafted this 1:1 behemoth using MCEdit, and the process took around eight months, even with the extra tools. The ship is simply massive, dwarfing most other builds and, thanks to the cutouts, you can see just how complex the structure is, with masses of floors, rooms, and chambers, all topped off with an intricately detailed exterior hull. Impressive. Most impressive.

Look at the size of that thing

The surface of the hull is extremely detailed

The interior is made up of a maze of corridors and rooms

The engines really show just how big this build is

Add a bit of image editing and you've got a space opera epic

The Rebel Blockade Runner chased by a Star Destroyer, as seen in the movie's opening

Han Solo's *Millennium Falcon* docked at Mos Eisley spaceport

STAR WARS – A NEW HOPE

Although this may not technically be just a build, there's no way to mention Minecraft and *Star Wars* without it. Created by Paradise Decay using nothing but vanilla Minecraft and some custom textures and artwork, A New Hope is a full recreation of the entire movie *Star Wars: Episode IV – A New Hope*. Every scene, character, and location are recreated within the Minecraft world, and edited into a full-length movie. The results so far are fantastic, although you have to play your own copy of the movie along with it to get the audio (copyright issues, and so on). The first 30 minutes and some trailers are available at the website, and the project is ongoing. ***paradisedecay.wordpress.com***. More on the next page!

A New Hope is a full recreation of the entire movie Star Wars: Episode IV – A New Hope. Every scene, character, and location are recreated within the Minecraft world, and edited into a full-length movie

The results so far are fantastic, although you have to play your own copy of the movie along with it to get the audio

A Jawa Sandcrawler

Just look at the detail on the exterior of the Death Star

Krayt dragon skeleton

Created by Paradise Decay using nothing but vanilla Minecraft and some custom textures and artwork

TERMINATOR – T-101

As this is a full 3D model, it doesn't qualify as simple pixel art, hence its inclusion here. This mammoth statue of one of Hollywood's most famous robotic stars is a Minecraft reproduction of the top half of the relentless T-101 Terminator. The endoskeleton is detailed, and the skull-like head looks menacingly on into the distance. The statue is enormous: user ShrubHerring put a lot of time and effort into creating the head, before deciding to carry on with the rest of the torso. The result is a statue that absolutely will not stop until your jaw drops.

If the Connors had to fight a Terminator this big, it's doubtful they'd make it past the first movie

It may lack legs, but as we saw in *Terminator 2*, this robot doesn't need legs to try and take out its targets

X-MEN – SENTINEL HEAD

Fans of Marvel's *X-Men* should appreciate this build. Rather than go for anything as passé as a building or simple location, user nizmoe decided to create a severed Sentinel head, presumably after a confrontation with the X-Men. Modeled on the giant robot Sentinels that hunt down mutant kind, the head is huge and rests on some sand dunes, probably contemplating its mistakes during the fight with the powerful super mutants.

You should see the other guy!

HARRY POTTER – POTTERCRAFT

We've got *The Lord of the Rings* and *Game of Thrones* in Minecraft, so it's pretty unsurprising that *Harry Potter* has also been recreated in the game. PotterCraft is another server-sized build project that's a haven for fans of all things magic and wizardry, and it recreates Hogwarts in great detail, including the Great Hall, Chamber of Secrets, Dumbledore's tower, and much more. You can find the server for this at ***pottercraft.simpleno.de***

You're a wizard, Harry, but even the chosen one can't build Hogwarts like this

Another server-sized build project that's a haven for fans of all things magic and wizardry

The castle has been reproduced, along with some of its more famous locations

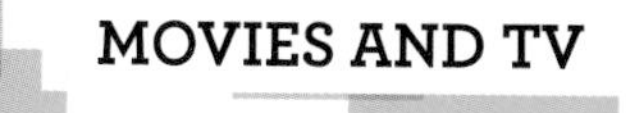

Hopefully there are no Death Eaters on the server trying to bring ruin to the splendid work on offer

PotterCraft recreates Hogwarts in great detail, including the Chamber of Secrets and Dumbledore's tower

King's Landing has to be one of the most impressive Minecraft builds around

Recreating Westeros isn't easy, especially when so many areas are to be included

GAME OF THRONES – WESTEROSCRAFT

Similar in scope to the Middle-earth project, this server is set to be a recreation of the world seen in the insanely popular *Game of Thrones*. The map recreates Westeros in full, including places like the Wall, Winterfell, King's Landing, Dorne, the Reach, and many more. The various regions will be populated by places from the series, producing a real, playable Westeros for Minecraft players. It's a very ambitious project, with a special launcher required to access the map. If you're a fan of *Game of Thrones*, you'll want to be part of this server. Find out more at *westeroscraft.com*

The map recreates Westeros in full, including places like the Wall, Winterfell, King's Landing, Dorne, the Reach, and many more

Seen from the top, King's Landing is even more impressive in terms of scale

The stoic sight of the Wall, Westeros's first line of defense against the coming winter

Castle Pyke sat precariously atop craggy stone

If you're a fan of Game of Thrones, you'll want to be part of this server

VIDEO GAME BUILDS

VIDEO GAME BUILDS

Minecraft is a video game, so unsurprisingly there are a lot of video game–themed builds out there. Such as these!

WORLD OF WARCRAFT – CRAFTING AZEROTH

When it comes to gaming, few worlds can approach the size of *World of Warcraft*'s Azeroth, and this build is recreating it within Minecraft. A 1:1 build, headed up by ramsesa, the project includes various regions from the MMORPG giant. The Howling Fjord, Icecrown Glacier, Dalaran, the Storm Peaks, and the Dark Portal are just some of the locations, and each has been created with keen attention to detail, replicating locations from the Blizzard hit.

This is world building +5, make no mistake

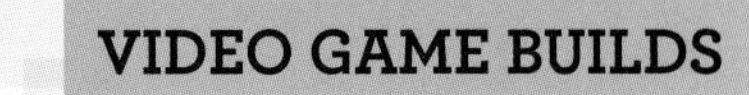

The fabulous worlds of WoW look very different from what we expect out of Minecraft

The city of Dalaran looking as splendid as ever

The Storm Peaks with precariously perched buildings

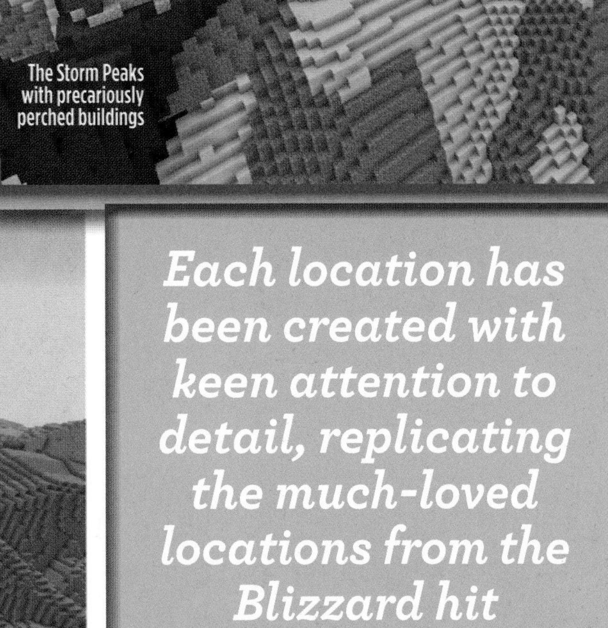
Now, it doesn't look like the owner will be very welcoming to visitors

Each location has been created with keen attention to detail, replicating the much-loved locations from the Blizzard hit

FINAL FANTASY VIII - BALAMB GARDEN

This is the Seed academy of Balamb Garden from *Final Fantasy VIII* (before it transformed into a hovering fortress). It's a large-scale build that bears all of the details from the Square RPG, including the elaborate floating decoration above, external grounds, and interior, all of which are recognizable if you've played the actual game. The build successfully captures the strange architecture and feel of the building, and it's clearly the work of a true fan.

The build successfully captures the strange architecture and feel of the building

The opening location from *Final Fantasy VIII* comes to life in Minecraft

The ornate crown of the building looks impressive here

It's a strange building, but what do you expect, it turns into a hover ship!

The interior reception looks good, and very much like the original game

The floating city of Columbia from *BioShock Infinite*

The huge city is only one location in the server's massive world, which also includes *BioShock's* Rapture

The server map showing Columbia to the bottom left, and Rapture north of the central island

The texture packs used on the server enable a closer likeness to the game

Another server overview, but this time as a striking isometric render

COLUMBIA AND RAPTURE

Although the Rapture by TraktorHagrid is great for a single-person build, the team on the server run by Adam "Ein" Shefki has crafted a world that's much larger in scale. This mammoth build is the result of a huge amount of work by a dedicated team. The Rapture build on its own is impressive, but with a version of Columbia on the same map, it's astounding. What's more, each and every block has been mined by hand. You can find out more and request to join the server at *bit.ly/1G4m3xU*

THE ELDER SCROLLS – TAMRIEL

The Elder Scrolls is set on planet Nirn, and the game series takes place in the continent of Tamriel. It's a huge, sprawling area that covers a wide selection of environments and distinct styles, and was last seen in *The Elder Scrolls Online*. It's impressive, then, that a project exists that aims to recreate Tamriel in Minecraft. Sadly, the project hasn't seen a great deal of movement of late, but even in its early days the build looked promising, and hopefully more builders will continue with the task.

The Imperial City is already included, sitting at the center of the world

Battleborn Castle, as seen in *Oblivion*

The scale of the map is huge, and there are plenty of regions to make use of Minecraft's varied biomes

It's impressive that a project exists that aims to recreate the continent of Tamriel in Minecraft

The central tower may be shorter than the original, but the detail here is still accurate

The layout of the buildings and sections of the pizza-style city is spot on

The walled city has many districts

It's almost like watching *Oblivion*'s intro video

Even the inside of the arena is included

THE ELDER SCROLLS IV: OBLIVION – IMPERIAL CITY

As a hugely popular open world game series, *The Elder Scrolls* presents builders with a raft of opportunities to create impressive structures and reproductions, and this offering from EpicQuestz is a very recognizable example. It's the Imperial City from *TES IV: Oblivion*, complete with the separate districts, Arena, and the central White Gold Tower. The layout of the buildings and sections of the pizza-style city is spot on.

DARK SOULS – LORDRAN

This has to be one of the most amazing video game builds we've seen, with nearly unrivaled attention to detail. The Lordran mega build is headed by builder Davweed, and it's an attempt to recreate the world from *Dark Souls* in 1:1 scale. The results so far are simply astonishing, with each and every location bearing an uncanny resemblance to the source material. Each location of the game is here, from the central hub of Firelink Shrine and the plague-filled Undead Burg to New Londo Ruins, Sen's Fortress, and the starting area of the Undead Asylum. There's already an impressive amount of progress, and work continues on this truly epic build. More on the next page, too!

The Undead Asylum, and the first bonfire you encounter on your perilous journey

An overview of the trap-ridden Sen's Fortress

Each location of the game is here, from the central hub of Firelink Shrine and the plague-filled Undead Burg to New Londo Ruins, Sen's Fortress, and the starting area of the Undead Asylum

New Londo Ruins, looking every bit as intimidating as in the game itself

The path leading toward Sen's Fortress

Blighttown, situated under the city, hopefully with a better frame rate

The city's foundations, seen from above, with the Blight Bog oozing poison

Firelink Shrine, one of only a few safe locations in the game

The entrance to Quelaag's domain found near Blighttown

The Undead Asylum, where future undead heroes are born

Your cell from the very beginning of the game

The Tower of Destiny, where Guardians rest, dance, and stand around in menus

Each section of the Tower is accurately reproduced, right down to small details like banners and lights

The main courtyard, bristling with detail

DESTINY – TOWER

The Tower in Bungie's *Destiny* is the central hub where players relax, manage their inventory, buy items, and play with floating balls in between missions. It's a very social area, and one that's been recreated in Minecraft several times. This version by builder ol_Nolbe_lo is one of the best and takes in all of the Tower's main sections, the Traveler, and even the city below. Each section of the Tower is accurately reproduced, right down to small details like banners, lights, and that weird gyroscope thing in the Speaker's office. There's a distinct lack of Carlton dances and slow claps, though. More on the next page!

The Crucible area, where Lord Shaxx dishes out PvP bounties and the odd quest

Here, the Vanguards decide the fate of mankind

The special event courtyard, home to the Iron Banner

The Speaker's office. He could tell you about the war, but he won't

The large castle is flanked by a small town and picturesque lighthouse

Fans of the RPG series will recognize this landmark

This epic fortress boasts plenty of added detail, such as the town and lighthouse sitting in the shadow of the mighty castle

Shown via a touched-up render, the castle looks stunning

FABLE – FAIRFAX CASTLE

It might not be as recognizable as landmarks from the likes of *Zelda*, *The Elder Scrolls*, the Mushroom Kingdom, and so on, but *Fable*'s Fairfax Castle is a huge royal edifice that looks great when recreated in Minecraft. Built by mikeack, this epic fortress boasts plenty of added detail, such as the town and lighthouse sitting in the shadow of the mighty castle, and the main building itself is fully explorable.

HALO – HALO RING

Halo is the Xbox's flagship title and, as such, it's inspired plenty of builds. This one such build is an actual halo—the giant space weapon ring the game is named after. The build features a halo ring, complete with varied climates and land masses, as well as a UNSC Pelican drop ship. There's even a working Forerunner teleporter situated in its own base. It's not to scale (the Pelican would be huge), but it's a clever piece of building, and the halo itself looks the part.

That's no moon... Sorry, wrong series

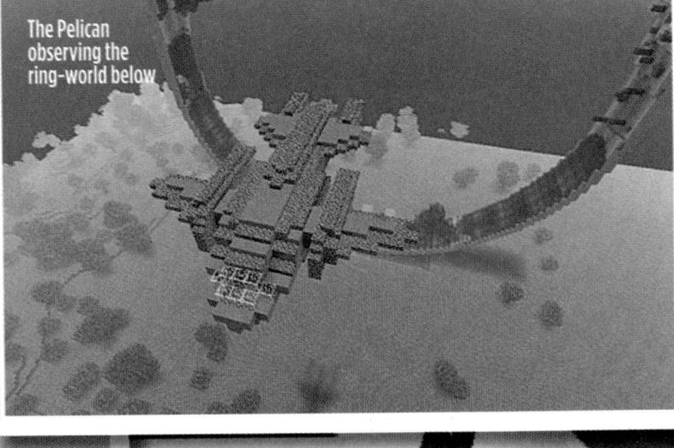

The Pelican observing the ring-world below

The same views of the ring seen in the game are recreated here

You wouldn't want to be under that thing if it started rolling

Alien technology adorns the ancient space structure

Hyrule from *Ocarina of Time*, recreated for Minecraft

Often topping best-video-game-ever lists, The Legend of Zelda: Ocarina of Time is one of the greatest games ever made

Hyrule Castle Town, complete with Happy Mask Shop

THE LEGEND OF ZELDA: OCARINA OF TIME – HYRULE

Often topping best-video-game-ever lists, *The Legend of Zelda: Ocarina of Time* is one of the greatest games ever made, and this project by user Kezsonaj is recreating the entire world of it in Minecraft. The world of Hyrule from *Ocarina* is here, from the Kokiri Forest and Great Deku Tree, to the Gerudo Desert and Ganon's Tower. There are even dual versions of some locations, reflecting both the young and adult Link time lines. Each area is wonderfully close to the original N64 classic, and we'd gladly play an actual game of *Ocarina of Time* in this Minecraft form. More on the next page!

Each area is wonderfully close to the original N64 classic, and we'd gladly play an actual game of Ocarina of Time in this Minecraft form

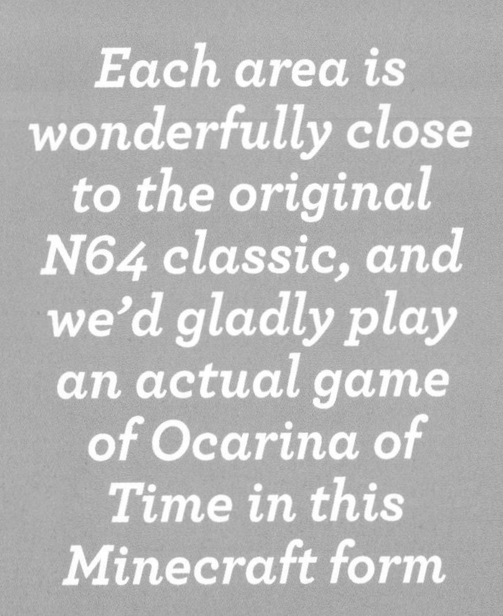

Kakariko Village sits in the shadow of Death Mountain

The Great Deku Tree, guardian of the Kokiri

Zora's Fountain is the home of Lord Jabu-Jabu. The whale can't swallow you yet, but the creator is working on it!

Ganon's Tower after Link has created the rainbow bridge

Gerudo Valley, home of Ganondorf's band of thieves

Although this build may look simple, it sticks close to the source material

Each location has been recreated with as much accuracy as possible

The various locations you adventure through in the real game are here

The familiar design adorns the Pokémon Center's floor

Shops and stores have been modeled, too

POKÉMON - KANTO REGION

A battle from *Pokémon* is all well and good, but how about an entire region to explore? This project by gmng24 recreates the series's famous Kanto region, packing in every town, city, and route, paying keen attention to each and every detail. Interiors are fully modeled, and seen from above the map looks exactly like the original layout.

SUPER MARIO

We can't have Nintendo characters and not have the man himself, can we? Here he is, in his classic, original guise from the first *Super Mario Bros.* This build by Justinheath905 keeps things simple, the way they should be, and it depicts Mario's famous jumping pose and his original NES-era limited colors. It's a perfect recreation of one of gaming's most famous heroes.

The jump-happy plumber looks right at home in the blocky world of Minecraft

He may be a little less rounded, but this is a faithful *Sonic*-style mini-game

SONIC THE HEDGEHOG

Sega's once-unstoppable mascot may have flagged in terms of popularity of late, but that hasn't stopped fans from paying tribute to the series. This build isn't just a simple map, but a fully functional racing mini-game, in which players are timed as they run around a circuit from checkpoint to checkpoint. It even has exploding jump pads, a working timer, and a huge Robotnik/Eggman face to run through. The whole map feels and looks like the Green Hill Zone, and other familiar items from the games include the checkered detail in the ground and palm tree decorations. You can download the map, created by Disco, from *www.ocddisco.com*. Toot, toot, Sonic warrior!

The map is complex and has multiple checkpoints to reach

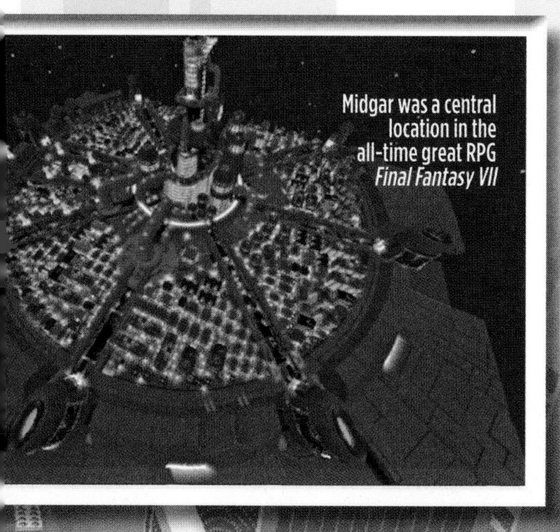

Midgar was a central location in the all-time great RPG *Final Fantasy VII*

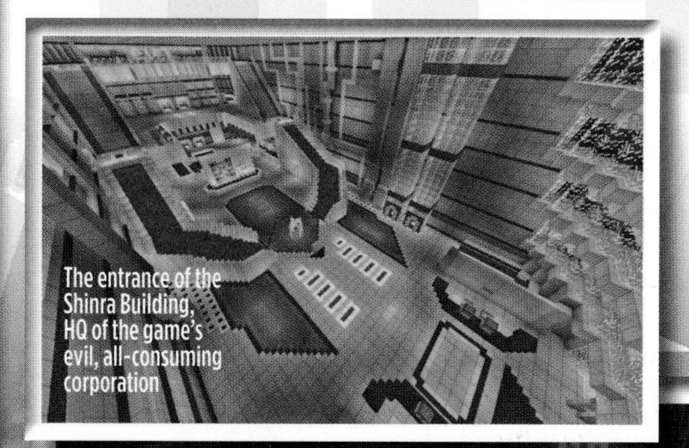

The entrance of the Shinra Building, HQ of the game's evil, all-consuming corporation

Even the Shinra logo looks the part

Every location has been carefully built with fine detail in mind

The offices of the Shinra Building are complex

FINAL FANTASY VII – MIDGAR

It took around two years for Killerx20 to create this masterpiece, with a little help from friends and other builders. It reproduces the city of Midgar from *Final Fantasy VII*, and is one of the most complex and intricate builds around. The project contains the entire city of Midgar, complete with various interiors, including the Shinra Building and Mako reactors. These interiors are modeled straight from the game and mirror the prerendered locations from the PlayStation classic.

MIRROR'S EDGE

The whitewashed, almost monochromatic city from EA's *Mirror's Edge* is very recognizable, and this recreation is very accurate. Created by Lord_Pancake, this pigment-light urban cityscape comes complete with red highlights to aid any free-running rebel on a mission, signifying spots that can be navigated in order to evade the police. The rendered scene looks like it was lifted from the actual game, so accurate is it in detail.

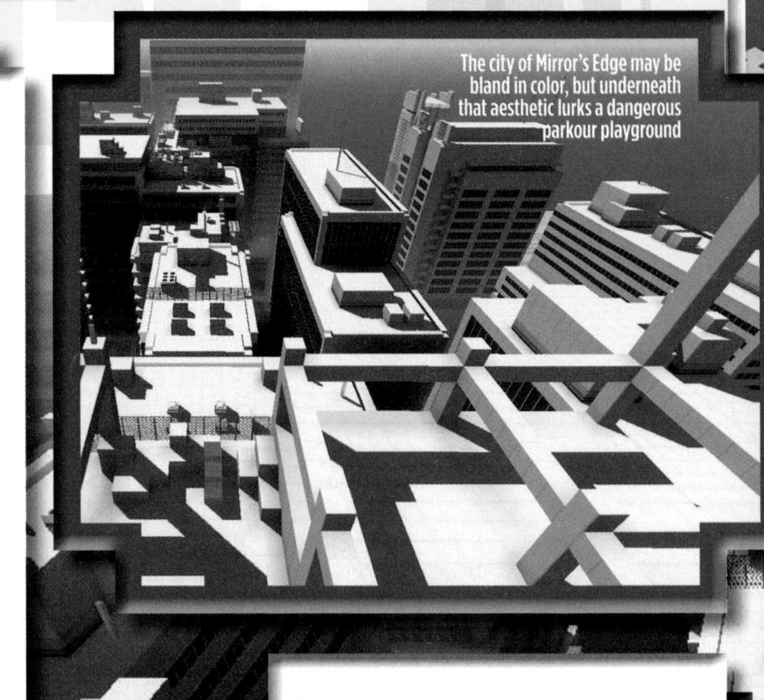

The city of Mirror's Edge may be bland in color, but underneath that aesthetic lurks a dangerous parkour playground

PORTAL – COMPANION CUBE

The game that launched a thousand memes, *Portal* is an internet hit, and this inanimate object is one of the most famous "characters" from the puzzler. Whether or not the cube actually contains human bodies (such is the theory), for a simple cube with a heart emblazoned on it, it's had quite a lot of success. It can now be found in many forms, including on mugs, plush toys, and in Minecraft builds. One example of the latter is this creation by user devatrox. It's a huge Companion Cube (which could contain a whole laboratory full of bodies), and bears all the details of the helpful cube.

The Weighted Companion Cube, only on a much larger and weightier scale

The *Normandy* SR-2 on station and ready for action

It's not to scale, but it's still a sizeable ship that took creator Tutifus four days to make

Doesn't look like there are any Mass Relays nearby

The SR-2 was larger than the original *Normandy* being built by Cerberus

Make sure you grab a Mass Effect skin or two, and you're all set

MASS EFFECT 2 – NORMANDY

Recreating famous vehicles is very popular in Minecraft, and one of the most famous video game vessels has to be the *Normandy* from *Mass Effect*. Here, we have the *Normandy SR-2* from *Mass Effect 2*, which is seen hovering above the ground. It's not to scale, but it's still a sizeable ship that took creator Tutifus four days to make. It nails the color scheme and the overall look, and although there may be no Reapers in Minecraft's world, it's all the safer for having the ship patrolling.

HALO – PILLAR OF AUTUMN

This build of the UNSC ship from the first game is a mammoth 1:3 replica, and not only does it look great from the outside, it also has a 1:1 interior, complete with cryo bay, where we first see the Master Chief as he's woken from his slumber. The build sees the ship in dry dock, with cranes and platforms granting access to it, and the inside includes the bridge and hangar bay.

The Pillar of Autumn from *Halo*

Currently in dry dock, the *POA* will soon tackle the Covenant threat

This is the cryo bay, where the pins are blown and the Master Chief awakes

The bridge of the ship, where Captain Keyes commands his loyal crew

The detail is excellent

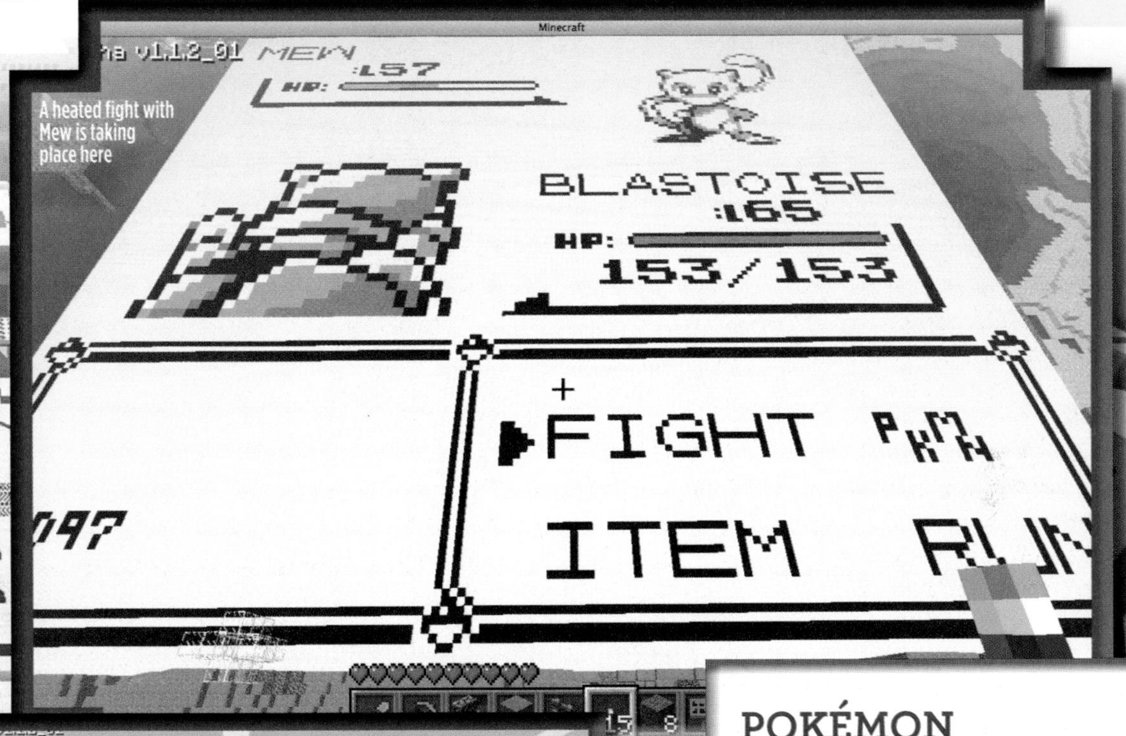

A heated fight with Mew is taking place here

Looking from the side, you can appreciate how many blocks went into this build

POKÉMON

Pokémon is one of Nintendo's most successful series, beginning life on the classic, monochrome Game Boy. The mixture of RPG adventuring and turn-based combat became an instant hit and remains so to this day. There have been many homages to the pocket monster phenomenon, including this unique creation. User KingDan97 has created an actual battle screen from the classic Game Boy iteration of the series, complete with menu system. The huge screen is a mixture of obsidian and snow blocks, and creates a realistic-looking scene from the game.

An actual battle screen from the classic Game Boy iteration of the series

BIOSHOCK – RAPTURE

Any large-scale build is challenging, especially underwater—the wrong block removed from the wrong place can lead to disaster. So, this underwater city by TraktorHagrid, inspired by Rapture from *BioShock*, is all the more impressive. It features a fully submerged structure, complete with submarine bay, observation windows, and that Jules Verne feel. All it's missing are some Splicers, Big Daddies, and Little Sisters running around.

It's not quite as big as the fictional city of Rapture in the game, but this is nonetheless quite the build

It may be an underwater dwelling, but it still has the home comforts

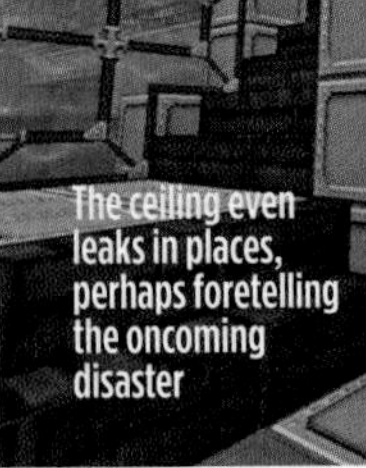

The ceiling even leaks in places, perhaps foretelling the oncoming disaster

The submarine bay, a possible escape, unless you're betrayed by an ally...

The texture pack adds plenty of atmosphere

No one actually knew Samus was female until they beat the game, back when the original was released in 1986

The detail of the Varia Suit is excellent, from the arm blaster to the neon green visor

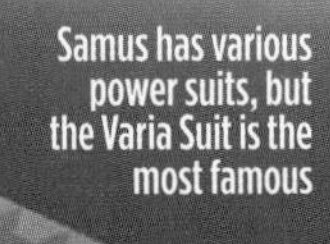

Samus has various power suits, but the Varia Suit is the most famous

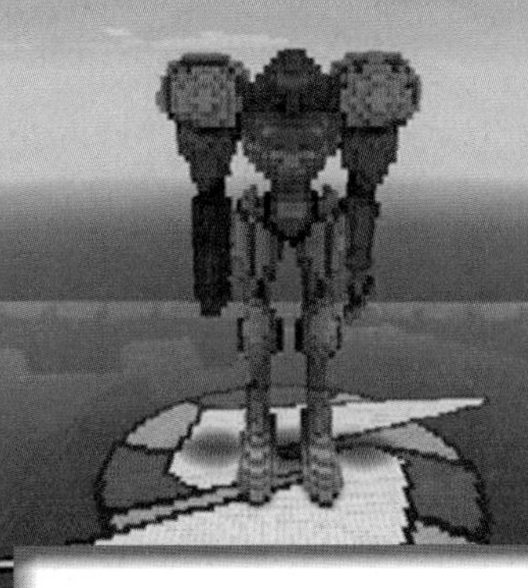

The color scheme is perfect, with the right blocks being used for just the right spots

Thankfully, there are no space jellyfish in the world of Minecraft

METROID – SAMUS ARAN

She's one of Nintendo's most-loved characters, and here we can see intergalactic bounty hunter Samus Aran in all her Varia-suited glory. The heroine from the *Metroid* series of games, Samus Aran and her instantly recognizable power suit have been modeled by user SoulSoda, complete with Samus's own logo functioning as an attractive base. The detail of the Varia Suit is excellent, from the arm blaster and bigger-than-the-'80s shoulder pads to the neon green visor. Let's just hope the last Metroid is still in captivity...

TECHNICAL BUILDS

TECHNICAL BUILDS

They may not always be pretty, but these builds take Minecraft to a whole different level

3D PRINTER

Created by ItsJustJumby, this is a masterpiece in Minecraft logic manipulation. Before the game had the /fill command added, it would have been very tricky to try something like this, but Jumby did and it works. This is a fully working 3D printer that lets users place blocks designed in various chests, using glass blocks for air spaces. Once the design's layers are assembled in the chests, the machine can "print" out the layers to form a 3D object. This can then be destroyed and the machine reset to print something else. The printer mechanics are a mass of command blocks, redstone, and hoppers, and just looking at it may give you a headache.

The printing space is the dark gray spot in the center of the room

A 3D-printed creeper sits waiting to be destroyed to make room for another print

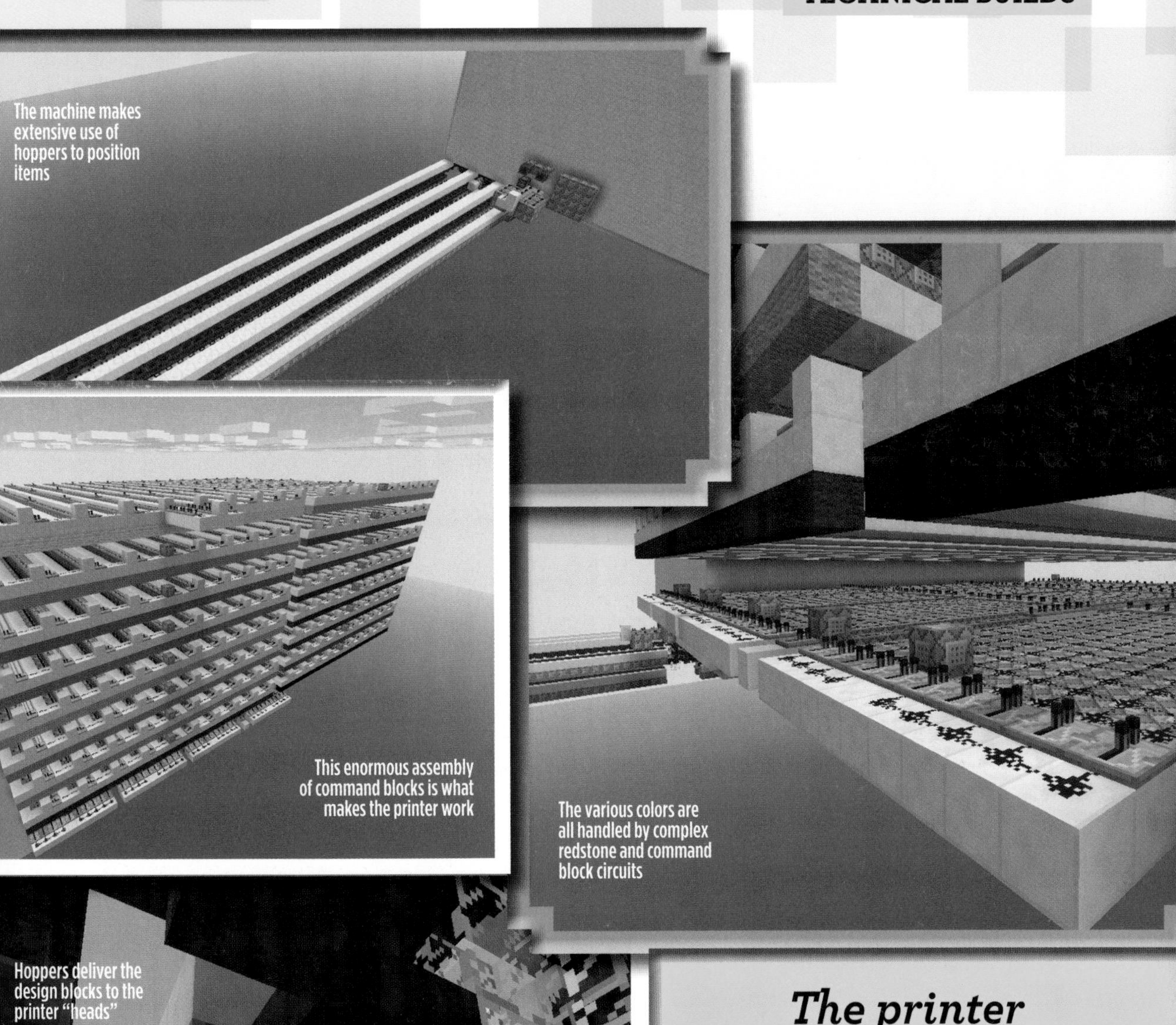

The machine makes extensive use of hoppers to position items

This enormous assembly of command blocks is what makes the printer work

The various colors are all handled by complex redstone and command block circuits

Hoppers deliver the design blocks to the printer "heads"

The printer mechanics are a mass of command blocks, redstone, and hoppers, and just looking at it may give you a headache

16-BIT ALU

The 16-bit ALU by theinternetftw was the first major step to a real, working computer within Minecraft. An ALU, or Arithmetic Logic Unit, is a basic building block of computing, and this was created using Minecraft's redstone system. It's a full 16-bit ALU, which theinternetftw intended on creation to be the first part of a full 16-bit system within the game. Notch himself praised the build, and it remains one of the most important user builds, which would lead to even more impressive creations...

With the ALU complete, the road to working Minecraft computers was paved

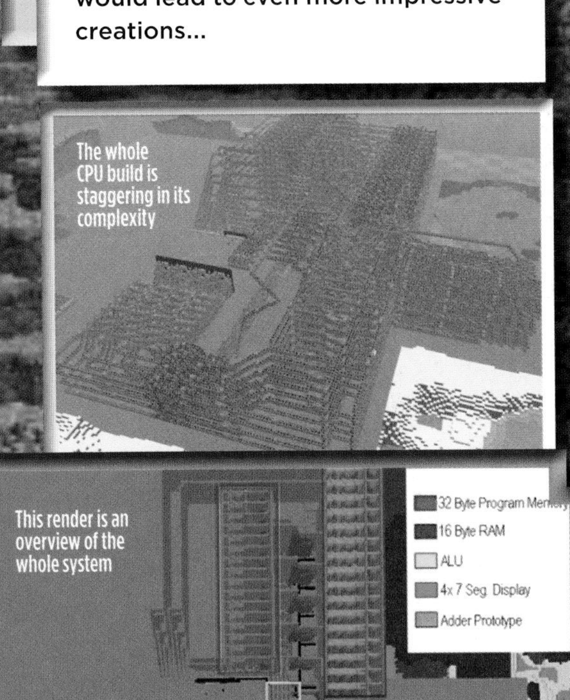

The whole CPU build is staggering in its complexity

This render is an overview of the whole system

WORKING COMPUTER

Since the 16-bit ALU, a lot of computers have been built within Minecraft, but this one by Salaja is one of the most impressive as it was one of the first. The complex maze of redstone circuitry spread throughout the elaborate structure shows just how difficult it must have been to build. The CPU can actually load up to 16 lines of code into its RAM, at which point it can execute operations to solve rudimentary problems, such as simple mathematics. The results can then be output onscreen via a hexadecimal display. Mind boggling.

The complexity of some Minecraft creations never ceases to amaze

Annotated overview of the system's rear

The top of the system

The specifications of the system are impressive, with 32 bytes of RAM, 256 bytes of ROM, and a variable-speed clock that equates to an average of 250 millihertz

16-BIT COMPUTER

Created by ohmganesha, this is a sprawling Minecraft computer system with working ALU and CPU. The system is based on the Hack platform, detailed in *The Elements of Computing Systems* *(www.nand2tetris.org)*, but also contains some new additions by ohmganesha, such as XOR and a random number generator. The specifications of the system are impressive, with 32 bytes of RAM, 256 bytes of ROM, and a variable-speed clock that equates to an average of 250 millihertz. More pictures on the next page!

The front of the system

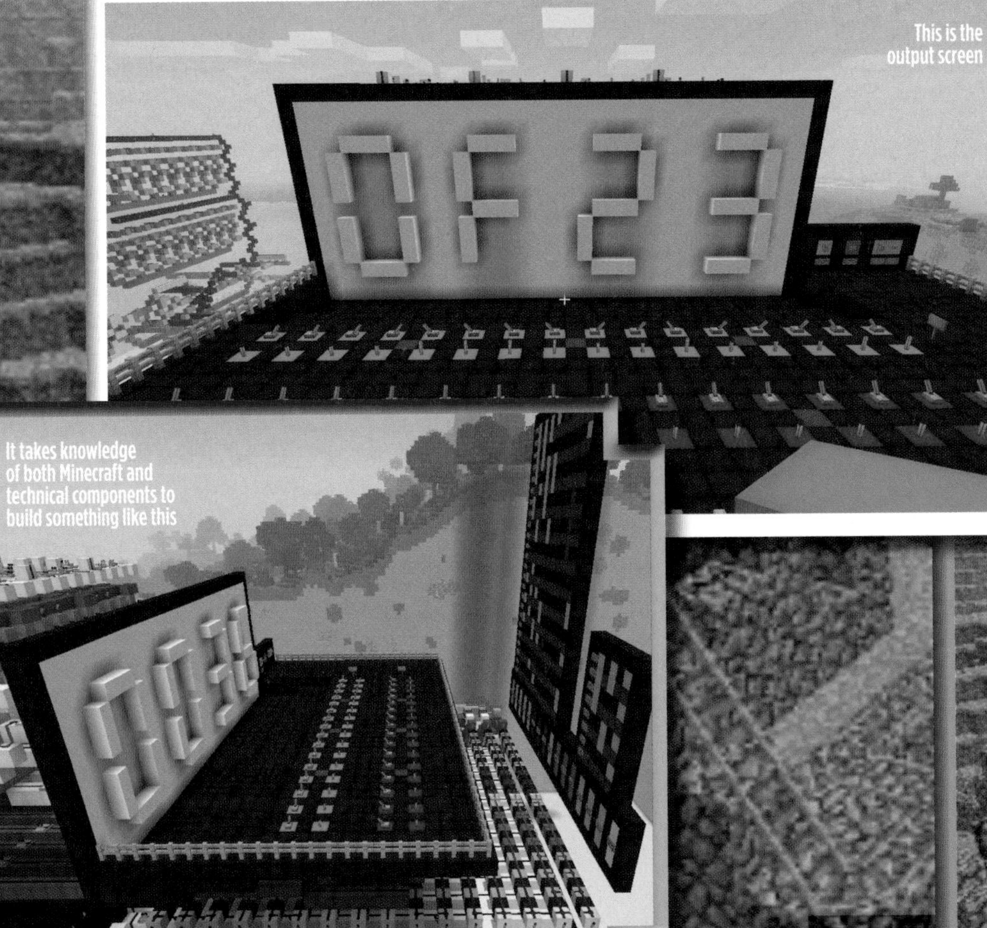

This is the output screen

It takes knowledge of both Minecraft and technical components to build something like this

Mixing a whole heap of TNT, animals in mine carts, and some clever building skill, this build creates a hilarious display of farm animal space launches

The cannon uses a channeled TNT explosion to launch critters skyward

Animals are stored in mine carts for easy loading

The whole contraption seen from above

ANIMAL CANNON

Not all inventive builds have to be technically proficient or able to run calculations. Some can be simple, stupid fun, and this creation from Keirshar certainly qualifies. Mixing a whole heap of TNT, animals in mine carts, and some clever building skill, this build creates a hilarious display of farm animal space launches, as an unfortunate creature is launched at extreme speeds into the great blue yonder. The animals are never seen again, and the pyrotechnics that precede this flight create quite a bang. Fun for all the family.

GRAPHING CALCULATOR

There have been a fair selection of devices created in Minecraft that can handle simple mathematical problems, but few are as impressive as this graphing calculator. It's a titanic build that doesn't attempt to hide any of the inner workings. Instead, the stunningly complex maze of circuitry takes pride of place, and you can easily see just how impressive the nature of this build is. What's more, the project's creator, IceGlade, built this when they were only 14, demonstrating a clear natural talent for such complex machinery. This all adds up to one of the most amazing technical builds we've seen.

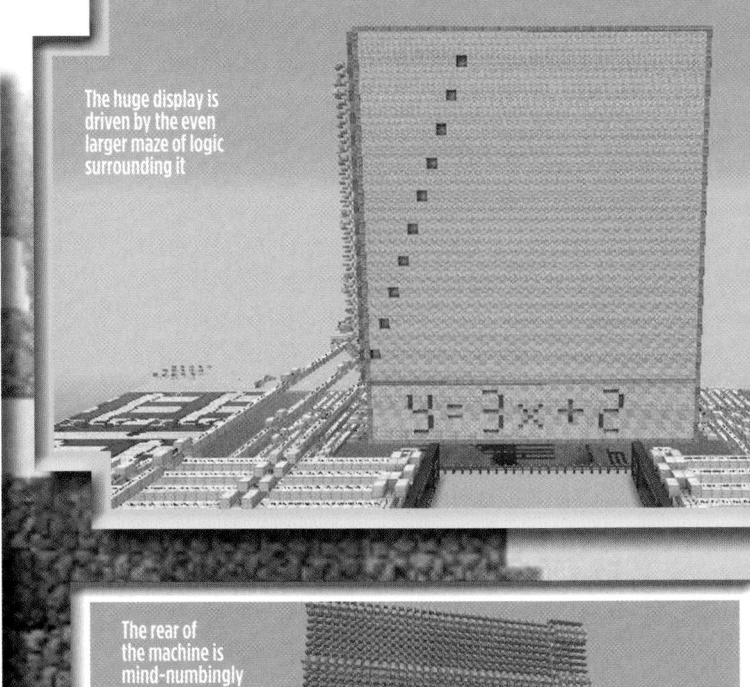

The huge display is driven by the even larger maze of logic surrounding it

The rear of the machine is mind-numbingly complex

This is the control room where the calculator is used

You can clearly see how the redstone wire works, and how it uses pistons and other blocks

From the outside, the house just looks like a simple hut

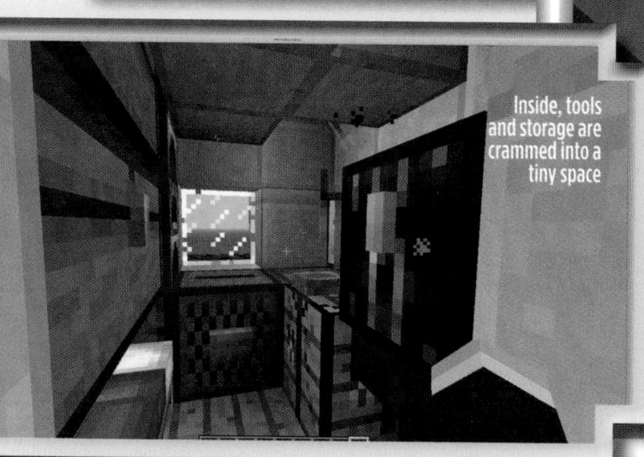
Inside, tools and storage are crammed into a tiny space

Below ground is an enchantment table and farm

jdmiller82 chose to create a house that contains everything in a 3x3 structure

The enchantment table is even fully boosted with a library

SUPER-COMPACT MINECRAFT HOUSE

When you're building your home, do you build a structure large enough to house all of your important tools? The answer is probably yes, and it's likely your house is fairly large to accommodate this. However, jdmiller82 chose to create a house that contains everything in a 3x3 structure. The house features a bed, three furnaces, two large chests, a cauldron, jukebox, crafting table, enchanting table, brewing stand, anvil, and ender chest. There's even a food dispenser. All crammed into a tiny space.

MINECRAFT INTERSTATE

This clever time-lapse video is built by Brett, who mined his way through the world in a straight line, cutting through cliffs, mountains, forests, and even crossing oceans, placing mine cart rail as he went. The final route, which took 24 hours over two months and spans eight miles, can be traveled from one end to the other and takes in some stunning sights as day descends into night. The route would take half an hour to travel by cart normally, but the time-lapse video compacts this to just over three minutes. You can see this at *www.youtube.com/watch?v=asImTDkPWKA*, where you can also download a link for the map, so you can travel the route yourself.

This render shows the entire Interstate. To give you an idea of how big this is, just the JPG file is nearly 15MB in size!

The view as you fly through the world via cart is beautiful

Make sure you check out the video on YouTube to see this in action

The whole machine is modeled on the original 1980 cabinet

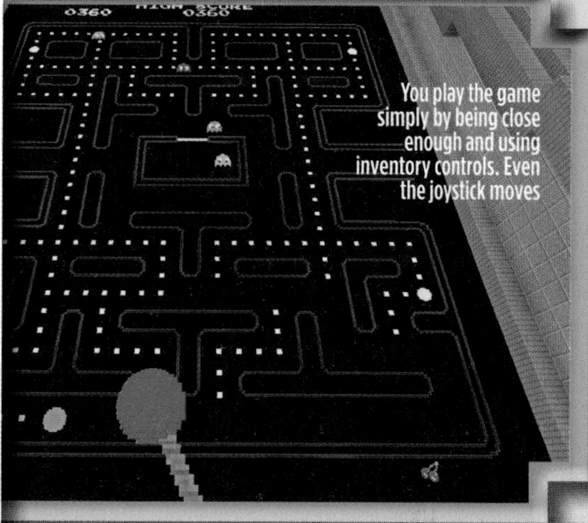

You play the game simply by being close enough and using inventory controls. Even the joystick moves

Artwork is made using Minecraft's blocks, and MrSquishyYT created his own for the actual game board

PAC-MAN ARCADE MACHINE

This is one of the most impressive technical Minecraft builds we've seen. MrSquishyYT has actually created a playable and accurate version of *Pac-Man* within Minecraft, contained within an original arcade cabinet. Players can load up the map and play full games of *Pac-Man*, with power pills, a high score, and lives. The project took a year to create, and MrSquishyYT used his own graphics and textures. However, and this is one of the most amazing parts, aside from the custom graphics, the rest of the build is in vanilla Minecraft, with no extra mods. The game also boasts the same AI routines of the original *Pac-Man*, in that the various ghosts behave differently. There are more pictures on the next page, too! You can also download the build itself from *bit.ly/1LH9BWL*.

The game even has the original music and sound effects

The game boasts the same AI routines of the original Pac-Man, in that the various ghosts behave differently

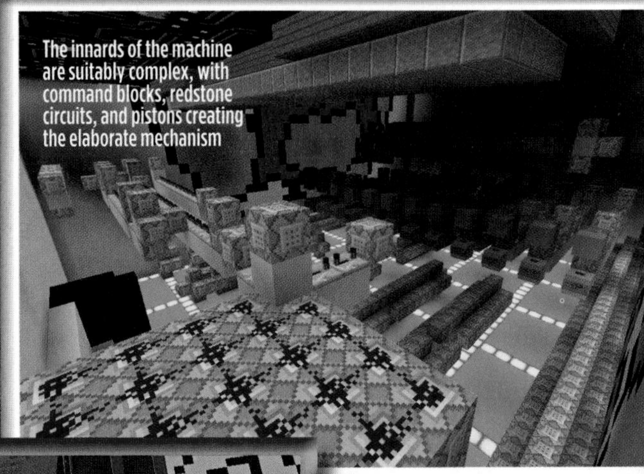
The innards of the machine are suitably complex, with command blocks, redstone circuits, and pistons creating the elaborate mechanism

The behind-the-scenes configuration is insanely clever

The Overworld map has been faithfully recreated with a 1:3 scale

THE LEGEND OF ZELDA

The *Pac-Man* arcade machine is amazing, but imagine how impressive a recreation of a game as complex as *The Legend of Zelda* for the NES would be if it were built within Minecraft. Actually, you don't have to imagine it, as a pair of talented Minecraft players are doing just that. Designer Evan Stanhope and programmer Jonathon Faulch are attempting to reproduce the Nintendo classic within Minecraft, right down to the actual programming. The end result will be a fully playable *Zelda* in first person within Minecraft. The project is still being worked on, but already it looks stunning, with a full *Zelda* map built and an ingenious logic system running behind the scenes that can detect where in the map the player is. This sensor system is used to control events of the game, such as spawning enemies. You can find out more about this amazing project at imgur.com/a/s9ITL. Always remember, though: It's dangerous to go alone. More pics on the next page!

The project is still being worked on, but already it looks stunning, with a full Zelda map built

The 3D versions of the traditionally 2D areas look great

Zelda fans will no doubt instantly recognize the areas, even in 3D

An ingenious logic system running behind the scenes can detect where in the map the player is

As the original game was so basic visually, a Minecraft recreation looks very authentic

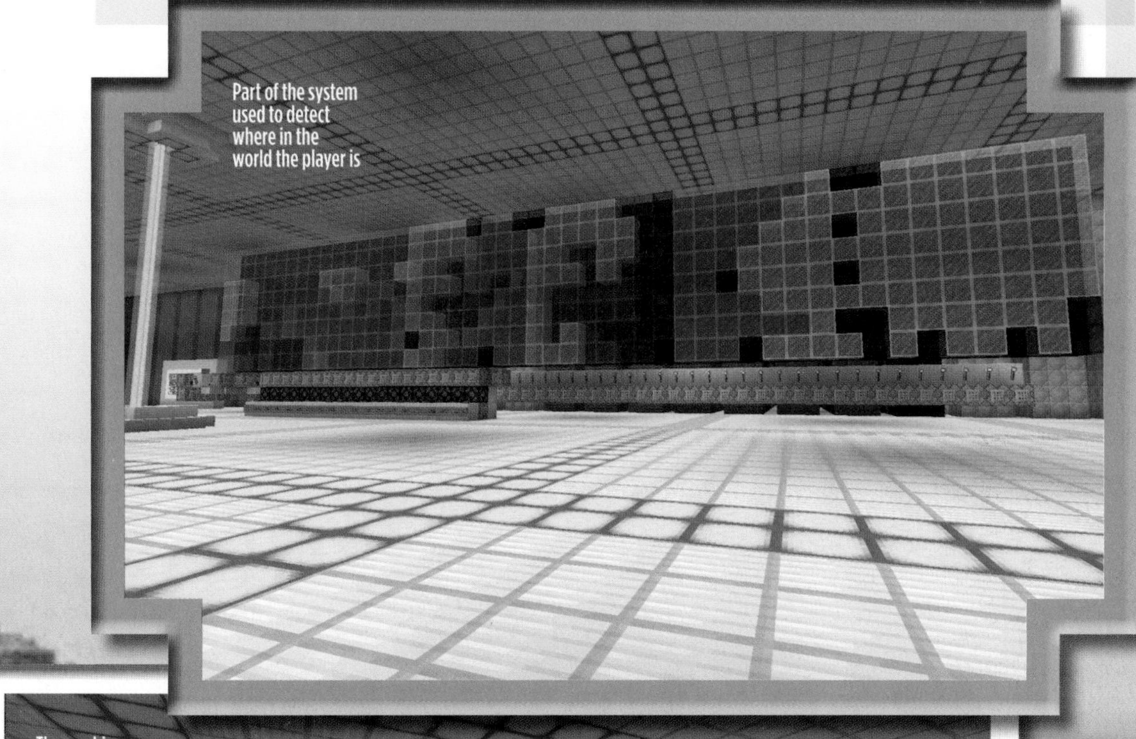

Part of the system used to detect where in the world the player is

The machinery behind the game's logic

The end result will be a fully playable Zelda in first person within Minecraft

ADVENTURE MAP BUILDS

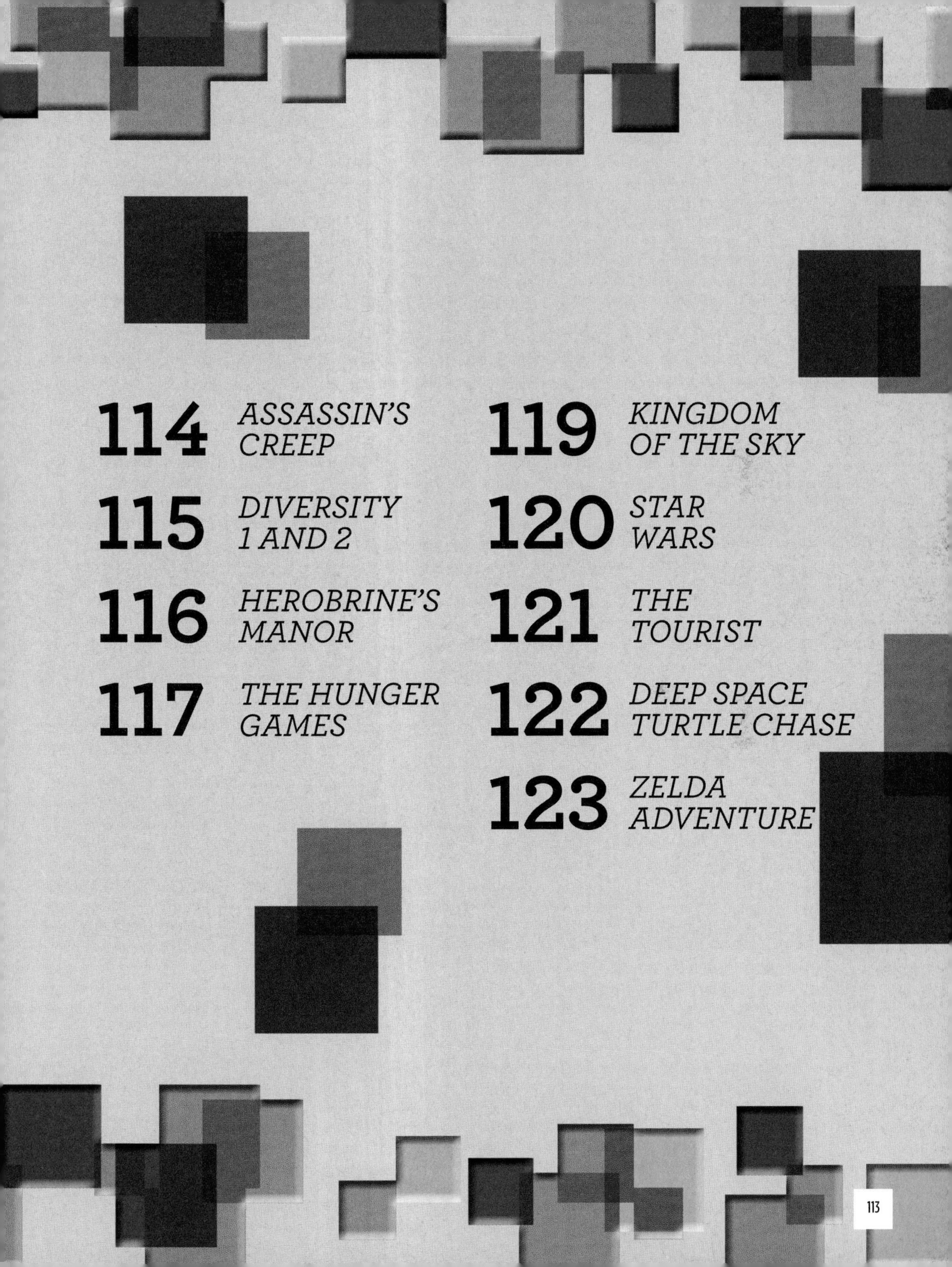

ADVENTURE MAPS

Survival and Creative aren't the only modes in Minecraft. Adventure mode allows for a different kind of build

ASSASSIN'S CREEP

Created by Selib and DrChriz, this Minecraft map is inspired by Ubisoft's *Assassin's Creed*. It's a parkour-themed map that challenges you to complete tasks to recover wool blocks. These blocks, as in many CTM (complete the monument) maps, allow you to access the final challenge. The map itself takes place in a well-designed location with plenty of typical *Assassin's Creed* features, such as rooftop running, jumping, and mantling, as well as the need to avoid guards and plan your actions. This can be grabbed from ***bit.ly/1bkAEXB***

There's a Roman theme to the location on offer

The area has been designed to offer plenty in the way of freerunning opportunities

This is the latest and best version of the Diversity adventure map

The adventure map is a quest for the item

TRIVIA BRANCH

Brains, not brawn, will help you in the trivia section

PUZZLE BRANCH

Puzzle solving can win you your needed item here

DIVERSITY 1 AND 2

CTM maps are very popular, and Diversity is undoubtedly one of the best around. Now in two versions, this adventure map tasks you with finding colored blocks of wool to complete the monument. The difference with this map is the variety of genres the adventure takes in. Each block is earned from a series of different challenges, such as puzzles, arena fights, freerunning obstacles courses, and more. There's a surprisingly varied amount of gameplay in these two maps, and they're well worth checking out if you like your Minecraft experience to be a little more, um ... diverse. The older, original map is only designed for 1.7.4, but the more recent Diversity 2 will work on the latest version of Minecraft. You can grab it from *bit.ly/1hZi7Uu*

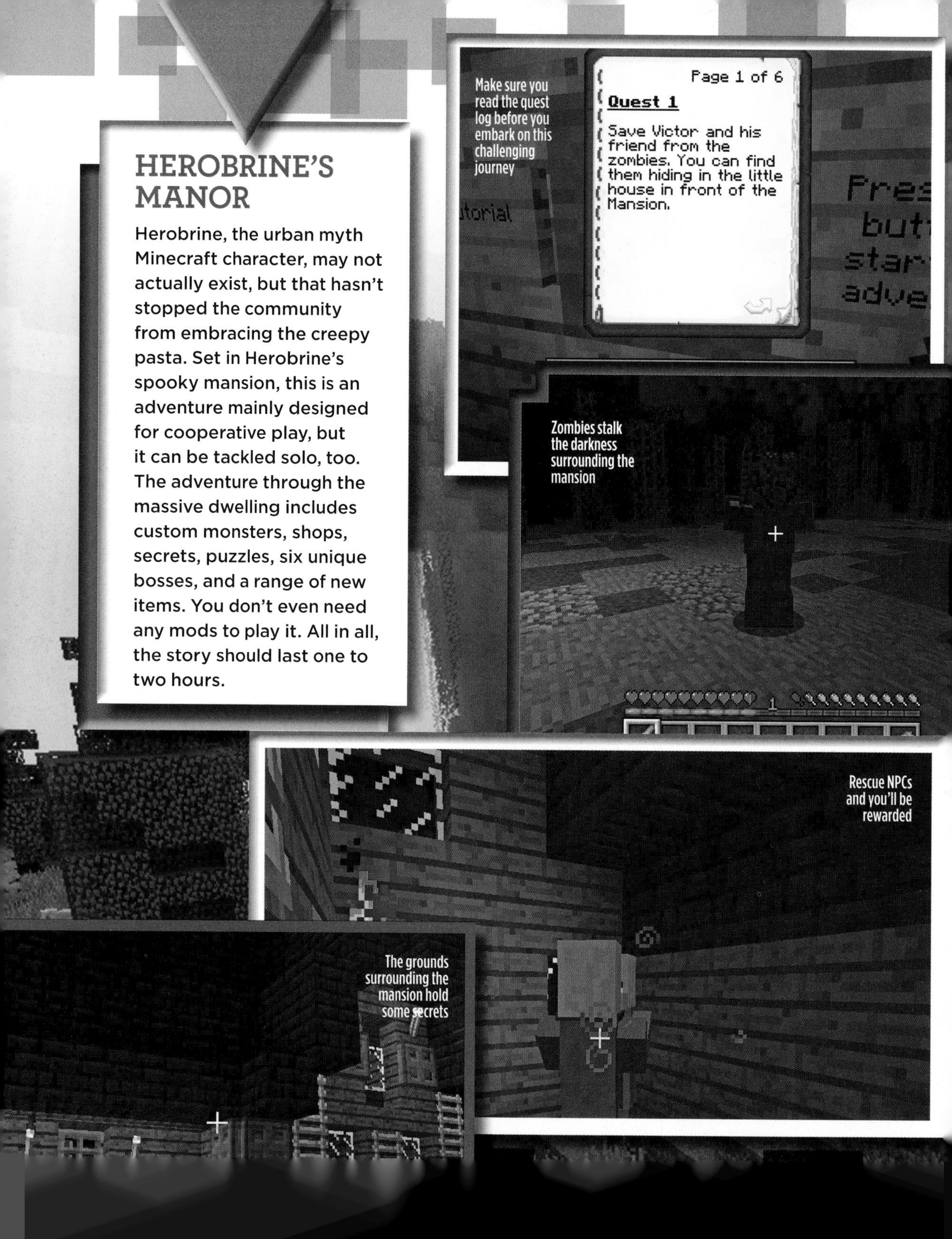

Page 1 of 6
Quest 1
Save Victor and his friend from the zombies. You can find them hiding in the little house in front of the Mansion.

HEROBRINE'S MANOR

Herobrine, the urban myth Minecraft character, may not actually exist, but that hasn't stopped the community from embracing the creepy pasta. Set in Herobrine's spooky mansion, this is an adventure mainly designed for cooperative play, but it can be tackled solo, too. The adventure through the massive dwelling includes custom monsters, shops, secrets, puzzles, six unique bosses, and a range of new items. You don't even need any mods to play it. All in all, the story should last one to two hours.

Make sure you read the quest log before you embark on this challenging journey

Zombies stalk the darkness surrounding the mansion

Rescue NPCs and you'll be rewarded

The grounds surrounding the mansion hold some secrets

THE HUNGER GAMES

This is a very popular adventure map, which is based on the books and movies of the same name. Created by Avocio, this is an adventure pack that doesn't require any special mods, and up to 24 players can take part in a very Minecraft version of the blood sport of the future. The map, which is encased in a giant dome, just as in the original stories, includes weapon chests, puzzles, hostile mobs, an optional timer, and a large, varied game world. There are a series of recommended rules for server admins to follow that enhance the map. The map itself can be found at ***bit.ly/1DtUd6F***

Admin Only
To enter the game simply step on any of the 24 pressure
Plates, if they are all taken you can enter spectate mode
by using the button beneath this set of instructions

The main building has an admin room where the game can be observed and controlled

Players spawn in the glass containers, and the mad dash for weapons begins

The central screen, complete with sponsor viewing rooms

More *Hunger Games* pictures on the next page →

Up to 24 players can take part in a very Minecraft version of the blood sport of the future

Chests contain different equipment and weapons. Choose wisely

There are various structures throughout the zone, with hidden puzzles and chests

The glass dome surrounds the arena, keeping participants confined to battle

As you progress, the map supplies links to YouTube clips that you need to listen to

Being a kingdom in the sky, there are plenty of precarious platforms

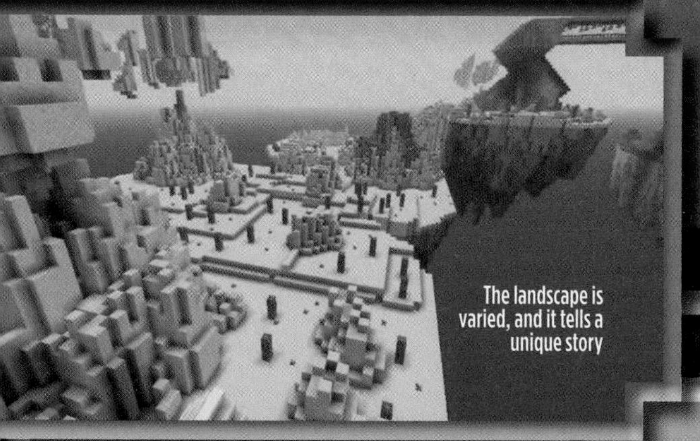

The landscape is varied, and it tells a unique story

Make sure you use the supplied texture pack, or the adventure won't work properly

KINGDOM OF THE SKY

This is one of the more inventive adventure maps around, not only due to the superb build, which thrusts you into a fantastic fantasy setting, but also the use of YouTube audio clips that serve as narration of the story. As you progress, the map supplies links to YouTube clips that you need to listen to. It's an interesting new way to tell a story within Minecraft. There's a sequel to this adventure, so when you're done, give the second map a try. You can get both, created by BlameTheController, from ***bit.ly/1vsXfJP***

You'll take in some fantastic sights during your adventure

STAR WARS

A Minecraft map based on *Star Wars*, with lightsabers, AT-ATs, the Millennium Falcon, Stormtroopers, a battle on Hoth, and an excursion to a Star Destroyer to face a Sith Lord. Yes, sign us up. This is a brilliant adventure map that features some excellent builds, including huge AT-ATs, expansive areas, and even a trip through space. There's plenty of combat, main and side quests, and it's designed for co-op play. It's created by Hypixel, and you can grab it from ***hypixel.net/threads/star-wars-adventure-map.29***

The Rebel base on Hoth is under attack, and you need to disable the incoming AT-AT

There are Stormtroopers aplenty for you to tackle with blaster or saber

AT-ATs are also a problem

There's plenty of combat, main and side quests, and it's designed for co-op play

Team up with friends to tackle this mini *Star Wars* tale

This adventure map has some high-quality builds within it

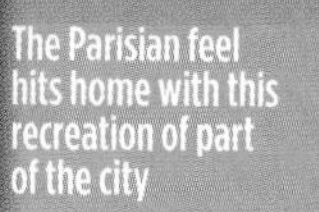

The Parisian feel hits home with this recreation of part of the city

The streets of Paris beckon

You'll explore many real-world locations

There's a custom GUI, so texture packs are recommended

THE TOURIST: A PLAYABLE ADVENTURE IN PARIS

This is a long adventure map, weighing in at around four hours, give or take. Set in Paris, it's a rather impressive build in its own right, and features some great architecture, including the Basilica of Montmartre, as well as a selection of mini-games and its own soundtrack. There's a decent story, too. It's a very well put together map, and a great achievement by builder Stratocrafteur. You can get the map from *www.planetminecraft.com/project/adventure-map-the-tourist*

DEEP SPACE TURTLE CHASE

Created by CaptainSparklez and members of The Voxel Box, this is one of the most impressive adventure maps in terms of scope and technical achievement. More of a total conversion than a simple map, this is an adventure in deep space, and brings a very different feel to Minecraft. It uses custom textures, sounds, items, and more, making for a map that really does make Minecraft feel like a very different game. It even has some impressive set pieces, and the whole adventure is obviously a labor of love. It's simply superb, and you should give it a try right away. Just be sure to back up your Minecraft data folder, as this is more complex than a simple map, and changes many settings. Grab from ***bit.ly/1HRC6Q3***

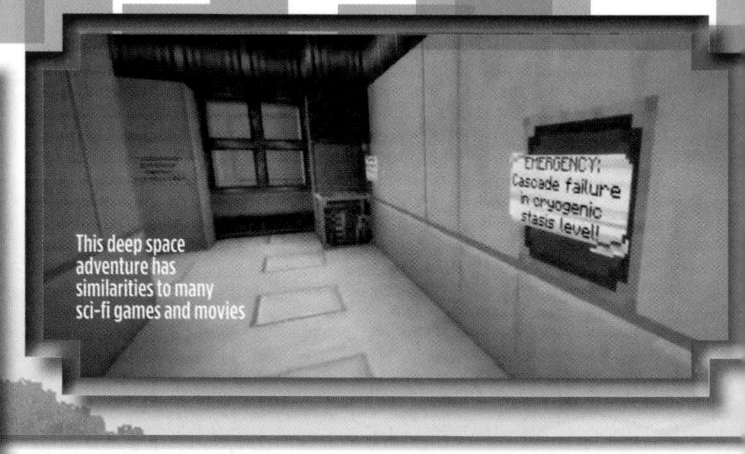

This deep space adventure has similarities to many sci-fi games and movies

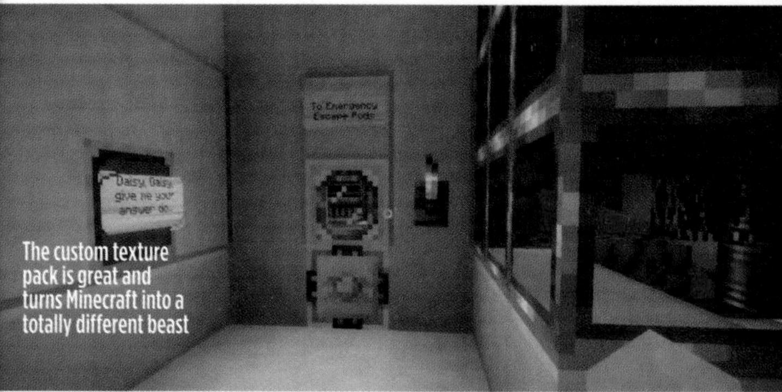

The custom texture pack is great and turns Minecraft into a totally different beast

More of a total conversion than a simple map, this brings a very different feel to Minecraft

Oh dear. The station begins to explode as you jettison to safety via escape pod

A range of elaborate and impressive locations are featured

ZELDA ADVENTURE

Few games match Nintendo's legendary *Zelda* series when it comes to action adventure, and builder Gary520 is obviously a fan, along with collaborator Spirale. They've spent a lot of time crafting this adventure map, which is inspired by the *Zelda* saga and uses a mod created by Cryect (AdventureCraft). It contains many familiar areas and situations from the RPG. In its latest version, the map should offer eight hours of gameplay, which is comparable to many full-price games, and it includes dungeons, puzzles, and even custom enemies and bosses. It also includes some *Zelda* sound effects for an authentic feel. Grab it at ***bit.ly/37sBs9l***

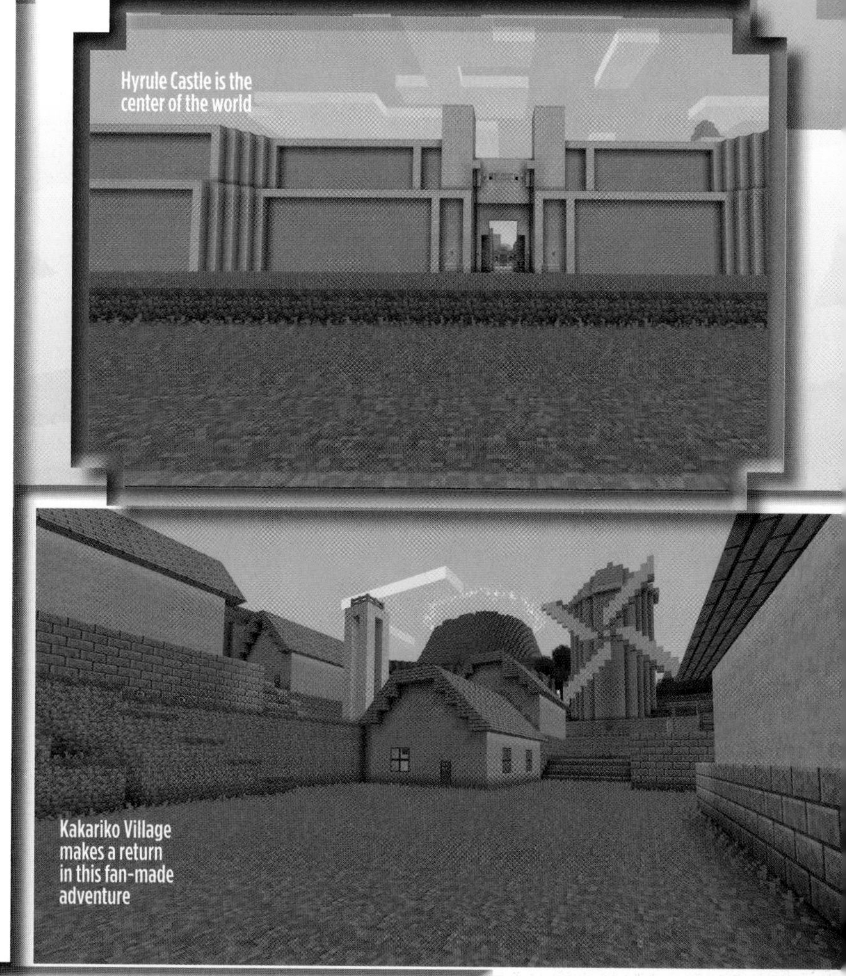

Hyrule Castle is the center of the world

Kakariko Village makes a return in this fan-made adventure

The ominous Death Mountain

Hyrule Castle Town, complete with Temple of Time

PIXEL ART

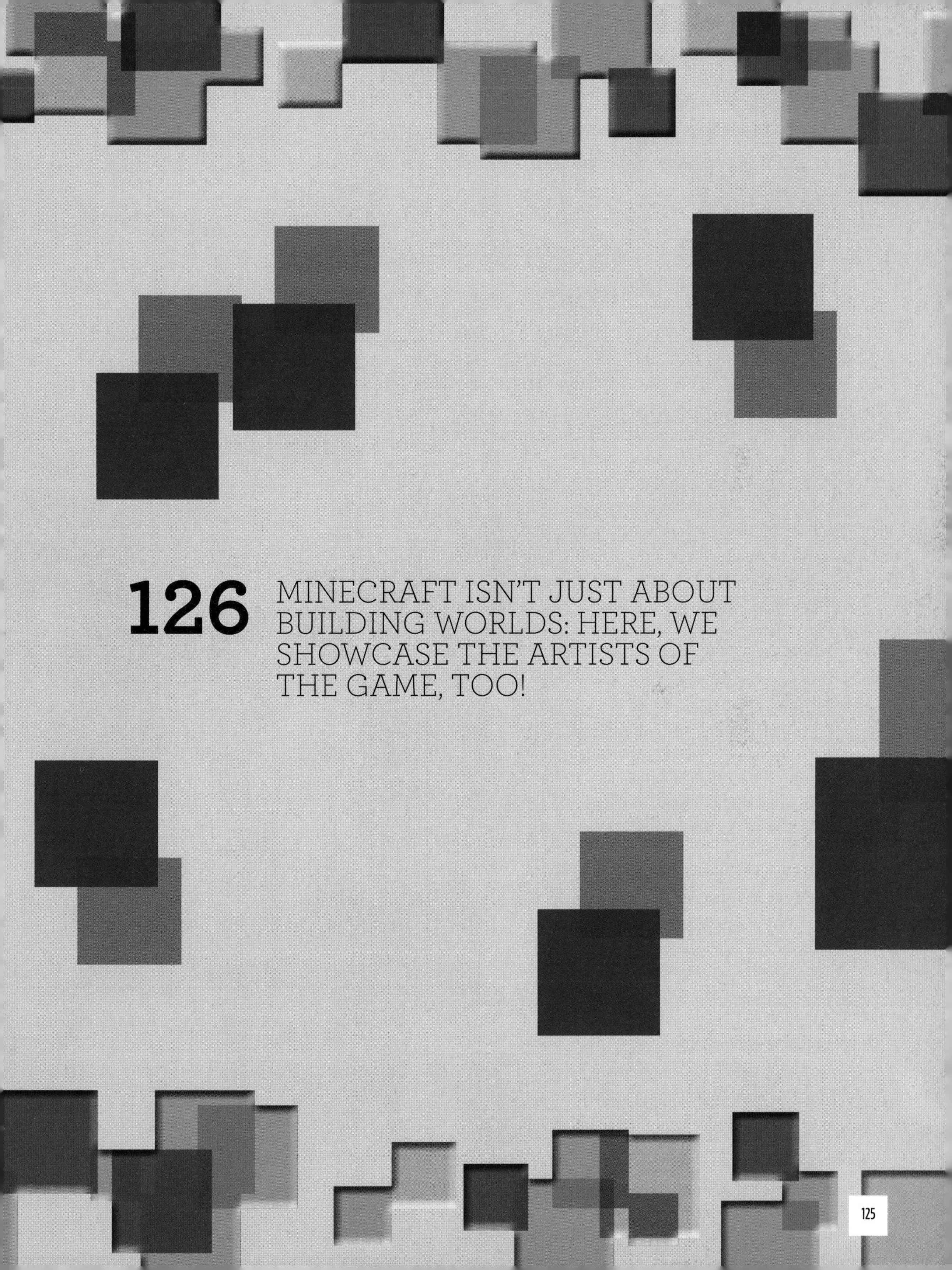

126 MINECRAFT ISN'T JUST ABOUT BUILDING WORLDS: HERE, WE SHOWCASE THE ARTISTS OF THE GAME, TOO!

PIXEL ART

Not all creations in Minecraft are structures and machines. Sometimes builders just want to express their artistic side

STARCRAFT – KERRIGAN

Currently, this Minecraft pixel art stands as the world record holder. The image uses over 1.1 million blocks and took 23 weeks to create. The creator of the record-breaking artwork, Tholar Tholarian, silenced critics who thought the image was faked by uploading a stream showing the final steps of the image's creation live to Twitch viewers. And if the fact that this amazing art was created in Minecraft isn't enough, he also takes any income from his streams and donates it to the Make-A-Wish Foundation. You can see the video at ***www.youtube.com/watch?v=vChMzRnw-Hc***

All of that detail and shading is built out of Minecraft blocks, in a normal Minecraft world

Tholar streamed the final stages of the image's creation, raising money for charity at the same time

When zoomed in, you can start to see how the image is made up

You can clearly see the various types of block used to make up this enormous image

PIXEL ART GALLERY

Meloetta (*Pokémon*) – vc1205

Nyan Cat – Dean0162

Ornstein (*Dark Souls*)

Artorias (*Dark Souls*) – Terminator8359

Hatsune Miku – Zczattis

Stormtrooper (*Star Wars*) – antonio

Android – Demon2113

Link (*Legend of Zelda*) – CaptainHarlock33

Pringles Man – BoxGamesTV

Rick (*Splatterhouse II*) – DamianDrake

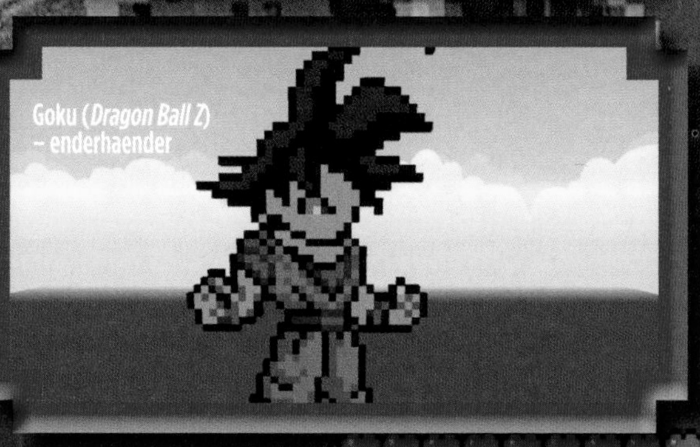

Goku (*Dragon Ball Z*) – enderhaender

Psy – MrSmiley101

Vault Boy (*Fallout*) – su_root

Slenderman – Ryantoy

Spider-Man – SilverTree

Mega Man – mrnada

Simon Belmont (*Castlevania*) – mrnada

Sonic and Tails – mrnada

Tails

Bart Simpson – rmtweb

Gir (*Invader Zim*) – DresdenDx3

Jimi Hendrix – GibsonAxe

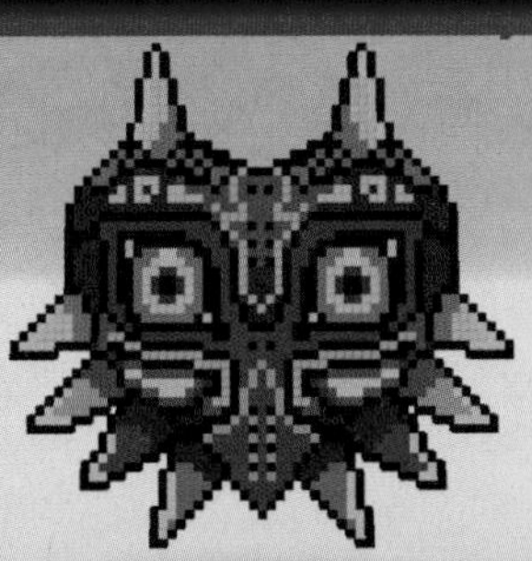

Majora's Mask (*Legend of Zelda*) – AguilaBDN

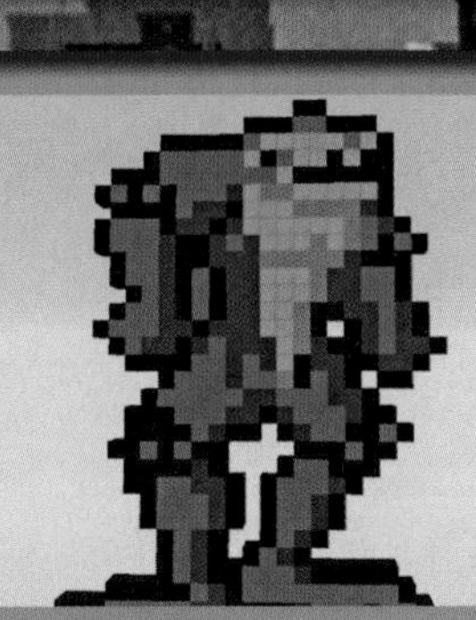

Rash (*Battletoads*) – CloudExSoldier

Pikachu (*Pokémon*) – Preatchman

Dalek (*Doctor Who*) - Ruyt

Diablo – galatasaray1905

Stewie (*Family Guy*) – DreamPhreak

Mythbusters – ert44

The 10th Doctor (*Doctor Who*) – ert44

Microsoft Office Clippy – Aerodrome

YOUR OWN BUILD

134 *INSPIRED TO CREATE YOUR OWN EPIC BUILD? TURN THE PAGE, AND WE'LL GET DOWN TO BUSINESS!*

TIPS FOR CREATING YOUR OWN EPIC BUILD

Creating large, complex builds isn't easy, but there are things you can do to make it easier

INSPIRATION

It's far easier to start your first epic build if you know exactly what you're going to create. It's tempting to craft that immense castle that's been rattling around your imagination, but a fictional structure like this can be hard to translate into Minecraft reality at first, especially on your first attempt at a large project.

It's also better to begin with a structure that actually exists, one that you can find pictures and drawings of. Using these, you can plan out a large structure without having to worry about any unknown elements.

This will get you used to creating larger builds and the pitfalls that can arise when you do. It will also refine your building techniques, so you'll be on top of your game when you come to build that impressive creation of your own.

Of course, even when picking an existing or real-world structure, know your limits. Start off with a realistic target. If you've never built a large, complex structure before, it's best not to try and reproduce an entire city or complicated building for your first try. Instead, pick a structure that's large and impressive, but a little more simplistic. This lets you focus on the bread and butter of planning and executing a large-scale build.

TAKE YOUR TIME

Whatever you decide to build, don't plan on doing so in one sitting. Although Minecraft may seem like a simple LEGO set, creating large and complex structures can take a very long time, even several months in some cases.

If you really want to create a huge, impressive build, you'll need to put in the time, work, and dedication, and do the various other tasks that most builders employ (which we'll cover elsewhere). The best builders don't just jump into the game and start building; a lot of time and effort goes into planning, and even more into building.

HAVE A PLAN

Before you fire up Minecraft, you'll want to do some rudimentary planning, and one of the best ways is to use good old pencil and paper. Graph paper, or any paper with a grid on it, is a great help, and using this you can easily draw up a basic plan that includes the dimensions of your build.

Alternatively, you can use software tools to plan out your builds. A perfect option is Minecraft Structure Planner (***bit.ly/2SPGWWS***). This is a program dedicated to planning out builds in Minecraft, and it uses a simple grid system that you can place blocks into, drawing them in just like an image editor. Once your schematic is ready, you can export this and use it as a guide, or pass the design onto others in your build team.

This will save you a huge amount of effort and cut down on guesswork and on-the-fly changes. Having exact measurements, even if only for the outer walls or general shape of your build, is a massive help. There's a reason real-world buildings and structures always have plans and schematics before the first brick is laid, and the world of Minecraft is no different.

Minecraft Structure Planner is a perfect way to plan your builds ahead of time

Complex structures, such as mazes like the one seen here, really need prior planning

SCOUT A GOOD LOCATION

Just as it's important to build in a good area when playing the game in Survival, so too is it important to pick the right place to build when creating your own epic build.

Although you can use tools to quickly clear an area, if you don't have such tools, it can take a very long time to clear an area for your build, so picking a good location is important and can save you a ton of time. Desert areas and flat lands are obvious prime spots, as they need much less clearing than a forest or uneven region.

Aside from the physical concerns of space to build, also consider what you're actually building and pick the right biome for the job. If you're going to build an ice castle, for example, you won't want to place it in a desert, as it just won't look right. A replica of London wouldn't really fit in a snowy forest, and a sandstone pyramid won't look great in the middle of a lush jungle (unless it's a stone Mayan temple, of course). If all else fails, take biomes out of the equation...

Desert biomes make perfect locations for certain builds, such as Egyptian-themed projects

Forests and jungles can make for a troublesome build area

Large hills and mountains can be a problem, but can also be of use if you're building large projects, as the mountain can be easily carved into

It's important to get the right area for your build, not picking one that's too uneven, which would create more work

GO SUPERFLAT

Many large-scale builds benefit from using a superflat world. This way, there are no biome-specific problems or other items in your way, and it's far easier to plan out and build. You don't need to clear areas or deal with different block types.

If you use this method, however, be sure to use the superflat world modifier to make the ground level higher, as the default places the superflat world just above bedrock. This means you won't be able to dig down if you need to, and an army of slimes will also spawn all over the place and can interfere with your build.

You can do this by selecting the superflat world and then picking a preset. Overworld is a good choice, as well as Tunneller's Dream and Bottomless Pit. These will give you plenty of room for underground structures, and a ground level high enough to stop irksome mob spawns.

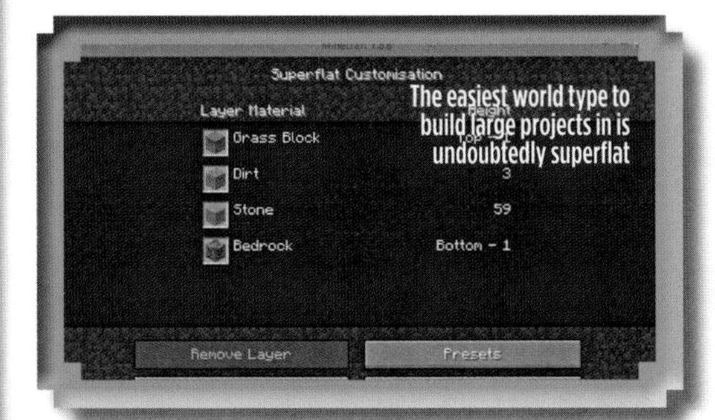

The easiest world type to build large projects in is undoubtedly superflat

UTILIZE CREATIVE MODE

Although it's a major achievement to build huge structures in Survival, as you have to mine and harvest your materials, doing so for your first couple of builds isn't advised. The amount of time that goes into a large-scale build is huge enough as it is, so adding in the need to gather resources and fight off mobs will make this even longer. Much longer.

It's best to start in Creative mode, as this gives you unlimited resources, the ability to fly (which is an enormous help when building large structures), and makes all mobs passive. This is perfect for focusing your attention on building.

Even advanced builders like those featured in this book mostly use Creative, as crafting these kinds of structures in Survival is just too time consuming, and life is too short. So, don't feel bad for switching to Creative and letting your imaginative juices flow.

BUILD WITH FRIENDS

A great deal of epic builds, especially those that take the form of large cities, are built on Minecraft servers by a team of people. Trying to build one on your own can sometimes be a little crazy, and things are always easier with help. Imagine how long it would take one man to build a skyscraper.

If possible, either start or join a server geared toward creating large builds, and draft in some friends to help. This can help in Creative mode, but since many servers actually use Survival mode, it's a tip that's almost essential.

Working in a team, you'll cut a huge amount of time off your build, and you can even assign people to specific roles. If you're building in Survival, for that ultimate achievement feeling, you could have a team of builders and a team of resource gatherers supplying the materials.

SCAFFOLDING

If you're a hardcore player, and you're just adamant that you want to build your structure in Survival, use special techniques to make things easier. For example, use soft blocks like dirt as scaffolding around your structure. Building steps and walkways can help you reach high places to build, and once you're done, the blocks are easily removed.

You can also build sand pillars to achieve the same result. Build the tower using sand blocks up to where you need to be, and when

A torch can destroy an entire sand pillar, making it a great technique for scaffolding

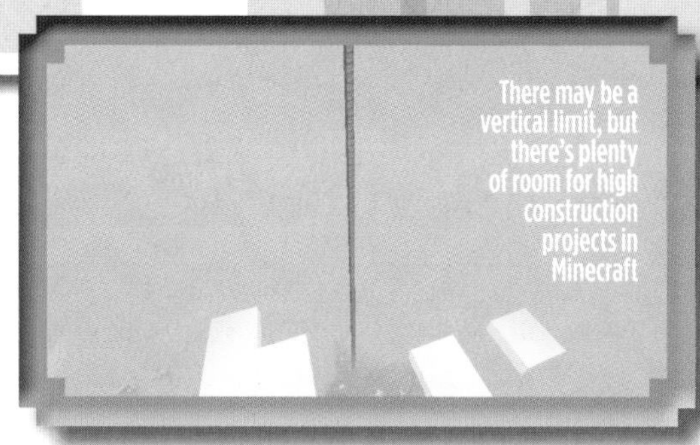
There may be a vertical limit, but there's plenty of room for high construction projects in Minecraft

you're done, simply replace the bottom block of the tower with a torch and the whole pillar will be removed. This can be tricky, as you need to be quick, but the whole pillar, regardless how tall, will be destroyed.

MIND YOUR HEAD

Minecraft's world, although almost infinite, has limits. One of these is the world height. Previously, the maximum altitude was 0-127, meaning 128 blocks above bedrock was the limit. Eventually this was enhanced, and now the limit is 0-255, allowing 256 blocks above bedrock to be reached. This is important for epic builds, as these will often be very tall and require as much height as you can possibly get. Even with this higher limit, you still need to plan your build accordingly, and try not to hit this limit and in turn cut off your structure early. Scale can help you out.

The maximum build height in Minecraft is 256 blocks above bedrock

SCALE IT BACK

One of the most tempting ideas to try when creating large builds is to create a true 1:1 replica of your subject. This is undeniably impressive, but it's also an idea that can lead to a failed project.

Given the height limit of the world in Minecraft, trying to build true 1:1 scale reproductions of famous landmarks can end in stunted, odd-looking results. There's just not enough vertical room to recreate 1:1 versions of some buildings. For this reason, you need to rein in your 1:1 ratio urges and start to scale things down. Doing this may end up with a smaller structure, but it's the only way to also ensure your build looks the part and has all of the detail you wish to include.

It's here where the tip of planning your build out on paper first comes in. Knowing the 256 block height limit, you can use this information to plan out a scaled-down version of your structure, and you won't run into any awkward surprises later on.

/FILL IT IN

Many builds require huge areas to be filled with blocks, and this can take a long, long time. There's a way around this, however, and it doesn't even need mods or extra tools. All you need is the built-in /fill command. This can be used to instantly fill in whole sections, and it can save a huge amount of time.

To use this, you need to have cheats enabled, so ensure you start a world with this option selected. When you're ready to fill an area, position yourself in the inner edge of one of the corners. Now, press F3 to display some important information.

This information will contain a section called Block. This is followed by three numbers that represent your X, Y, and Z coordinates. Note these down.

Next, move to the opposite corner and repeat the same process. So, looking at a square plot from above, if you started on the northwest (or top left) corner, you'd move to the southeast (bottom right).

Now, press T to open up the chat/command window. Type "/fill" followed by the first and second set of coordinates. For example, you

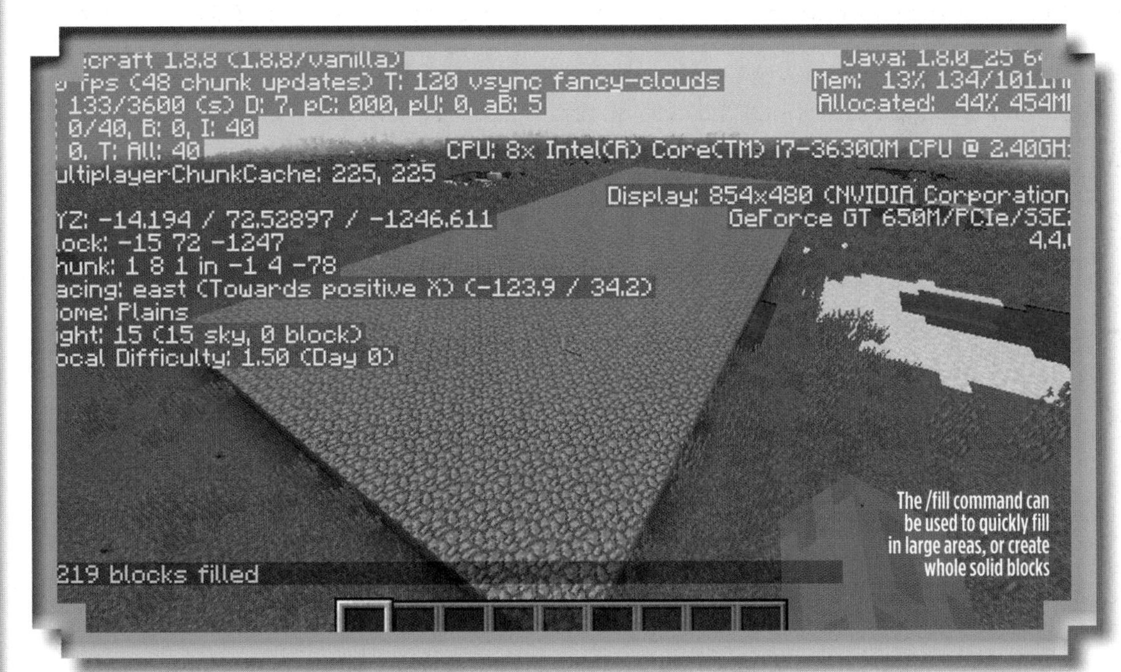

The /fill command can be used to quickly fill in large areas, or create whole solid blocks

may type "/fill 40 64 -1271 -12 64 -1249".

After the numbers, put a space and then type a technical name for the blocks you wish to use in the fill process. Each block in the game has a technical name, such as "minecraft:stone", or "minecraft: redstone". If you now press tab, you'll see a list of some block variants. Pick one from this list to continue. Using minecraft.air will place empty space. Press space again and enter the block variant number. This is used to pick variants like the different types of wood block. You can leave this as the default 0 if you would prefer.

Finally, press space again and type in the command used to place the blocks. This includes the following:

- **Replace** – Replace any blocks in the way with your specified block.
- **Destroy** – Destroy all blocks, clearing the space. Use with minecraft.air to mine out a whole section.
- **Keep** – Leaves all blocks already present in the specified area alone.
- **Hollow** – Only fills the outer border of your coordinates and destroys any blocks within, leaving a hollow interior.
- **Outline** – Only fills the outer area of your coordinates with blocks, but leaves any inside the area alone.

Once you've done this, press enter and the command will be run. It takes some practice to get used to the command, but with time it becomes an essential time-saver.

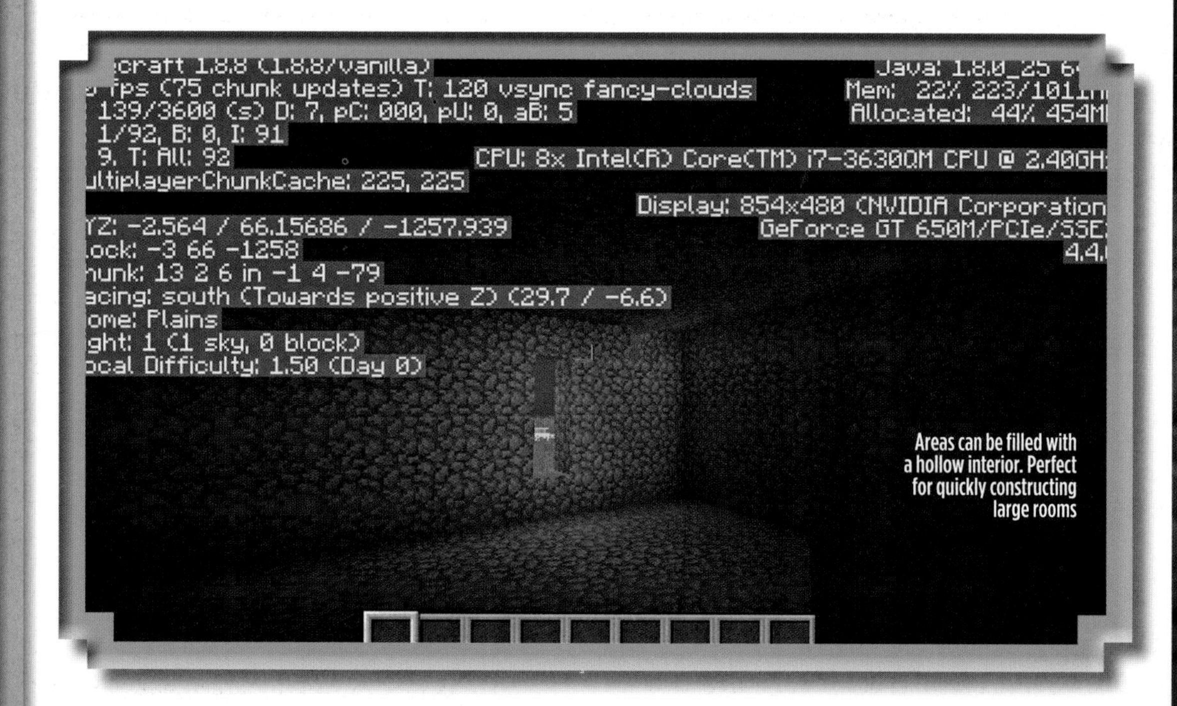

Areas can be filled with a hollow interior. Perfect for quickly constructing large rooms

EDITING MODS

Although many people indulge in the sheer challenge of building structures from scratch by hand, either in Creative or Survival, often the best way to achieve your goal is to cheat. Just a little. This helping hand comes in the form of world building modifications, or mods, for Minecraft.

WORLDEDIT

These third-party applications can be used to build huge structures and complex creations far easier. Perhaps the most popular of these is WorldEdit (***minecraft.curseforge.com/projects/worldedit***). This is a really brilliant add-on that gives you a selection of useful commands and tools within the game itself. These commands are similar to the built-in /fill command, but are much more powerful and flexible.

For example, instead of messing around with entering specific coordinates to select areas, you simply use the wooden axe tool to select bounding blocks. This shows a wireframe selection area, so you can see the area you're changing visually. You can then use a multitude of commands to edit the world, including options to fill, replace, and alter the size of an area.

You can even use a copy and paste command to copy whole sections of a build and paste them elsewhere. This is an immensely useful feature when crafting large builds with many repeated sections, and it saves a huge amount of time.

All commands are prefixed by "//" and not just "/" as used by Minecraft's default commands, and all are pretty easy to use. For example, to specify a zone manually, you can use the commands "//pos1" and "//pos2". When used, these set the position point to the block directly above the point you're standing on. This defines the area. "//hpos" sets the area to the block you're looking at, and "//chunk" selects the whole chunk you're currently in—very useful for those very large builds that span multiple chunks.

As well as the copy and paste commands, you can even use "//flip" and "//rotate" to move blocks, and there are even commands that will automatically generate a specified shape, such as a cylinder ("//cyl") or sphere ("//sphere"). There's also an option to alter the "brush" size and shape, and things like spheres can be created with a single click.

WorldEdit is a highly recommended tool, and it's also free, as it's open source, so feel free to grab it. You'll first need to

You can hollow out large sections with a single mouse click using WorldEdit's brushes

Shapes and other items can be created with a click of the mouse

install Minecraft Forge (***files.minecraftforge.net***) to use it, but once you have it installed you'll have a great deal of power to create whatever you like in Minecraft.

MCEDIT

Another very popular editor is MCEdit (***www.mcedit.net***). Unlike WorldEdit, which is a selection of commands and items for use within the main game, MCEdit is an actual editor in which you can view the world and use a range of dedicated tools. As a result, some would argue it's the best editor out there, and even more powerful than the brilliant WorldEdit.

You don't so much wander around the world as your character here, but instead you float around out of body from your avatar in an editing mode. The inventory bar becomes a toolbar, and this lets you excavate and edit the world, from small adjustments to huge-scale excavations. You move a block-shaped cursor around to select point A and, once selected, you simply drag a selection box over the area to be edited. Once the second point is selected, you can work with the area, and delete, fill, and populate whole areas or chunks.

As well as this, MCEdit features the ability to create specific shapes, like spheres, diamonds, and boxes, and you can export schematics for use in other builds. So, if you create an impressive structure, you can export the blueprint for this, which is very useful.

MCEdit is a huge favorite among builders, and rightly so

TOOMANYITEMS

Another very popular mod used by world builders is TooManyItems. This is an inventory mod that includes a number of new item types and, more importantly, a far easier way to manage Minecraft's huge selection of block types, which includes a search function. This is a godsend when building large, complex structures that utilize a wide range of blocks.

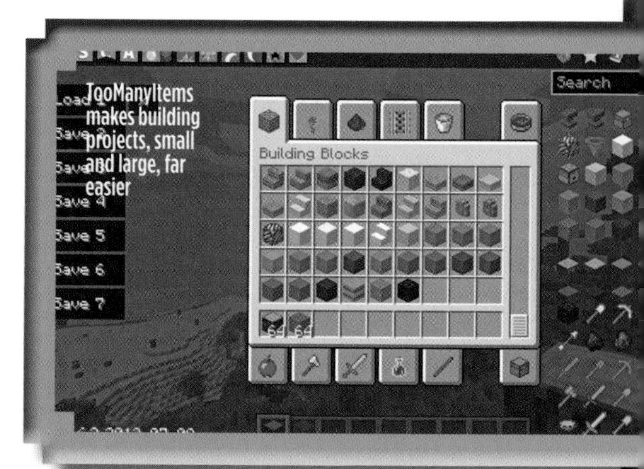

TooManyItems makes building projects, small and large, far easier

TooManyItems also features extra tools, like the ability to easily switch games modes, change the time of day, control weather, and save and load inventory setups. It's a major help when creating your own epic builds, and is a highly recommended tool. You can get it from ***file-minecraft.com/toomanyitems-tmi***.

PIXEL PLANNING

If you're thinking of creating some impressive Minecraft pixel art, Minecraft Structure Planner (***minecraftstructureplanner.com***) is a fantastic help. Although originally designed for planning structures, this app now includes a pixel art tab, which can be used to create your work of art, again, just like using an image editor. Once you're done, this can then be exported into another editor for fine tuning, and exported into a format recognized by MCEdit, which can effortlessly place the artwork into Minecraft.

ADDED TEXTURE

Minecraft's visual aesthetic is well established and recognized the world over, and the unique, retro-inspired look is great. However, if you're trying to recreate specific landmarks, or build new, themed locations, the basic graphical appearance can sometimes be very limiting.

Luckily, the game supports texture packs, which can be applied, changing the way blocks, mobs, and even the GUI look. There's a huge number of texture packs available, and you can grab them either online from numerous websites on the PC, or via your console's online store.

This can help greatly when trying to create a specific build, especially one that has an existing look or feel, such as builds based on TV shows, movies, or games. Simply changing textures can improve the appeal of a build tenfold. Happy building!

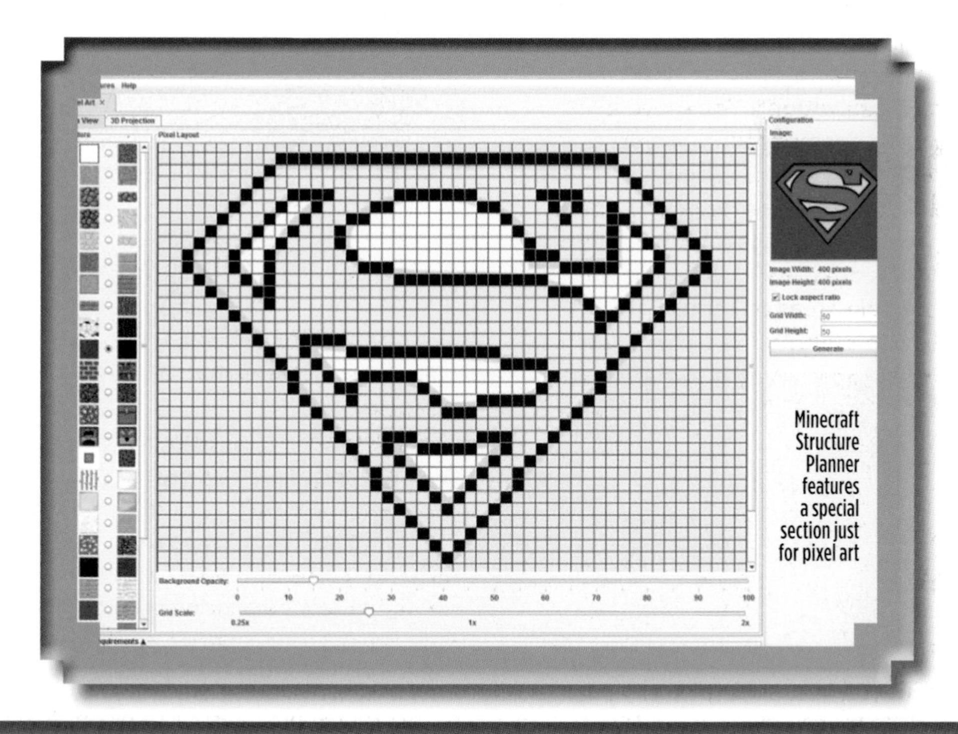

Minecraft Structure Planner features a special section just for pixel art

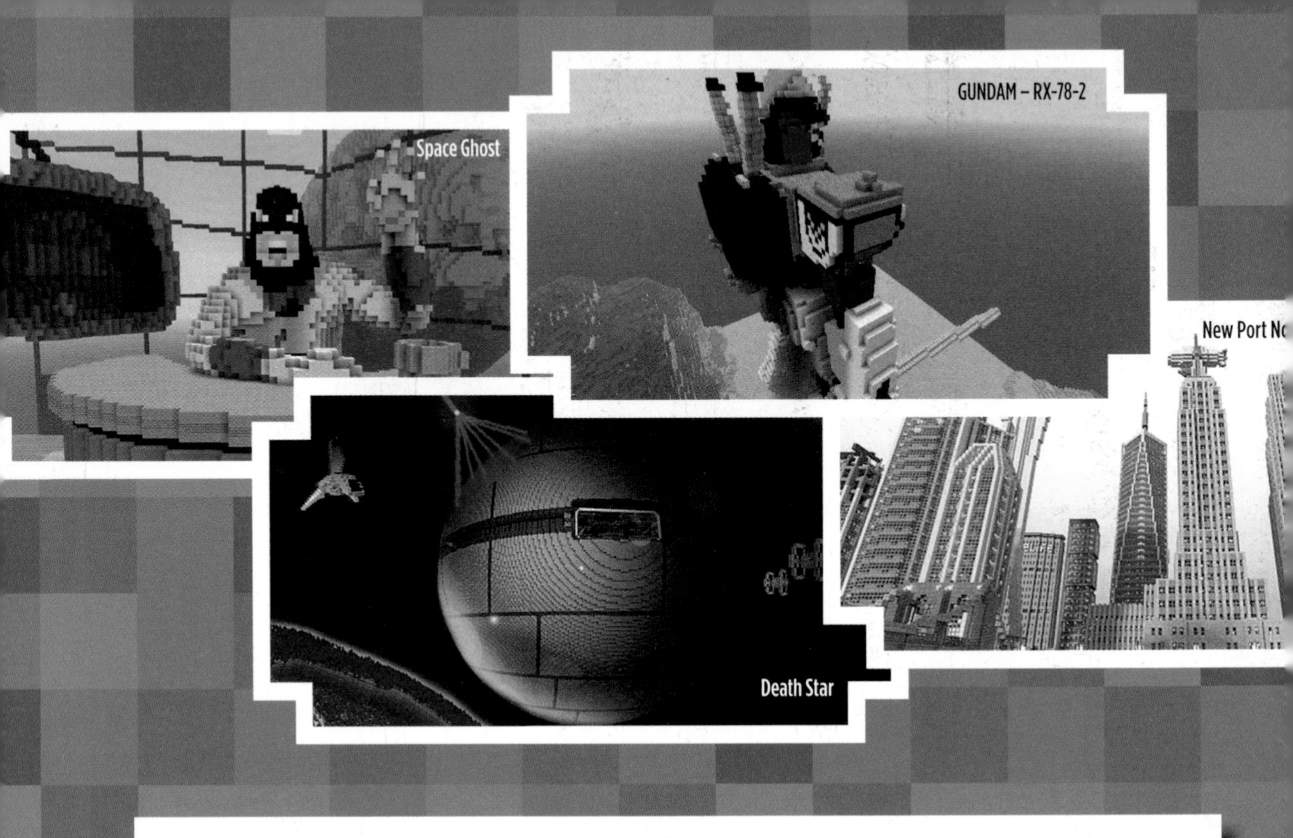

Published by Scholastic, Inc., 557 Broadway, New York, NY 10012

Editorial: Aaron Birch, Simon Brew, John Moore
Art Editor: Laura Passmore
Production Editor: Rachel Storry

PRINT Printed in U.S.A 40
ISBN: 978-1-338-71785-3
8 7 6 5 4 3 2 22 23 24 25 26

DISCLAIMER
Minecraft is a registered trademark of Mojang Synergies AB ("Mojang"). The screenshots and artwork shown in this publication were taken from Minecraft, a game published by Mojang, and from Microsoft XBOX websites. Game design, programming and graphics for Minecraft were authored by Notch (Markus Persson), officers, employees and/or freelancers of Mojang. This is a 100% unofficial and independent publication which is in no way licensed, authorized or endorsed by or otherwise connected in any way with Mojang or any other individuals who are authors of Minecraft.

Names, brands, and logos mentioned in this publication may be protected by trademark or other intellectual property rights of one or several legal jurisdictions. Any reference to such marks in no way implies that they are not protected under applicable law, nor is it implied that there is any commercial or other relationship between the publisher and that trademark holder.

The publisher excludes all liability for the content and services provided by any websites or other third party publications, or games reviewed and shall not be responsible for and does not endorse any advertising, products, or resources including those available from any third party external resources including websites, and we shall not be liable to any party for any information, services, or resources made available through them.

All copyrights recognized and used specifically for the purpose of criticism and review.

Projects and images are the work of their original creators. All rights acknowledged.

© Scholastic, Inc., may not be reproduced in whole or part without the consent of the publishers. Scholastic and associated logos are trademarks and/or registered trademarks of Scholastic Inc.
2020

W9-CEE-658

As he laye unravelling in the agonie of death, the Standers-by could hear him say softly, I have seen the Glories of the world.

C 16 80

john aubrey

the minutes of lives

brief lives
S
SANDMAN
(t h e)

neil gaiman
writer

penciller
jill thompson

vince locke
inker
dick giordano
inker

todd klein
letterer
danny vozzo
colorist
dave mckean
covers and design

foreword by
neil gaiman

afterword by
peter straub

featuring characters created by
gaiman, kieth and dringenberg

SANDMAN

(the) *brief lives*

Published by DC Comics.

Cover and compilation copyright © 1994 DC Comics
(All Rights Reserved.)

Originally published in single magazine form as THE SANDMAN 41-49.
Copyright © 1992-93 DC Comics.
All Rights Reserved.

VERTIGO and all characters, their distinctive likenesses and related elements featured in this publication are trademarks of DC Comics.
The stories, characters and incidents featured in this publication are entirely fictional. DC Comics does not read or accept unsolicited submissions of ideas, stories or artwork.
The song lyrics on Pages 19 and 20 are from "Tear In Your Hand," from the album Little Earthquakes by Tori Amos. Copyright © 1991 Warner Music UK Ltd. Published by Sword in the Stone. Used by permission.

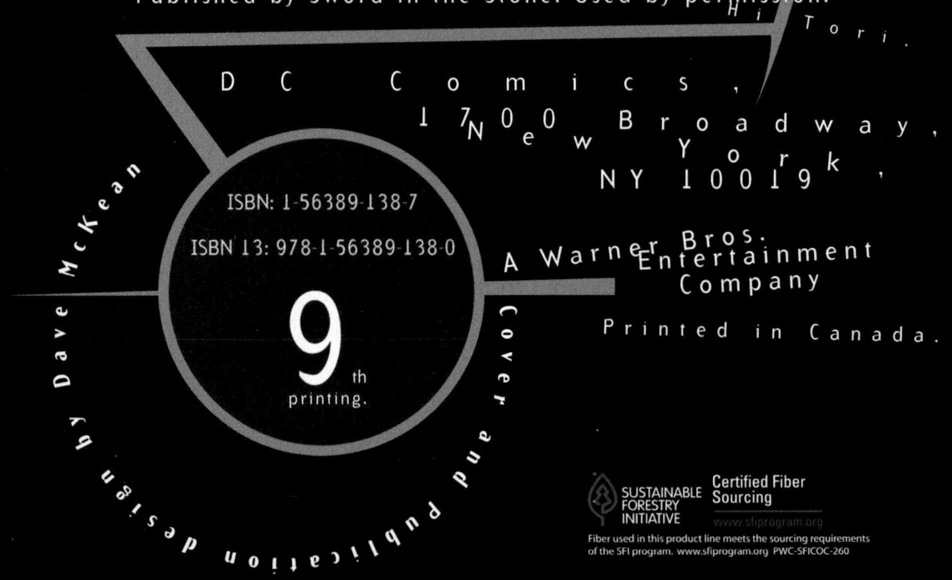

karen berger
vp-executive editor & editor-original series

lisa aufenanger, shelly roeberg
assistant editors-original series

bob kahan
editor-collected edition

robbin brosterman
senior art director

paul levitz
president & publisher

georg brewer
vp-design & dc direct creative

richard bruning
senior vp-creative director

patrick caldon
senior vp-finance & operations

chris caramalis
vp-finance

terri cunningham
vp-managing editor

stephanie fierman
senior vp-sales & marketing

alison gill
vp-manufacturing

rich johnson
vp-book trade sales

hank kanalz
vp-general manager, wildstorm

lillian laserson
senior vp & general counsel

jim lee
editorial director-wildstorm

paula lowitt
senior vp-business & legal affairs

david mckillips
vp-advertising & custom publishing

john nee
vp-business development

gregory noveck
senior vp-creative affairs

cheryl rubin
senior vp-brand management

jeff trojan
vp-business development, dc direct

bob wayne
vp-sales

not (an introduction)
a few words.
19 94
(neil gaiman)

Peter Straub has done a real, honest-to-goodness introduction to the book, which, for reasons of not wanting to give too much away up front, we placed at the end of the book, after the story's over.

You can go and read it now, if you like: it's a very wise and wonderful introduction. Or you can wait until the end, in which case it will be a similarly wise and wonderful conclusion.

But that's the introduction, not this. This is just a few words at the beginning, to say hello, and tell you what you need to know before you start.

Hello.

What you need to know before you start: there are seven beings that aren't gods, who existed before humanity dreamed of gods and will exist after the last god is dead. They are called The Endless. They are embodiments of (in order of age) Destiny, Death, Dream, Destruction, Desire, Despair and Delirium.

Approximately three hundred years ago, Destruction abandoned his realm.

That's all you need.

The artist is always an important force in comics, and, for a writer, a vital collaborator; but I'd like to take this opportunity to extend my particular thanks to Jill Thompson for her contribution to this book, and to both Jill and Vince for their professionalism and skill. I couldn't have done it without you.

And thank you: to Danny Vozzo for all the colors; to Todd Klein, letterer's letterer; to Lisa Aufenanger; to Dick Giordano (for bailing us out); to Karen Berger, the very best editor a boy could wish for; and to Shelly Roeberg, small miracle.

Once again, Bob Kahan has turned a group of comics into a book with persnickety panache.

For Dave McKean, my friend and collaborator and my hardest critic, who, in seven years, hasn't stopped surprising me with the covers or design, thanks seem somewhat inadequate. But thanks, Dave.

This story was written in England and Australia and Waikiki and all over North America. My thanks to all my hosts and friends for permitting me to intrude upon their lives, however briefly.

ded(ication)
for Bob and Allison on the occasion of their engagement
Pete and Dana on the occasion of their wedding,
a n d
Beth and Chris, on the occasion of my dedicating a book to them.
neil
for Basil
jill t.
to Mom and Dad for their encouragement and support
and to Khrysta for helping me through the rough times.
vince

chapter 1

Rain
in the
doorway

"The
number
you have
dialed..."

IT IS, OF COURSE, A MIRACLE.

ANDROS CAN NEVER GET OVER THE HONOR DAILY DONE TO HIM AND TO HIS FAMILY. THEIR PRIVILEGE AND THEIR BURDEN, AS CUSTODIANS, GUARDS, AND PRIESTS.
AS WITNESSES TO THE MIRACLE.

HE IS THE OLDEST, NOW. THE HEAD OF THE FAMILY.
EACH MORNING, AT DAWN, HE CLAMBERS AWKWARDLY UP THE CONCEALED STEPS CARVED INTO THE ROCK-FACE OF THE HILL.

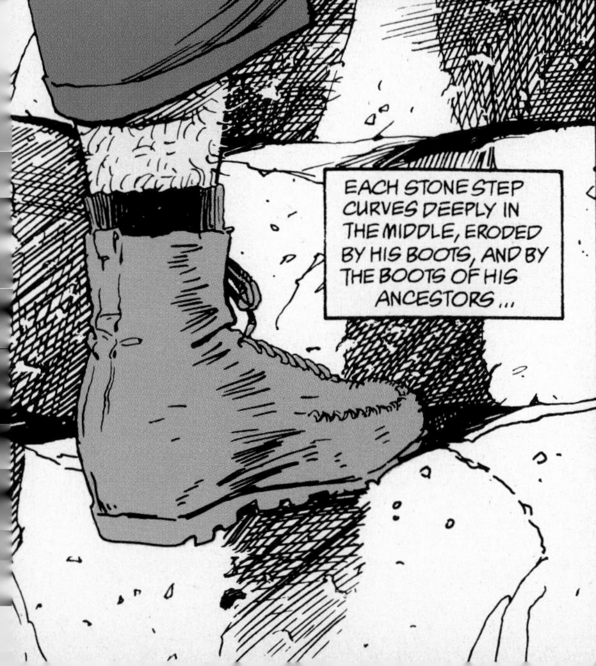
EACH STONE STEP CURVES DEEPLY IN THE MIDDLE, ERODED BY HIS BOOTS, AND BY THE BOOTS OF HIS ANCESTORS...

AT THE TOP OF THE HILL HE PAUSES TO CATCH HIS BREATH. HE'S GETTING OLD.

LADY JOHANNA CONSTANTINE
born 1760
died 1859
"Be to her Virtues very Kind.
Be to her faults a little Blind."

THERE.

EVERY SPRING DAY FOR OVER SIXTY YEARS HE HAS PICKED A BLOSSOM FROM THE CHERRY TREE; EVERY SPRING DAY HE HAS PLACED IT ON THE LADY'S GRAVE, AS HIS FATHER AND HIS GRANDFATHER DID BEFORE HIM.

KRIS IS HIS SON-IN-LAW. TWENTY YEARS AGO HE CAME TO THE ISLAND, FLEEING A WAR IN A FAR LAND, DRIVEN BY DARK DREAMS.
ANDROS'S FAMILY TOOK HIM IN: THEY HAD BEEN EXPECTING HIM.
HELLO, PAPA.
HOW WAS HE TONIGHT?
HE SLEPT FOR A FEW HOURS. THEN HE WANTED TO LOOK AT THE MOON. THEN HE WAS SILENT. NOW, HE SLEEPS ONCE MORE.
HM. TELL YOUR HALF-WIT OF A SON THAT I SAW HIM, WHEN I WAS COMING UP THE PATH. **BEAT** HIM FOR ME.
HE'S TOO **OLD** FOR A BEATING, ANDROS.
HE SHOULD NOT BE SEEN, WHEN HE IS ON GUARD.

BEAT HIM, AND AS YOU DO, TELL HIM THAT WHEN THEY STOLE OUR CHARGE, TWO HUNDRED YEARS AGO, IT WAS **THIRTY** YEARS BEFORE HE RETURNED TO US.
THIRTY **YEARS.**
IT WILL **NEVER** HAPPEN AGAIN.
HE **KNOWS** THAT, PAPA.
IF HE **TRULY** KNEW THAT THEN HE WOULD NOT HAVE LET HIMSELF BE **SEEN.**
GO DOWN AND EAT, KRIS. GO SLEEP. I WILL SEE YOU AT DUSK.

GOOD MORNING, ANDROS.

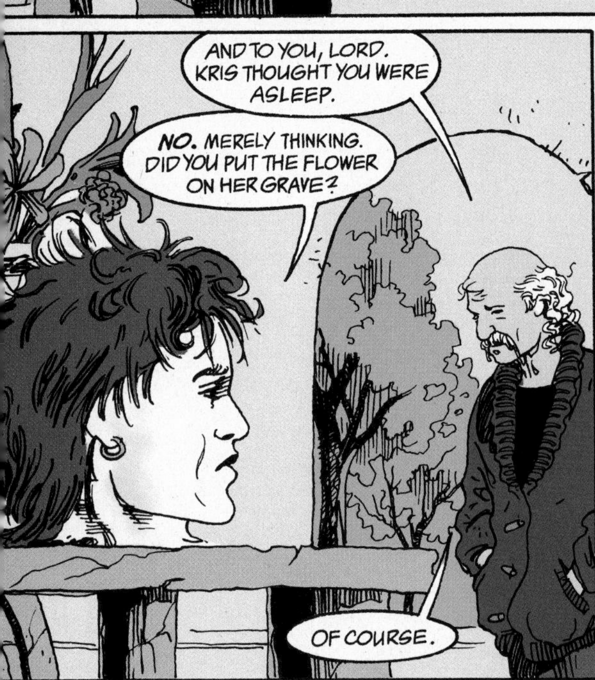
AND TO YOU, LORD. KRIS THOUGHT YOU WERE ASLEEP.
NO. MERELY THINKING. DID YOU PUT THE FLOWER ON HER GRAVE?
OF COURSE.

SHE WAS A REMARKABLE WOMAN.
ALL WOMEN ARE REMARKABLE.
THE EAST WINDOW, I THINK. I WANT TO SEE THE SUN RISE.

HE STARES UNBLINKING INTO THE LIGHT.
THEN HE BEGINS TO SING TO HIMSELF, HIS VOICE LITTLE MORE THAN A WHISPER. HE SINGS TO THE SUNRISE, IN A LONG-FORGOTTEN TONGUE.

ANDROS LISTENS TO THE SONG OF ORPHEUS, AND THE ACHE IN HIS JOINTS EASES; THE COLD LEAVES HIS FINGERTIPS.
THIS IS WHAT MAKES HIM GET UP IN THE DARKNESS, SUMMER OR WINTER, RAIN OR MIST...
THE SONG. IN HIS SOUL HE FEELS YOUNG AGAIN.

FROM THE EAST WINDOW ONE CAN LOOK ACROSS THE BAY.
THERE IS A HOUSE, ON THE HILL ACROSS THE BAY, AND OCCASIONALLY ANDROS (WHOSE EYES HAVE LOST NONE OF THEIR KEENNESS, IN THEIR SEVENTY YEARS ON THIS EARTH) SPIES TINY FIGURES THERE. TOURISTS, PERHAPS, OR VISITORS TO THE ISLAND.
HE WONDERS WHAT THEY SEE, FROM THEIR VILLA.
A LITTLE TEMPLE, ON A CLIFF.
THAT'S ALL. NOTHING SPECIAL.
THE ISLANDS ARE LITTERED WITH THEM. OLD SHRINES TO GODS LONG DEAD.
THE PRIESTS OF ORPHEUS HAVE HAD THOUSANDS OF YEARS TO LEARN THE ART OF MISDIRECTION.
EVEN THE MOST INQUISITIVE TOURIST WOULD FIND IT ALMOST PHYSICALLY IMPOSSIBLE TO FIND HIS WAY TO THE TEMPLE.
AND IF IT CAME TO MORE THAN THAT..?
WELL, THE CUSTODIANS HAVE NOT BEEN IDLE.
KRIS HAS DRAWN UP PLANS THAT COVER ALMOST ALL EVENTUALITIES -- UP TO AND INCLUDING A HELICOPTER ASSAULT ON THE TEMPLE...
THIRTY YEARS. IT SHALL NOT HAPPEN AGAIN.
"THERE. ENOUGH."

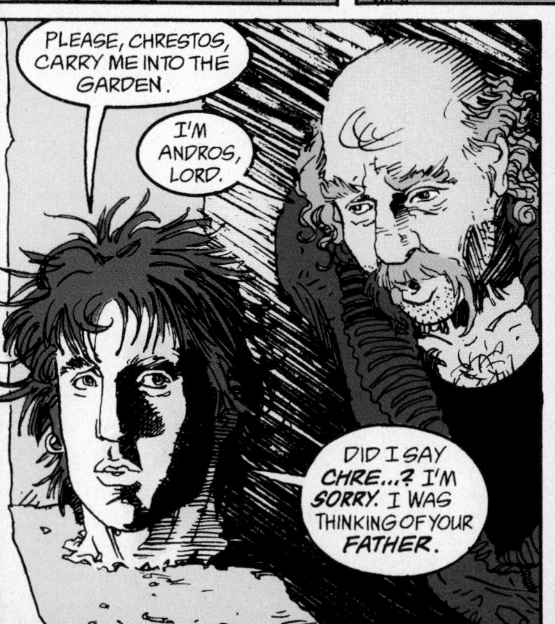
PLEASE, CHRESTOS, CARRY ME INTO THE GARDEN.
I'M ANDROS, LORD.
DID I SAY *CHRE...?* I'M *SORRY.* I WAS THINKING OF YOUR *FATHER.*

NO, THINKS ANDROS RHODOCANAKIS. YOU WERE THINKING OF MY GRANDFATHER.
BUT HE SAYS NOTHING.
IT IS GOING TO BE A BEAUTIFUL DAY.

BLOSSOM FOR A LADY—RAIN IN THE DOORWAY—NOT HER SISTER—WANT/ NOT WANT—THE VIEW FROM THE BACKS OF MIRRORS—JOURNAL OF THE PLAGUE YEAR—"THE NUMBER YOU HAVE DIALED..."
HORVENDILE'S
GOT ANY SPARE CHANGE, LUVVY? I NEED ANOTHER 50p TO PUT PETROL IN ME ROLLS ROYCE. HEE.
YEAH. HOLD ON.
HERE YOU GO. NOT A NICE NIGHT TO BE OUT.
NO. AT LEAST IT'S WARMING UP A BIT, THOUGH. THE WINTER WAS SOMETHING CRUEL.
WHAT ABOUT YOUR FRIEND?
THIS END
HER? SHE'S ASLEEP. I THINK. SHE WAS HERE WHEN I GOT HERE.
IT'S A SHAME, WHEN IT'S THE KIDS. I FIGURE, US OLD FOLKS, WELL, WE'VE HAD A GOOD INNINGS.
BUT KIDS. TCH.
I HAD A SON ONCE, DEAR, BUT HE'S NO LONGER WITH US. WELL, THEY SAID IT WAS A HINDUSTRIAL HACCIDENT, BUT I KNEW WHAT WAS WHAT, OH YES. I WASN'T BORN YESTERDAY.
IT'S NOT FAIR, WHEN THE YOUNG ONES DIE BEFORE THE OLD ONES. I MEAN, THEY'RE ALL WE'VE GOT TO LOOK FORWARD TO.
6

YEAH. WELL. GOOD LUCK.
IT'LL TAKE MORE THAN LUCK TO HELP ME, DEARIO. YOU'VE A GOOD HEART.
THERE, NOW, LOVE. THAT WAS ONE THER NICE ONES.
THIRTY PEE AND A BIT OF A NATTER, AND I DUNNO, SOMETIMES I THINK A KIND WORD'S BETTER THAN THE RHINO...
YOU SHOULD MOVE UP A BIT THERE, LOVE. YOU'LL GET POSITIVELY SOAKED.
I'VE BEEN. WET. BEFORE. I THINK.
OH. YOU'RE AWAKE. FEELING BETTER?
I FEEL LIKE... I DON'T KNOW. SOMEPLACE NOBODY EVER GOES ANY MORE.
I DON'T KNOW.

SPARE CHANGE?
AREN'T YOU COLD, DRESSED LIKE THAT? AND LOOK AT YOU. HOW OLD ARE YOU REALLY? RUN AWAY FROM HOME, HAVE YOU?
YOU SHOULD GO BACK TO YOUR MUM AND DAD, LOVE. I MEAN, THEY'LL FORGIVE AND FORGET. PARENTS DO. I WOULD'VE FORGIVEN MY STEVEN.
HINDUSTRIAL HACCIDENT MY AUNT FANNY.

I HAVEN'T GOT ANY PARENTS. THERE WAS A BIG FLOOD ONCE AND I GOT REALLY WET IN THAT, ONLY IT WASN'T RAIN, IT WAS THE GUNKY STUFF INSIDE PEOPLE'S. EYES.
I WISH I COULD REMEMBER WHAT IT'S CALLED...

YOU LOST BOTH PARENTS? TSK. POOR DEAR.
I DIDN'T LOSE MY PARENTS.
I LOST MY BROTHER...
WHAT A SHAME. MY STEVEN DIED. THEY SAID IT WAS A HACCIDENT. BUT I'VE GOT PAPERS. OH YES. I WASN'T BORN YESTERDAY.

SO, LUVVY. HOW DID YOUR BROTHER DIE?
HE'S NOT DEAD. I JUST LOST HIM, OKAY?
WELL, PARDON ME FOR BREATHING.
SPARE A LITTLE CHANGE, LOVE?
THANKS.
CHANGE.
THAT WAS ALWAYS KIND OF THE PROBLEM, KIND OF...
UM SOME DAYS I FEEL LIKE RITA MARLOWE IN THE WAYWARD BUS. YOU EVER SEE THAT MOVIE?
CHANGE. CHANGE. CHANGE. CHANGE... CHANGE. CHANGE. CHAAAANGE.
WHEN YOU SAY WORDS A LOT THEY DON'T MEAN ANYTHING. OR MAYBE THEY DON'T MEAN ANYTHING ANYWAY, AND WE JUST THINK THEY DO.
WHERE YOU GOIN'?
I NEED A CHANGE...
8

AND WHERE DO YOU THINK YOU'RE GOING?
INSIDE. IT'S RAINING OUT HERE. BUT NOT THE JELLY STUFF IN PEOPLE'S EYES.
PRIVATE PARTY. INVITATION ONLY. STRICT DRESS CODE. GO FIND A WAREHOUSE BASH, EH, KID?
CLEAR OFF.
UM. I'VE GOT AN INVITATION. AND I'M DRESSED PROPERLY. AREN'T I?
OH. YEAH. SORRY. GO ON IN, LOVE.
AQUEOUS SOMETHING. OR VITREOUS.
PARDON?
IT'S THE NAME OF WHAT I CAN'T REMEMBER. IN PEOPLE'S EYES.
pervy
'Going down'
Viv!
LOVE
All the WORLD Just stopped Now, So you say You DON'T wAnn A STAY toGether ANY MORE, let me take A deep breAth babe...
...WHEN I TOLD HIM THE NEWS ABOUT FREDDIE HE SAID, "OH. ANOTHER ONE BITES THE DUST." I SAID, DAHLING, WHEN GOD PUT TEETH IN YOUR MOUTH, HE RUINED A PERFECTLY GOOD ARSEHOLE...
GOD, WHAT I WOULDN'T GIVE TO LOOK LIKE HER. LOOKS LIKE BUTTER WOULDN'T MELT BETWEEN HER LEGS...

I DIDN'T LOSE HIM. I MEAN, IT WASN'T ME. I WANTED HIM TO STAY. I NEVER THOUGHT HE'D GO. I ASKED HIM. NOT TO.
IT WASN'T ME. HONESTLY.
...MAYBE SHE'S JUST PIECES OF ME YOU'VE NEVER SEEN...
AND I THINK. AND I THINK. AND I THINK. AND I...
I DON'T. FEEL VERY WELL.
I WANT MY FAMILY BACK. I WANT MY...
YOU?
CUTTING MY HANDS UP EVERY TIME I TOUCH YOU
YOU CAME TO SEE ME. I'M SORRY. I SORT OF GOT MY HEAD A BIT TANGLED. UM.
SHALL WE GO BACK TO YOUR PLACE?
YOU'RE A BIT AHEAD OF YOURSELF, AREN'T YOU? BIT TOO GRUBBY FOR ME BUT I DUNNO. BUY ME A DRINK AND WE CAN TALK ABOUT IT.
I'M LISA. WHO'RE YOU?

I... I'M SOMEBODY ELSE. THE WRONG PERSON.
I THOUGHT YOU WERE MY SISTER.

I WANT HER.
I WANT MY SISTER.
I WANT MY SISTER!
I WANT MY SISTER.
ER... ARE YOU ALL RIGHT, LOVE?
DO YOU WANT SOME FRESH AIR? OR SOME WATER?
CHRIST. WHERE DO THEY DIG THEM UP FROM?
KIDS. NO RESPECT FOR THE SCENE. SOME PEOPLE JUST BLITHELY RUIN IT FOR EVERY-ONE.
I THINK SHE'S ILL...
E'D OUT OF HER LITTLE BONCE, I EXPECT. OR WHATEVER THEY'RE DOING NOWADAYS. CHRIST. IT'S PATHETIC.
DO YOU WANT ME TO GET A DOCTOR, LOVE?
SHE'S FINE. I'LL TAKE CARE OF HER.
OH YEAH? AND WHO ARE YOU?
WELL...
SOMETIMES...
I'M HER SISTER.

HONESTLY, GIRL. SHE'S RIGHT: YOU ARE PATHETIC, MAKING A SCENE LIKE THAT. I COULD HEAR YOU SCREAMING TWO CONTINENTS AWAY.
DESIRE?
WHO ELSE?
EXCUSE ME. I'VE BEEN WATCHING YOU. UM. I MEAN. YOU'RE GORGEOUS. SO. UH. WHAT'S YOUR NAME?
NO.
YOU SEE THAT YOUNG LADY IN RED? OVER THERE?
GO AND TALK TO HER. HAVE A PASSIONATE WEEKEND DURING WHICH BOTH OF YOU MAKE LOVE UNTIL YOU'RE SORE AND BLEEDING. THEN, WITHOUT KNOWING WHY, REFUSE TO SEE HER AGAIN.
SHE'LL PHONE YOU UP, AND HANG AROUND YOUR HOUSE. WHEN YOU ASK HER TO LEAVE YOU ALONE SHE'LL JUST CRY AND NOT SAY ANYTHING-- LOOK AT YOU WITH HURT EYES AND FOLLOW YOU AROUND.
EVENTUALLY THIS WILL MAKE YOU SO ANGRY YOU'LL FIND YOURSELF NEEDING DESPERATELY TO MAKE HER SAY SOMETHING. TO MAKE HER REACT. TO HURT HER. TO GET HER EYES OUT OF YOUR MIND.
AFTER THAT IT WILL BE JUST A MATTER OF TIME.
CHK
UH. OKAY...
THANKS. YEAH. WOW. THANKS A LOT.
WILL YOU. WILL YOU TAKE ME AWAY FROM HERE?
PLEASE?
HOLD MY HAND. WE'LL GO TO MY PLACE.
12

"I HAVEN'T SEEN YOU THIS BAD IN A WHILE. ROTTEN NIGHT, HUH?"
"I. I'M FINDING IT HARDER TO HOLD ON."
"HOLD ON TO WHAT?"
EVERYTHING. IT ALL KEEPS MOVING AND IT WON'T STOP AND I JUST WANT IT TO STOP AND THEN I WON'T STOP AND THEN I THINK WHAT IF IT GETS WORSE? I MEAN, YOU KNOW?
WHAT IF IT GETS WORSE?
OH COME ON, LITTLE SISTER. PULL YOURSELF TOGETHER.
DELIRIUM? COME ON, SIS...
13

I'M TOGETHER. AREN'T I? I... I KNOW I USED TO BE.
I DON'T KNOW.
YES. YOU USED TO BE.
DESIRE? I MISS HIM SO BADLY.
HE WAS ALWAYS KIND TO ME.
INDEED.
AND I'M NOT?
...I DIDN'T MEAN IT LIKE THAT.
DESIRE? DO YOU KNOW WHERE HE IS?
NOT ONLY DO I NOT KNOW, LITTLEST SISTER, BUT I
DON'T
CARE.
DO YOU THINK IT'S IN THE BIG BOOK?
I MEAN, EVERYTHING'S IN THE BIG BOOK. MAYBE HE'D SHOW IT TO US. AND THEN WE COULD ALL BE TOGETHER AGAIN. ONE BIG HAPPY FAMILY.
IF OUR PRODIGAL BROTHER WANTED US TO FIND HIM I'M SURE HE'D LET US KNOW.
YES...
LOOK--DEL. HE'S NOT HERE, OKAY? HE'S NOT ONE OF THE FAMILY ANY MORE. JUST ACCEPT IT.
I WANT HIM BACK!
DROP IT, DEL. JUST DROP IT.
14

HAHAHA HAHA... HAA...HAAAA... HH.
HAHA HAHA HAAA...
WHAT'S SO FUNNY?

WELL, YOU.
TELLING ME NOT TO WANT SOMETHING. I MEAN, THAT'S ALL YOU ARE. WANTING. I MEAN, IT'S KIND OF FUNNY...

ISN'T IT? ISN'T IT FUNNY?
WELL, ISN'T IT?

DESIRE? CAN I USE YOUR GALLERY?
HMPH. WHAT'S WRONG WITH YOUR OWN GALLERY?
I LOST IT. IT'S SOMEWHERE IN MY OWN REALM. I'M NOT SURE WHERE.

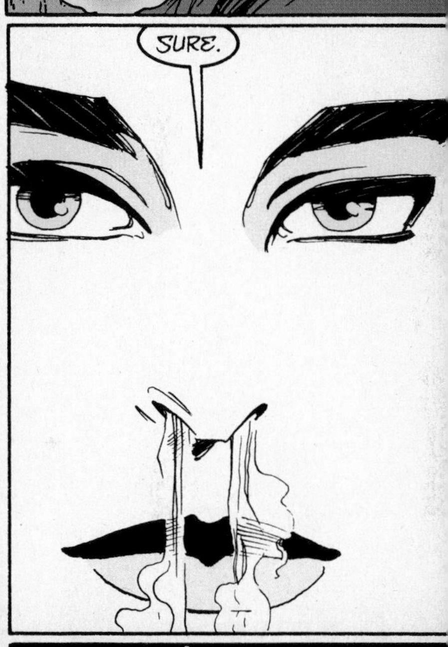
SURE.

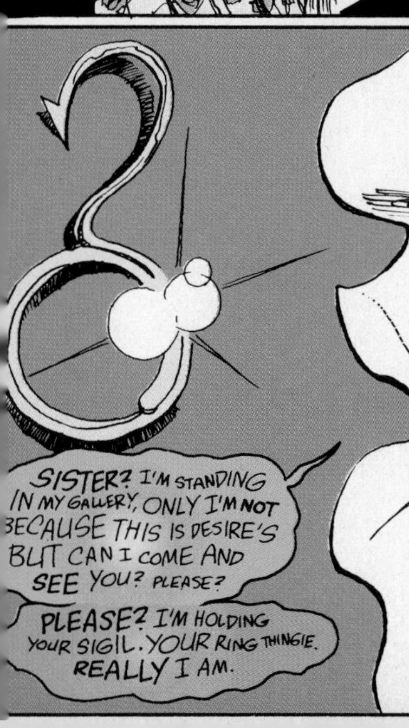
SISTER? I'M STANDING IN MY GALLERY, ONLY I'M NOT BECAUSE THIS IS DESIRE'S BUT CAN I COME AND SEE YOU? PLEASE?
PLEASE? I'M HOLDING YOUR SIGIL. YOUR RING THINGIE. REALLY I AM.

OBVIOUSLY SHE DOESN'T WISH TO BE DISTURBED.
PLEASE?

TCH.

DELIRIUM HAS, FROM TIME TO TIME, VISITED DESPAIR'S GRAY REALM. IT IS THE ANTITHESIS OF HER OWN CHURNING DOMAIN: FORMLESS AND SILENT AND STILL. APATHY HANGS LIKE DAMP MIST IN THE CHILL AIR.
NO WINDS BLOW, NO BIRD SINGS, NOTHING MOVES.
SHE FEELS THE COLD TOUCHING HER, SOBERING HER. COOL TENDRILS MOVE INSIDE HER, QUESTING, WHISPERING...
SHE STARES AT THE WORLD WITH TWO MISMATCHED EYES: ONE EMERALD GREEN, THE OTHER PALE BLUE THROUGH WHICH SILVER FLECKS FLICKER AND SWIM LIKE A SHOAL OF TINY FISH.
DELIRIUM SEES THE GRAY PLACE THAT WAITS ON THE OTHER SIDE OF EVERY MIRROR.
AND SHE SHIVERS.
UM. HELLO.
SHHH... WAIT...
SO. ER. WHO IS HE?
HE MANAGES A SUPERMARKET IN A SMALL TOWN IN NEBRASKA.
YESTERDAY HIS WIFE FOUND A COLLECTION OF PORNOGRAPHIC PHOTOGRAPHS HIDDEN IN THEIR GARAGE.
16

MOST OF THEM SHOWED SMALL CHILDREN PERFORMING VARIOUS SEXUAL ACTS WITH ADULTS.
SHE RECOGNIZED HER HUSBAND, AND THEIR FIVE-YEAR-OLD NIECE.
SHE LEFT HIM, TAKING THE PHOTO-GRAPHS WITH HER. HE FEARS SHE MAY ALREADY HAVE GIVEN THEM TO THE POLICE.
TODAY HE'S SITTING IN THEIR FAMILY ROOM, REALIZING THAT HIS LIFE IS OVER, WONDERING IF HE HAS THE COURAGE PHYSICALLY TO END IT.
HE DOESN'T.
ISN'T IT BEAUTIFUL?
IT'S OKAY. I SUPPOSE. IF YOU'RE INTO THAT KIND OF THING.
LISTEN. I UM SORT OF HAVE TO TALK TO YOU.
AH? SO TALK.
IT'S ABOUT, UM, OUR FAMILY.
WHAT ABOUT IT?
I ALWAYS THOUGHT THAT MAYBE I OUGHT TO HAVE A PET. I MEAN, YOU'VE GOT YOUR RATS AND OUR SISTER'S GOT HER GOLDFISH AND I MEAN EVEN STUFFY DREAM'S GOT THAT BIG BLACK BIRD.
AND DESTINY'S GOT THE LITTLE FLAPPY THINGS...
I DON'T KNOW. WHAT DO YOU THINK?
WHAT ABOUT OUR FAMILY?
OH YEAH. I THINK MAYBE SOMEBODY SHOULD DO SOMETHING. THAT'S ALL.
ABOUT WHAT, DELIRIUM?
DIDN'T I SAY?
NO.
OH. I THOUGHT MAYBE I DID.
LOOK, DESPAIR, DO YOU REMEMBER... UM...
I MEAN, DO YOU REMEMBER...
REMEMBER WHAT?
THE NAME OF THE GUNKY JELLY STUFF IN PEOPLE'S EYES?
VITREOUS HUMOR.
OH YEAH. I KNEW THAT. THANKS. WELL... HANG IN THERE. I MEAN, I'LL SEE YOU. B'BYE.

DELIRIUM? IS THAT ALL YOU WANTED TO KNOW? THE NAME OF THE JELLY IN PEOPLE'S EYES?
NOT REALLY. THERE'S SOMETHING ELSE. YOU PROMISE YOU WON'T BE MAD IF I TELL YOU?
I DON'T GET MAD.
OKAY, THEN, YOU HAVE TO PROMISE IF I SAY SOMETHING YOU DON'T LIKE YOU WON'T DO THAT VOICE THAT SOUNDS LIKE PEOPLE WITH WET AND BUBBLY STUFF IN THEIR LUNGS BURIED UNDER THE GROUND BEING CRUSHED TO DEATH BY GIANT WORMS TALKING.
HHHH... I PROMISE.
OUR BROTHER. I THINK WE SHOULD GET IN TOUCH WITH HIM.
WHY?
HE MIGHT BE. HURT. HE MIGHT NEED US.
SO?
I MISS HIM.
SO?
WILL YOU HELP ME FIND HIM?
DO YOU HONESTLY THINK HE WANTS TO BE FOUND?
I DON'T KNOW. BUT I WANT TO FIND HIM. I JUST THOUGHT YOU COULD MAYBE. HELP ME.
18

IF I SAY NO, WHAT WILL YOU DO THEN?
ASK THE REST OF THE FAMILY, I SUPPOSE. DESIRE SAID NO ALREADY. SO I THOUGHT, OKAY, I'D ASK YOU NEXT. IT'S JUST ALL BEEN DIFFERENT SINCE HE WENT. IT'S SOUR AND ROTTEN AND I'M LONELY. WE NEVER SEE EACH OTHER. HE MADE THINGS OKAY.
NO. I WON'T HELP YOU.
OH.
WELL, THANK YOU FOR NOT DOING THE VOICE, ANYWAY.
SO WHO WILL YOU ASK NOW?
UM. DREAM, I SUPPOSE. HE'S THE NEXT OLDEST, AFTER...
HE'LL SAY NO. YOU KNOW THAT?
ARE YOU SURE YOU WON'T CHANGE YOUR MIND? I MEAN, DREAM'S MUCH SPOOKIER THAN YOU ARE. AND I'M ALWAYS SCARED HE'S LAUGHING AT ME, BEHIND HIS FACE.
I HAVE MY OWN RESPONSIBILITIES. AND I RESPECT OUR BROTHER'S PRIVACY.
AND YOU DON'T WANT TO UPSET DESIRE, DO YOU?
PLEASE. DON'T LOOK AT ME LIKE THAT. I. UM. I...
I'M GOING BACK TO MY OWN HOME. I'M GOING TO THINK.
19

THREE BLIND HUMMINGBIRDS HANG IN THE AIR LIKE JEWELS OF IRIDESCENT SCARLET AND COBALT; THEN, ONE BY ONE, THEY FADE, ALL COLOR LEECHED FROM THEM, AND FALL LIFELESS INTO THE MISTS, TO BE EATEN BY THE RATS.
DESPAIR FEELS UNCOMFORTABLE.
IN HER WORLD THERE ARE SO MANY WINDOWS. EACH OPENING SHOWS HER AN EXISTENCE THAT'S FALLEN TO HER--SOME ONLY FOR MOMENTS, OTHERS FOR LIFETIMES.
ABLE AT THIS MOMENT NEITHER TO SAVOR THEM, NOR TO UNDERSTAND HER OWN DISQUIET, SHE STARES AWAY FROM ALL WINDOWS AS SHE WALKS.
SILENT RATS RUN UNMINDFULLY OVER HER FEET, INVISIBLE IN THE MIST.
SHE MISSES HIM.
IT IS OVER THREE HUNDRED YEARS SINCE LAST SHE AND HER BROTHER WERE ALONE TOGETHER...
LIKE A FLOOD, THE MEMORIES COME, AND SHE IS DROWNING IN THEM.
AGAINST HER WILL HER CHEST HEAVES, AND SHE BEGINS TO WEEP: DEEP, HELPLESS, RACKING SOBS...
NO.
DESPAIR PLACES THE COLD METAL BARB OF HER HOOK ONTO THE SURFACE OF HER EYE. AND THEN SHE PUSHES (PIERCING CORNEA AND LENS) AND RIPS (FREEING THE AQUEOUS HUMOR AND VITREOUS HUMOR TO RUN LIKE TEARS DOWN HER CHEEK, INTO HER HAND)...
THE PAIN DISTRACTS HER, A LITTLE.
BUT STILL, SHE REMEMBERS...

THE CITY FOLK HAD KILLED THE CATS AND THE DOGS BECAUSE THEY MIGHT HAVE HELPED SPREAD THE DISEASE; AND IF THEY COULD, THEY WOULD HAVE KILLED EACH OTHER.

Lord Have mercy upon uf.
LACKING THAT POWER, THEY IMPRISONED EACH OTHER IN THEIR HOUSES ON THE FIRST SUSPICION OF DISEASE. A ROUGH RED CROSS WAS PAINTED ON THE DOOR: WRITTEN ON A PAPER THE WORDS "LORD HAVE MERCY UPON US".
THE DOOR WAS THEN SEALED, AND A WATCHMAN PLACED OUTSIDE, UNTIL ALL THEREIN HAD BEEN UNTOUCHED BY THE DISEASE FOR FORTY DAYS, OR WERE DEAD.

SHE HEARD THE SCREAMS OF TWO CHILDREN IN A HIGH ATTIC ROOM, THEIR PARENTS LONG DEAD. A NEWBORN BABY SUCKLED THE MILK AND THE PLAGUE FROM A COLD BREAST...
DESPAIR WALKED THE STREETS OF LONDON IN 1665, THE PLAGUE YEAR.

ON THE EMPTY STREET, A CORPSE LAY, WAITING FOR THE CART TO TAKE IT TO THE PLAGUE PIT; NEXT TO IT LAY A POOR PIPER, UNTOUCHED BY DISEASE, BUT DEAD DRUNK.
HE WOULD COME TO HIS SENSES IN THE EARLY HOURS OF THE FOLLOWING MORNING, IN THE PLAGUE PIT, WITH SOFT EARTH ON HIS FACE, AND COLD FLESH BENEATH HIM, AND BELIEVE HIMSELF IN HELL...

"LET ME OBSERVE HERE," SAID DEFOE, WRITING SOMEWHAT AFTER THE EVENT, "THAT WHEN I SAY THE PEOPLE ABANDONED THEMSELVES TO DESPAIR, I DO NOT MEAN TO RELIGIOUS DESPAIR, OR A DESPAIR OF THEIR ETERNAL STATE; BUT I MEAN A DESPAIR OF THEIR BEING ABLE TO ESCAPE THE INFECTION, OR TO OUTLIVE THE PLAGUE...
"THE PEOPLE WERE BROUGHT INTO A CONDITION TO DESPAIR OF LIFE."
WHEN DESPAIR READ THAT, THROUGH A MIRROR, SHE NODDED WITH THE SATISFACTION OF ONE WHO HAD PERFORMED HER DUTY WITH DILIGENCE AND CARE.
WELL-MET, SISTER. LONG IT IS, SINCE LAST I SAW YOU AWAY FROM YOUR DOMAIN.
TRUE. SOMETIMES REFLECTIONS ARE NOT ENOUGH. AND YOU? SHOULD YOU NOT BE IN YOUR KINGDOM?
I GET LITTLE CHANCE FOR THAT IN THESE DAYS. I WALK THIS WORLD MORE AND MORE...
THE WHEEL NEVER CEASES FROM TURNING.
STILL-- HAH HAH HAH! I HAVE NOTHING TO COMPLAIN OF, DO I?
I NEVER COMPLAIN.
NO.
SO, MY SISTER. THIS IS A GOOD TIME FOR YOU.
YES.
ARE YOU PLEASED?
PLEASED, OH MY LORD OF DESTRUCTION? I AM NEITHER PLEASED NOR DISPLEASED.
I SIMPLY AM.
OH.

THIS WON'T LAST FOR MUCH LONGER. ALREADY THE DEATHS ARE GETTING FEWER...
PLAGUES COME AND GO.
YES.
AND THEN IT'S MY TURN.
THINGS ARE CHANGING, MY SISTER.
THINGS NEVER CHANGE.
OH, BUT THEY DO. THAT'S MY PROVINCE, AFTER ALL.
SOME THINGS ARE CHANGELESS.
PEOPLE LOVE, AND DIE, THEY DREAM, DESTROY, DESPAIR, GO MAD. THEY FULFILL THEIR DESTINIES, LIVE OUT THE COURSE OF THEIR LIVES.
WE FULFILL OUR FUNCTION, AS THEY FULFILL THEIRS...
THAT WILL NOT CHANGE.
YOU THINK NOT?
AHHH. AYE WELL, PERHAPS YOU ARE RIGHT, AFTER ALL.
WE WILL SEE.
AH, ME. I HAVE MUCH TO DO, SCANT TIME TO STAND HERE GABBLING. FARE YE WELL, MY LITTLE SISTER. 'TIL NEXT I SEE YOUR PRETTY FACE...
HIS BEARD WAS ROUGH AGAINST HER SKIN.
NO ONE EVER KISSED DESPAIR, SAVE HER BROTHER.
BUT WHEN SHE NEXT SAW HIM IT WAS IN DESTINY'S HALL, THIRTY YEARS ON...
FOR THE LAST TIME.

DESPAIR? SWEET TWIN? I, DESIRE, CALL YOU. I STAND IN MY GALLERY AND I HOLD YOUR SIGIL.
WILL YOU TALK TO ME?

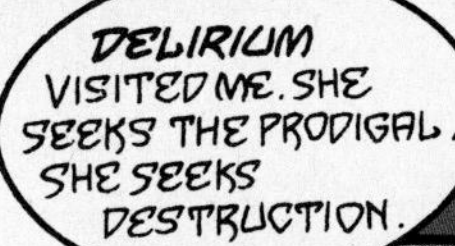
DELIRIUM VISITED ME. SHE SEEKS THE PRODIGAL. SHE SEEKS DESTRUCTION.

WHAT DID SHE SAY TO YOU? WE HAVE TO TALK...
HELLO?

YOU KNOW HOW SHE IS WHEN SHE GETS AN IDEA INTO HER HEAD. I MEAN, WHEN ONE FINALLY PENE-TRATES.
I'M... I'M REALLY WORRIE ABOUT THIS.
SHE'LL GO AFTER HIM. I KNOW SHE WILL. AND WHAT IF SHE INVOLVES OUR ELDERS IN HER MADNESS?

DESPAIR?
I'M IN MY GALLERY.
I'M HOLDING YOUR SIGIL.
I KNOW YOU'RE THERE.
TALK TO ME.

WE HAVE TO STOP HER.
PLEASE?
SISTER?
TALK TO ME?

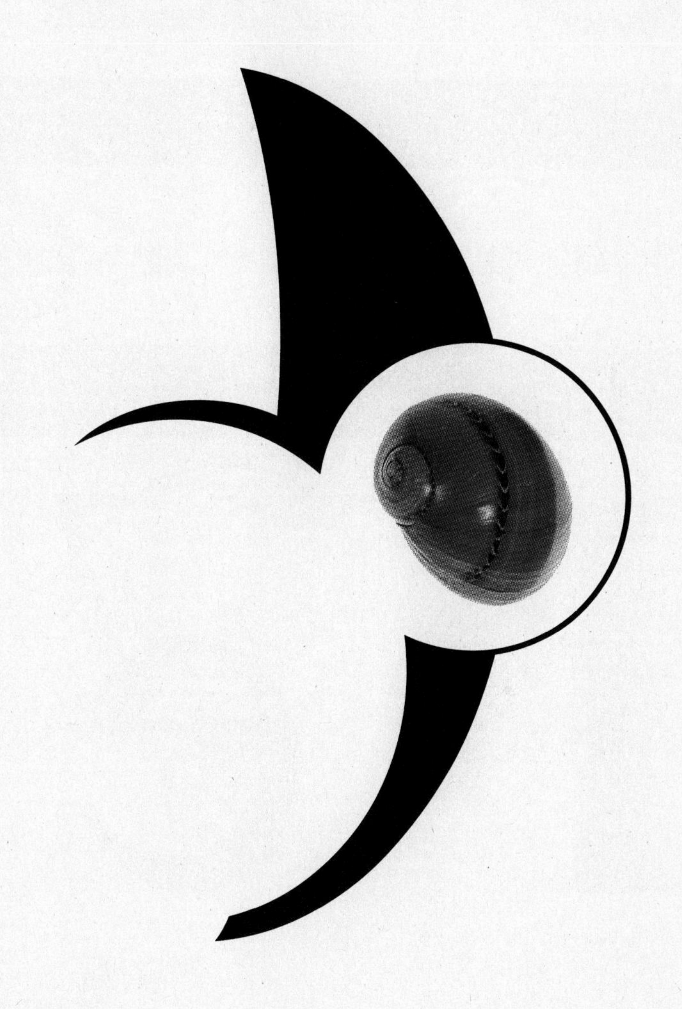

It always rains on the unloved
Wet dreams
A fishing expedition
She kisses Wyverns
(the Disneyland analogy)
Dinner etiquette and chocolate lov
Desire swears by the first circle
"Things are changing"
What can possibly go wrong?

chapter 2

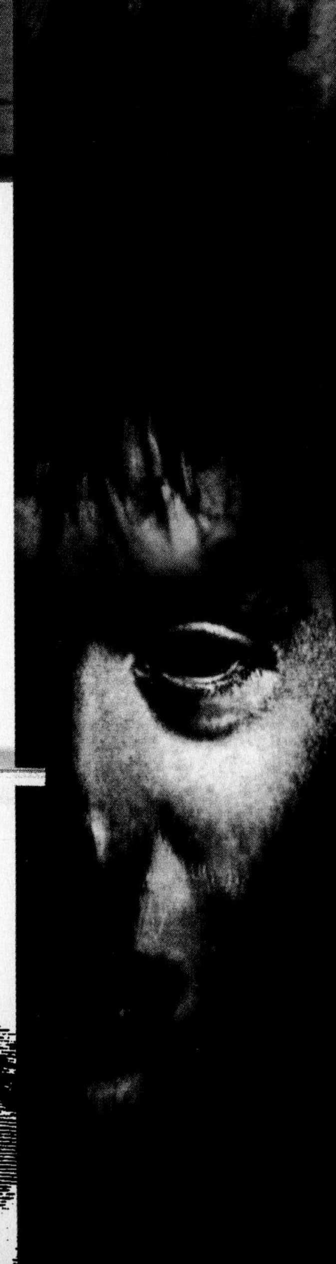

She...
She has decided she no longer loves me.

LORD?
MY LORD, YOU ASKED TO BE TOLD WHEN THE YOUNG LADY HAD LEFT THE CASTLE.
YES, WELL. SHE'S GONE. ON HER WAY BACK TO THE WAKING WORLD.
AND THE, UH, THE PALACE STAFF WERE WONDERING, LORD...
WHAT WOULD YOU LIKE DONE WITH THE SUITE OF ROOMS YOU CREATED FOR HER?
Erase them.
2

TWO: IT ALWAYS RAINS ON THE UNLOVED—WET DREAMS—A FISHING EXPEDITION—SHE KISSES WYVERNS (THE DISNEYLAND ANALOGY)—DINNER ETIQUETTE AND CHOCOLATE LOVERS—DESIRE SWEARS BY THE FIRST CIRCLE—"THINGS ARE CHANGING"—WHAT CAN POSSIBLY GO WRONG?

WELL, I SPOKE TO HIM ABOUT THE ROOMS.
HE WANTS THEM ERASED. HMM. TO BE ON THE SAFE SIDE YOU'D BETTER REMOVE THAT WHOLE WING OF THE CASTLE.
AND HE DOESN'T WANT TO BE REMINDED OF HER.
DON'T SAY HER NAME. DON'T MENTION HER UNLESS HE MENTIONS HER FIRST, WHICH HE WON'T-- AND EVEN IF HE DOES, PRETEND THAT YOU'VE FORGOTTEN SHE EVER EXISTED.
PASS THE WORD ALONG.
UM. MISTER LUCIEN? SHE GAVE ME THIS. WHEN SHE WAS LEAVING. AS A PRESENT. FOR BEING HER MAID.
IT'S REALLY PRETTY. AND SHE WAS SO NICE TO ME. CAN'T I KEEP IT?
PLEASE, MISTER LUCIEN?
BAA-BOOM
I SUPPOSE SO, NUALA. BUT DON'T LET HIM SEE IT.
BRRRR. LISTEN TO THAT THUNDER.
POOR LORD MORPHEUS. HE MUST BE VERY SAD.

NAH. HE ENJOYS IT.
I MEAN, HELL, IT'S A POSE. Y'KNOW?
PHHHHT.
NOW, GUYS LIKE ME, ORDINARY JOES, WE JUST SHRUG OUR SHOULDERS, SAY, HEY, THAT'S LIFE, FLICK IT IF YOU CAN'T TAKE A JOKE.
HE SPENDS A COUPLA MONTHS HANGING OUT WITH A NEW BROAD. THEN ONE DAY THE MAGIC'S WORN OFF, AND HE GOES BACK TO WORK, AND SHE TAKES A HIKE.
NOT HIM. OH NO. HE'S GOTTA BE THE TRAGIC FIGURE STANDING OUT IN THE RAIN, MOURNIN' THE LOSS OF HIS BELOVED. SO DOWN COMES THE RAIN, RIGHT ON CUE.
IN THE MEANTIME EVERYBODY GETS DREAMS FULLA EXISTENTIAL ANGST AND WAKES UP FEELING LIKE HELL.
AND WE ALL GET WET.
I'M SURE WE'RE ALL GRATEFUL FOR THOSE PRICELESS GEMS OF WISDOM, MERVYN.
HEY, I SPEAK MY MIND, LOOSH. YOU GOTTA PROBLEM WITH THAT?
I DO FEEL SORRY FOR HIM. HE REALLY LIKED HER.
5

AND WHY DO MY GUYS HAVE TO DISMANTLE THE WHOLE WING? HELL, HE COULD VANISH IT INNA BLINK.
BLINK! IT'S GONE!
LIKE THAT.
WELL, HE'S ON THE BALCONY OUTSIDE HIS QUARTERS, MERVYN.
WHY DON'T YOU GO UP THERE NOW, AND SUGGEST IT TO HIM?
BA-BOOM
OOOKAY. I'LL GO GATHER THE WRECKING CREW.
SEEYA, TOOTS. LATER, LOOSH.
LUCIEN? YOU'VE KNOWN HIM FOR A LONG TIME...
HE REALLY DID LIKE HER, DIDN'T HE?
YES, MY DEAR.
I'M VERY MUCH AFRAID THAT HE DID.

...IT'S BEEN A WHOLE WEEK, FOR CHRISSAKES! ISN'T HE TIRED OF RAIN YET?
I VERY MUCH DOUBT IT, MATTHEW.
SO, ANY IDEA HOW LONG IT'LL TAKE HIM TO GET OVER THIS?
I MEAN, DOES THIS ALWAYS HAPPEN WHEN A GIRLFRIEND WALKS OUT ON HIM?
NOT AT ALL. FOR EXAMPLE, AFTER THE NADA AFFAIR HE RAZED THE DREAMING. IT WAS A BLEAK, LONELY DESERT FOR CENTURIES.
I REMEMBER THE FIRST FLOWER THAT GREW. THE FIRST TIME HE SMILED AGAIN...
CALLIOPE? WELL, THAT AFFAIR HAD RUN ITS COURSE FOR BOTH OF THEM. HE MOPED A BIT, BUT I THINK ON THE WHOLE HE WAS RELIEVED.
POOR DEAR ELEANORA...? HMM. HE THREW HIMSELF INTO HIS WORK AFTER THAT ONE BIT THE DUST. HE WOVE DREAMS AND CRAFTED NIGHTMARES FOR A HUNDRED YEARS, SCARCELY RAISING HIS HEAD.
SO, NO, THIS ISN'T USUAL.
BUT THEN, WHAT IS?
I NEVER LIKED HER. I KNEW SHE'D DO SOMETHING LIKE THIS.
YOU KNOW, I WENT UP THERE AND TRIED TO SNAP HIM OUT OF IT. I MEAN, I WAS UP THERE FOR LIKE, HOURS.
OH YES?
WENT DOWN LIKE A DEAD BALLOON.
YOU KNOW WHAT HE SAID TO ME?
NO.
"NOTHING."
"ABSOLUTELY NOTHING."

UH, OKAY, MM GOLDIE.
THE UH SUHSOMETHING NASTY IN THE MM SUB-BASEMENT SAYS IT ER DOESN'T MUHMUH MIND BERBEING UNDERWATER.
IT SUHSORT OF, HMM, LIKES IT EVEN.
YOU ER LEARN SOMETHING NEW EVERY DUH-DAY.
TWENTY-ONE DAYS OF, HH, SOLID RAIN. JUST WHAT WE NEEDED--I UH DUHDON'T THINK.
ARE YOU UH ALL RIGHT UP THERE?
urkle.
WELL, I'VE MUHMADE LOTS OF SANDWICHES. ENOUGH FOR ANOTHER TUH-TWO WEEKS. AND I'VE BUH-BROUGHT MY, ER, FISHING ROD. AND YOU'VE GOT YUH-YOUR FISHING ROD.
HAS THE B-B-BOTTLE IMP GOT ITS FUHFISHING ROD?
Glurk.
HAH! WE'LL HAVE FUN, WERWON'T WE? WE CAN S-SING LITTLE MM SONGS TO EACH OTHER. YES?
PUH-PUH-PACK UP YOUR TROUBLES IN YOUR MM HM ER OLD KIT BAG AND SMILE, SMILE, SMILE...
NEARLY THERE...
YAAARR!
SNAP
meep?
8

This is foolish...
Why do I hurt so?
I scarcely knew her.
A handful of months, little more...
I would have given her worlds of her own, strung like sapphires and emeralds on a silken cord.
I would have given her...
I keep thinking of her eyes, toward the end. Cold eyes, weighing me dispassionately, finding me wanting...
And in the end, she told me. But I knew before she told me. It was there in her eyes.
She had decided she no longer loved me.

MY LORD?
WE HAVE CAPTURED
AN INTRUDER.
SO?
MY LORD,
SHE CLAIMS
TO BE YOUR
SISTER.
10

HERE SHE IS, MY LORD. THE INTRUDER. WE HAVE HER SAFE.
FHEE FHED FHEE WOV WOR FHIFHTER.
I'm afraid she IS my sister, Wyvern. Put her down.
WHEEEE!
Gently.

WHEEEE!
MY-- MY LADY-- I MUST-- I--HAD I BUT KNOWN-- I THOUGHT--
S'OKAY. I MEAN, I LIKED IT. IT WAS LIKE DISNEYLAND.
I ESPECIALLY LIKED THE SWINGING BIT.
Delirium.
What are you doing here?
I CAME TO SEE YOU. I MEAN I WANTED TO TALK TOO. NOT JUST SEE
Why didn't you call me? You have a gallery.
I DIDN'T WANT TO.
IF I CALLED AND YOU SAID NO THEN THAT WOULD MEAN YOU WOULDN'T TALK TO ME AND THE LAST TIME I CALLED YOU YOU SAID NO AND THE TIME BEFORE THAT SO I THOUGHT YOU PROBABLY DIDN'T WANT TO TALK TO. ME. SO I THOUGHT IF I JUST TURNED UP THEN...
PLEASE DON'T MAKE ME GO AWAY.
Are you hungry?
...MAYBE.
Very good. I will find us something to eat.

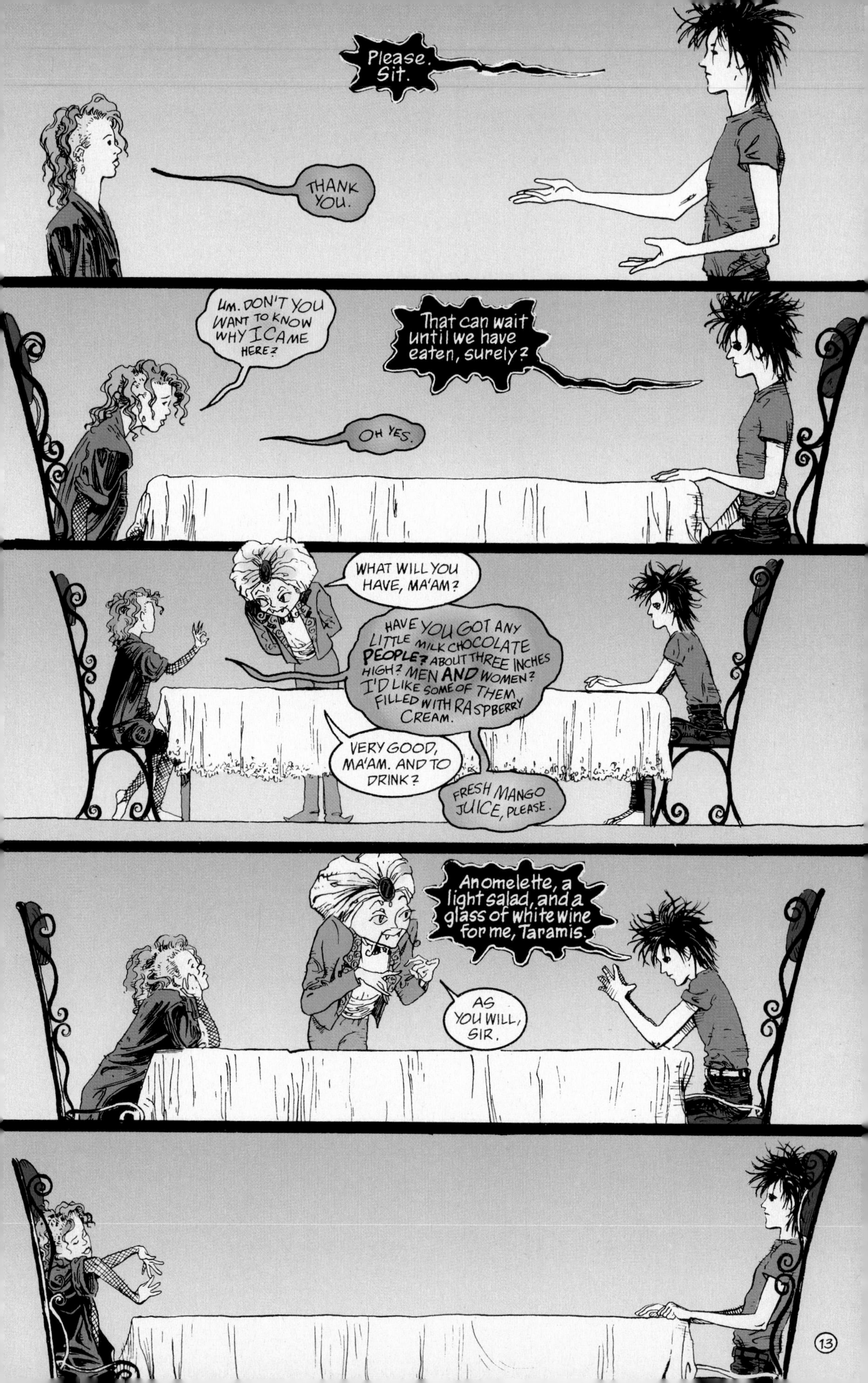
Please. Sit.
THANK YOU.
UM. DON'T YOU WANT TO KNOW WHY I CAME HERE?
That can wait until we have eaten, surely?
OH YES.
WHAT WILL YOU HAVE, MA'AM?
HAVE YOU GOT ANY LITTLE MILK CHOCOLATE PEOPLE? ABOUT THREE INCHES HIGH? MEN AND WOMEN? I'D LIKE SOME OF THEM FILLED WITH RASPBERRY CREAM.
VERY GOOD, MA'AM. AND TO DRINK?
FRESH MANGO JUICE, PLEASE.
An omelette, a light salad, and a glass of white wine for me, Taramis.
AS YOU WILL, SIR.

UM. HAVE YOU SEEN ANY OF THE FAMILY RECENTLY?
No.
I HAVE. I SAW DESPAIR AND DESIRE.
Ah. And how are they?
FINE. JUST FINE.
Ah.
I SAW IT WAS RAINING OUTSIDE. WATER. OR WHAT IT RAINS IN DREAMS, ANYWAY.
Yes.
YOU MUST BE IN A VERY BAD MOOD.
Must I?
DINNER IS SERVED, SIR.
Thank you, Taramis.
OH, LOOK! THEY'VE ALL GOT LITTLE EYEBROWS.
FIRST OF ALL I BITE THEIR LITTLE HANDS OFF, ONE TWO THREE... THEN I BITE THEIR LITTLE NOSES...
Indeed.

LOOK. THESE TWO ARE MAKING LO-OVE...
K. I. S. S. I. N. G.
Stop that.
SORRY...
UM. THEY WEREN'T REALLY KISSING. THEY WERE UM.
SQUIDGING.
IT'S OKAY. I'M FINISHED. MOSTLY. THEY'VE GONE ALL STICKY ANYWAY. AND I DON'T LIKE MANGO JUICE.
IT'S YECCHY.
KISSING.
Is this formal family business, sister?
OH YES. I THINK. I MEAN KIND OF. MOSTLY. MAYBE.
Then I think my Gallery might well be the best place to conduct discussions, don't you?
WHATEVER.
THEY LEAVE THAT PLACE, ALMOST IMPERCEPTIBLY.
TOUCHED BY HER FINGERS, THE TWO SURVIVING CHOCOLATE PEOPLE COPULATE DESPERATELY, LOSING THEMSELVES IN A MELTING FRENZY OF LUST, SPENDING THE LAST OF THEIR BRIEF BORROWED LIVES IN A SPASM OF RASPBERRY CREAM AND FEAR.
15

Now, what exactly do you wish to talk to me about?
Delirium? You are beginning to try my patience.
Is... something the matter?
Here. Use this.
TH-THANK YOU.
And wipe your nose.
Little sister, what exactly is the problem?
Snorrk
16

I WAS AFRAID YOU'D PROBABLY BE ALL HORRIBLE TO ME, AND YOU'RE SO SCARY, SO I THOUGHT I'D REALLY TRY TO BE GOOD AND I WAS TRYING SO HARD TO BE GOOD AND YOU WERE STILL BEING HORRID TO ME AND I WAS DOING MY BEST AND THEN I MESSED IT ALL UP AND NOW YOU'LL SAY NO AND BE HORRIBLE AND IT'S ALL A MESS AND IT'S MY FAULT.

I...
I'm sorry.
I've been a little distracted recently.
I wasn't angry with you, sister.
If I have behaved badly, as your host, then please, accept my apologies.

ARE YOU MAKING FUN OF ME?
ARE YOU?

Why would I do that?
ALL THAT APOLOGIZING.
YOU'VE NEVER APOLOGIZED TO ME. YOU JUST ACT LIKE YOU KNOW STUFF I DON'T KNOW THAT MAKES EVERYTHING YOU DO OKAY.

I see.
Well, I have apologized. And I was not making fun of you.
Now, why don't you tell me why you came here.

I WAS THINKING ABOUT THINGS. AND I WAS THINKING THAT WE SHOULD GO AND FIND OUR BROTHER.
Yes?
WELL, I MISS HIM. AND HE COULD BE HURT OR SOMETHING AND WE SHOULD DO SOMETHING.

So?
THAT WAS JUST WHAT DESPAIR SAID. SHE SAID "SO?"
You've asked her, then?
YES. SHE SAID NO. SHE SAID YOU'D SAY NO, TOO.
And Desire? I take it you asked Desire as well.

OH YES.
I WAS IN DESIRE'S HOUSE WHEN I HAD THE IDEA.
I'm sure you were.
SO WILL YOU COME WITH ME TO LOOK FOR HIM? PLEASE?

Will you excuse me for one moment?
I S'PPOSE so.

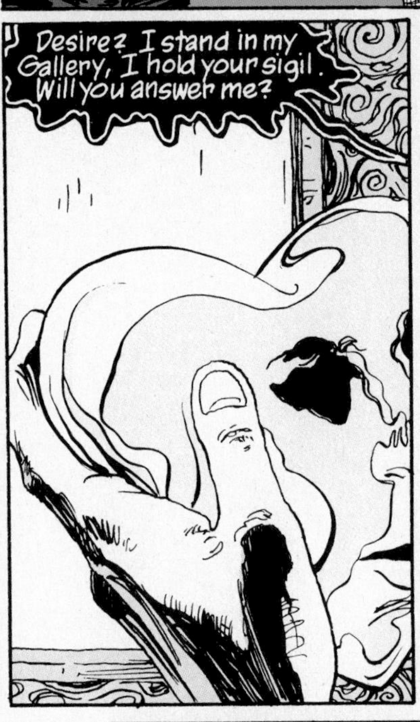
Desire? I stand in my Gallery, I hold your sigil. Will you answer me?

DREAM? IT'S BEEN TWO YEARS SINCE I LAST SAW YOU.
AT THAT LITTLE FAMILY GET-TOGETHER. REMEMBER?
OF COURSE YOU DO.

Delirium is in my realm.
YES. I THOUGHT SHE'D BE ARRIVING SOONER OR LATER. IT'S TAKEN HER LONGER THAN I THOUGHT TO GET THE NERVE UP, THOUGH. ARE YOU COMING THROUGH?

No. I'll stay between realms, if you have no objection.
SUIT YOURSELF.
She wants to find our lost brother.
I KNOW.

This affair has your marks all over it, Desire. She tells me she decided on this idiotic course while in your domain.
SHE DID.
BUT I HAD NOTHING TO DO WITH IT.
And I suppose you had nothing to do with my recent troubles?
YOUR LITTLE AFFAIR, AND ITS MESSY ENDING?
I HATE TO DISAPPOINT YOU, DREAM, BUT YOU MANAGED TO SCREW THAT ONE UP ALL ON YOUR OWN.
ALTHOUGH I DID FIND IT EXTREMELY AMUSING.
Are you telling the whole truth?
I'M AFRAID SO.
YOU DON'T BELIEVE ME, DO YOU?
No.
VERY WELL. I HAVE TOLD YOU THE TRUTH: I SWEAR IT BY MY HEART. THERE. SATISFIED?
Will you swear it by the first circle?
HMM. THAT TAKES ME BACK.
BUT YES: I SWEAR BY THE FIRST CIRCLE. AND BY THE OTHER SIDE OF THE SKY. AND BY THE SWORD AND THE--
Enough.
I JUST WANTED TO SHOW YOU I WAS SERIOUS.
AND I AM.
NEITHER DELIRIUM'S NEW OBSESSION NOR YOUR LITTLE HEARTBREAK ARE OF MY DOING.
NOW. SOME OF US HAVE BUSINESS TO ATTEND TO.
SO WHY DON'T YOU GO BACK TO YOUR GALLERY, TELL THE LITTLE GLEET TO BUZZ OFF AND BOTHER SOMEONE ELSE, SO YOU CAN GET BACK TO FEELING SORRY FOR YOURSELF?
Hmm.

DELIRIUM STANDS IN DREAM'S GALLERY, WAITING FOR HIS RETURN. REMEMBERING:
THE MOMENT SHE REALIZED WHAT WAS HAPPENING, THAT THE UNIVERSE WAS CHANGING, THAT SHE WAS GROWING UP OR AT LEAST GROWING OLDER...
SHE WAS NO LONGER DELIGHT; AND THE BLOSSOMS HAD ALREADY BEGUN TO FALL IN HER DOMAIN, BECOMING SMUDGED AND FORMLESS COLORS, AND SHE HAD NO ONE TO TALK TO...
THEN SHE WENT TO SEE HIM. SHE REMEMBERS THE LIGHT GLINTING GOLD IN HIS BEARD AND EYELASHES. AND HE PUT HIS ARM AROUND HER SHOULDERS AND THEY STOOD ON THE HILL (BECAUSE THIS WAS ON EARTH IN THE DAWN DAYS, EVEN THEN HE SPENT A LOT OF TIME ON EARTH).
AND HE SAID, "DEL, IT'S OKAY." AND THEN HE SHUT UP, AND THEN SHE STARTED GIGGLING UNCONTROLLABLY, AND HE DIDN'T SAY ANYTHING, HE JUST HELD HER UNTIL SHE GAINED CONTROL ONCE MORE. THEY WATCHED THE SUNSET FOR A BIT.
THEN HE SAID, "DEL. THINGS ARE CHANGING."
SHE KNEW IT WAS TRUE.
AND THERE WAS NOTHING SHE COULD DO ABOUT IT.
20

Little sister?

OH. YOU'RE BACK.
Yes.

I WAS THINKING. I CAN DO THAT. THINK. STILL DO THAT. I MEAN, EVEN WHEN I FORGET HOW TO... HOW TO...
WHAT WAS I SAYING?

I have spoken to Desire.
YES. I'VE DONE THAT, TOO.
DREAM?
Yes.
I WAS LYING TO YOU. EARLIER. WHAT I SAID. IT WASN'T TRUE.

Really?
YEEES. I DO LIKE MANGO JUICE REALLY.
If you were to seek our brother, where would you start looking?

UM. I DON'T KNOW.
I SUPPOSE I'D START BY FINDING HIS OLD FRIENDS AND ASKING THEM IF THEY KNEW. I MEAN, I'D ASK THEM REALLY NICELY.
Did you know any of his friends?
A FEW.

He's been gone three hundred years.
I MADE A LIST OF HIS FRIENDS I KNEW. I WROTE IT MYSELF. IN WRITING.
I'm impressed.
UM. WHAT DID DESIRE SAY?
Nothing important.
I'M SORRY I MADE YOU ANGRY.
What are you going to do now?
OUR OLDER SISTER. I'LL ASK HER. AND IF SHE SAYS NO, I'LL ASK DESTINY. AND IF HE SAYS NO I'LL GO AND LOOK ON MY OWN.
I CAN DO IT ON MY OWN IF I WANT TO.
IT'S JUST I MIGHT GET DISTRACTED, AND I GET LOST KIND OF EASILY, AND SOMETIMES I HAVE REALLY BAD DAYS...
...WHEN, YOU KNOW, I JUST WANT TO HIDE OR SCREAM OR BLEED OR SOMETHING, AND... ALL THAT...
Hmm.
Lucien?
LORD.
Lucien. You remember my sister?
INDEED. A PLEASURE, MA'AM.
YOU'VE GOT POINTY EARS.
INDEED.
22

Lucien, I will be taking a short journey, with my sister.
If any matters arise that require my attention, please feel free to contact me.
VERY GOOD, LORD.
We'll be travelling in the Waking World. Let Pharamond know that we will be calling on him. I trust that he still oversees transportation?
I HAVE HEARD NOTHING TO THE CONTRARY, LORD.
Good.
YOU MEAN YOU'LL ACTUALLY COME WITH ME? AND LOOK FOR HIM? HONESTLY?
Yes.
OH.
WOW.
MY LORD? MIGHT I HAVE A BRIEF WORD WITH YOU?
Certainly, Lucien.
IF YOU'LL FORGIVE MY SPEAKING PERHAPS A LITTLE BLUNTLY, LORD...
DO YOU REALLY FEEL THAT THIS IS A WISE COURSE OF ACTION?
My brother had his reasons for leaving, Lucien. He desires his privacy, and I respect his wishes.
We will not find him.
THEN, WHY...?
Because I need something to take my mind off my recent misadventure, perhaps?
Because it has been a long time since I walked abroad.
And because I wish to.
VERY GOOD, LORD.

AND YOU WILL BE BACK...?
When Delirium loses interest in the quest, as she will.
Or, when I lose interest, and feel I am ready to return.

OR WHEN YOU HAVE FOUND YOUR BROTHER?
It won't happen.
MY LORD, ARE YOU SURE THIS IS WISE?

It will be a brief diversion, Lucien. Nothing more.
We will see a few people, a few sights. I am but a step away from the Dreaming should you need me here.
I see no reason to worry.

"You worry too much, Lucien. I've noticed this before.
"After all, this is completely straightforward. What could possibly go wrong?"
"WHATEVER YOU SAY, LORD.
"WHATEVER YOU SAY."

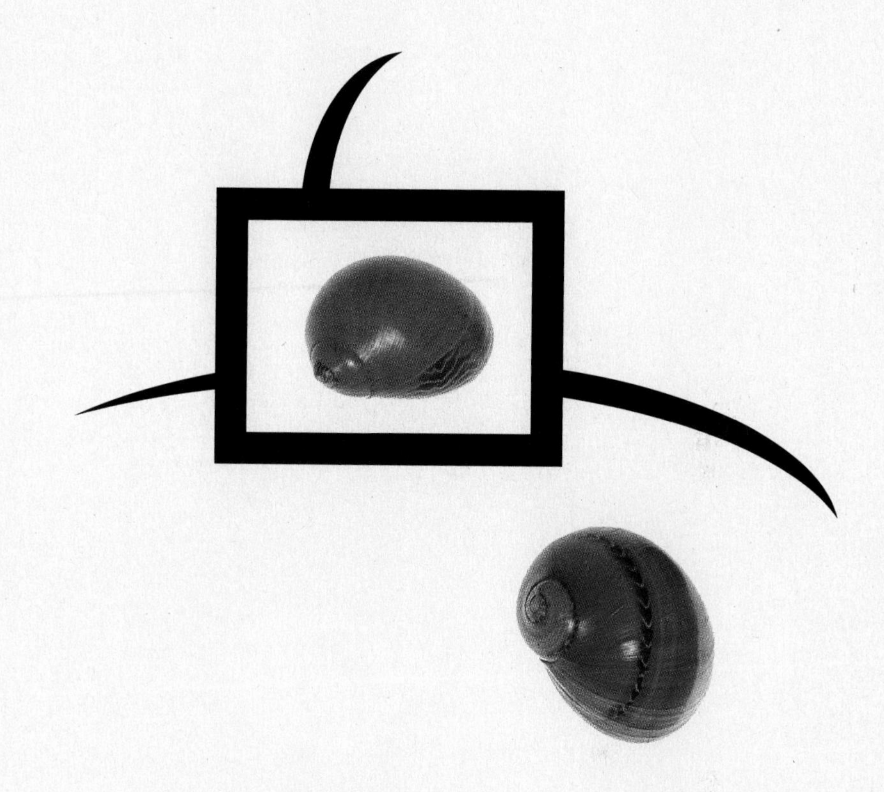

The people who remember Atlantis

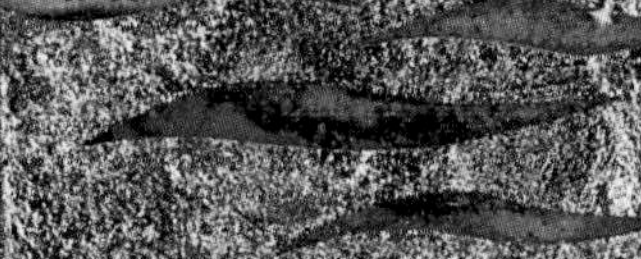

Concerning mammoths and falling walls

chapter 

"When I dream, sometimes I remember how to fly"

Ancestral voices prophesying

Bored, she makes little frogs

Who controls transportation?

THERE ARE NOT MANY OF THEM, ALL THINGS CONSIDERED: THE TRULY OLD.

EVEN ON THIS PLANET, IN THIS AGE, WHEN PEOPLE CONSIDER A MERE HUNDRED YEARS, OR A THOUSAND, TO BE AN UNUSUAL SPAN.

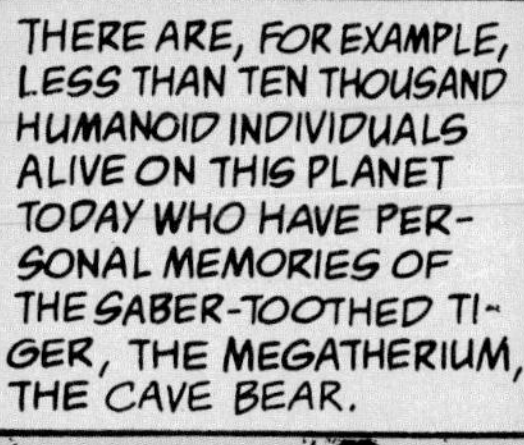

THERE ARE, FOR EXAMPLE, LESS THAN TEN THOUSAND HUMANOID INDIVIDUALS ALIVE ON THIS PLANET TODAY WHO HAVE PERSONAL MEMORIES OF THE SABER-TOOTHED TIGER, THE MEGATHERIUM, THE CAVE BEAR.

THERE ARE TODAY LESS THAN A THOUSAND WHO WALKED THE STREETS OF ATLANTIS (THE FIRST ATLANTIS. THE OTHER LANDS THAT BORE THAT NAME WERE SHADOWS, ECHO-ATLANTISES, MYTH LANDS, AND THEY CAME LATER).

THERE ARE LESS THAN FIVE HUNDRED LIVING HUMANS WHO REMEMBER THE HUMAN CIVILIZATIONS THAT PREDATED THE GREAT LIZARDS. (THERE WERE A FEW; FOSSIL RECORDS ARE UNRELIABLE. SEVERAL OF THEM LASTED FOR MILLIONS OF YEARS.)

THERE ARE ROUGHLY SEVENTY PEOPLE WALKING THE EARTH, HUMAN TO ALL APPEARANCES (AND IN A FEW CASES, TO ALL MEDICAL TESTS CURRENTLY AVAILABLE), WHO WERE ALIVE BEFORE THE EARTH HAD BEGUN TO CONGEAL FROM GAS AND DUST.

HOW WELL DO YOU KNOW YOUR NEIGHBORS? YOUR FRIENDS? YOUR LOVERS?

WALK THE STREETS OF ANY CITY, AND STARE CAREFULLY AT THE PEOPLE WHO PASS YOU, AND WONDER, AND KNOW THIS:

THEY ARE THERE TOO. THE OLD ONES.

BERNIE CAPAX IS ON HIS WAY IN TO WORK. HE'S A LAWYER ; A JUNIOR PARTNER IN COLUM, MARTINDALE AND GRANT.
FROM TIME TO TIME HE'S DONE OTHER THINGS, BUT MOSTLY HE'S BEEN A LAWYER OF ONE KIND OR ANOTHER.
PEOPLE ALWAYS NEED LAWYERS.

HE'S THINKING ABOUT A HORROR MOVIE HE SAW LAST NIGHT ON TV: ONE OF THE VILLAINS WAS THE MARQUIS DE SADE, DEPICTED AS AN ATHLETIC, DEBONAIR PSYCHOPATH: THE EMBODIMENT OF PURE, VICIOUS EVIL.

HE'S THINKING ABOUT THE MARQUIS HE KNEW, A PALE LITTLE ASTHMATIC, TERRIBLY OBESE FROM HIS YEARS IN PRISON, WHO STARTED AT SHADOWS AND WROTE OBSESSIVELY ABOUT ACTIONS HE DARED NOT PERFORM.
COMICS SOLD HERE
CLASSIC AUTO
BABY!

HE'S THINKING OF A DREAM HE HAD JUST BEFORE WAKING, WHICH REMINDS HIM OF SOMETHING FREUD ONCE SAID TO HIM, ABOUT HOW WE DON'T SMELL ANYTHING IN DREAMS, AND HE'S THINKING HOW THAT JUST ISN'T TRUE.
LOST

HE'S THINKING OF THE MAMMOTHS HE DREAMED OF THIS MORNING, STEAM RISING FROM THEIR THICK BROWN COATS IN THE CHILL OF THAT INTERMINABLE WINTER.
IN HIS DREAM THE RANK, HIGH SMELL OF THEM HUNG ON THE AIR, AND HE WALKED AMONG THE HUGE BEASTS, FINGERS STROKING THEIR ROUGH HIDES.
DANGER
DANGER! CONSTRUCTION
IN ITS 8TH SMASH YEAR
Cats
Sweeney Todd
The Musical
POST NO BILLS
LOST

IT WAS THE SMELL OF MAMMOTH. HE'S CERTAIN OF IT. NOTHING ELSE SMELLS LIKE THAT. HE HASN'T SMELLED IT SINCE HE WAS A CHILD...
DANGER
IN ITS 8TH SMASH YEAR
Cats
LOST

BERNIE CAPAX REMEMBERS; ALTHOUGH AT THIS MOMENT HE SUDDENLY REALIZES HE IS UNSURE WHETHER HE'S REMEMBERING HIS CHILDHOOD IN THE STEPPES, OR HIS DREAM OF THIS MORNING, INTERRUPTED BY THE SHRILL OF THE ALARM.
HEY!
HE HEARS THE SHOUT, AND TURNS, AND LOOKS...
DANGER
IT'S HAPPENING SLOWLY. MUCH TOO SLOWLY. BUT THERE'S NOWHERE TO RUN. NOWHERE TO GO.
HE CAN HEAR HIMSELF SCREAMING, AS THE WALL COMES DOWN, AND HE'S SURPRISED WHEN HE HEARS WHAT THE WORDS ARE.
"NOT *YET*..."

I DON'T BELIEVE IT.
IN ITS 8TH SMASH YEAR!
DANGER CONSTRUCTION
Sweeney Todd
The Musical!
I DID IT AGAIN. I DID IT A-FRIGGIN'-GAIN.
I'M NOT EVEN HURT.
WELL, THAT'S ONE WAY OF PUTTING IT.
BUT YOUR BODY IS UNDER THERE.
NO. PLEASE NO. NOT AFTER ALL THIS TIME. I MEAN, A STUPID ACCIDENT.
4

BUT I DID OKAY, DIDN'T I?
I MEAN I GOT, WHAT, FIFTEEN THOUSAND YEARS. THAT'S PRETTY GOOD. ISN'T IT? I LIVED A PRETTY LONG TIME.

YOU LIVED WHAT ANYBODY GETS, BERNIE.
YOU GOT A LIFETIME.

NO MORE.
NO LESS.

YOU GOT A LIFETIME.

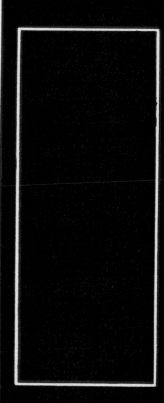

THE PEOPLE WHO REMEMBER ATLANTIS—CONCERNING MAMMOTHS, AND FALLING WALLS—WHO CONTROLS TRANSPORTATION? —BORED, SHE MAKES LITTLE FROGS—TRUTH OR CONSEQUENCES, AND OTHER PLACES—ANCESTRAL VOICES PROPHESYING—THE DOGS OF ART—"WHEN I DREAM, SOMETIMES I REMEMBER HOW TO FLY."

WHAT'S THE NAME OF THE WORD FOR THE PRECISE MOMENT WHEN YOU REALIZE THAT YOU'VE ACTUALLY FORGOTTEN HOW IT FELT TO MAKE LOVE TO SOMEBODY YOU REALLY LIKED A LONG TIME AGO?

There isn't one.
OH. I THOUGHT MAYBE THERE WAS.
No. There isn't.

WHERE ARE WE?
In Dublin.
OH. RIGHT.

WHY ARE WE IN DUBLIN?
We are arranging transportation.
OH. WHY ARE WE ARRANGING TRANSPORTATION?
Because we will be travelling in the waking world, while we search.
WHY?

In here.

FARRELL
TRAVEL
GOOD AFTERNOON. CAN I HELP YOU?
We will talk with Pharamond.
I'M SORRY? I DON'T THINK WE HAVE ANYONE OF THAT NAME HERE.

CASTLE
Who rules here?
I'M SORRY. I DON'T FOLLOW YOU.
To whom do you report? Who employs you? Who controls transportation?
WOULD YOU BE TALKING ABOUT OUR MR. FARRELL?
Yes. Call him.

MR. FARRELL DOESN'T SEE PEOPLE WITHOUT AN APPOINTMENT.
He will see me. Please, let him know that I am here.

CAN I HAVE A NAME?
DON'T YOU HAVE ONE? THAT'S SAD, NOT HAVING A NAME. I USED TO HAVE ONE NAME, THEN I HAD TO GET ANOTHER ONE.
IF YOU DON'T HAVE A NAME, WHAT DO PEOPLE CALL YOU? I MEAN, DO THEY JUST WAVE AND SMILE, OR JINGLE LITTLE SILVER BELLS OR WHAT?

CAN I HAVE YOUR NAMES?
YOU DON'T WANT MY NAME. TRUST ME. YOU REALLY DON'T. SOMETIMES I DON'T WANT MY NAME, AND I'M SORT OF USED TO IT BY NOW. IT WOULD REALLY MESS YOU UP.

I'M SORRY. IS THIS PERSON WITH YOU?
I'M NOT A PERSON.
We are together. Now, inform Pharamond-- your Mister Farrell--that an old acquaintance is here, and wishes to see him.

RIGHT. NOW, IF YOU SIT DOWN OVER THERE I'LL PUT A CALL THROUGH TO HIS SECRETARY FOR YOU. BUT I, Uh, ***DON'T*** THINK HE'S IN THE OFFICE TODAY.
He is.
Now, please call him.
SHE CALLED ME A PERSON. DID YOU HEAR?
HELLO? ***AISLEEN?***
IT'S MARIE ON RECEPTION. LISTEN, THERE'S A COUPLE O HIPPIES OR SOMETHING DOWN HERE ASKING TO SEE MR. FARRELL...
YES I ***TOLD*** THEM THAT... ONE OF THEM SAYS HE'S AN OLD FRIEND...
NOT MUCH... OKAY.
TOURS
EXCUSE ME, SIR?
I SPOKE TO HIS SECRETARY. I'M AFRAID IT'S ***NOT*** POSSIBLE TO MAKE AN APPOINTMENT TODAY.
BUT IF YOU CAN LEAVE YOUR NAME AND YOUR BUSINESS WITH ME, AND A TELEPHONE NUMBER WE CAN GET YOU ON, I'M ***SURE*** MISTER FARRELL WILL GET BACK TO YOU.
Marie. I wish to see your employer. I have no intention of leaving, nor, indeed, of waiting longer.
Call back, and have the following message given to him. Tell him that we drank wine in Babylon together.
I ***CAN'T*** JUST...
Tell him.

AISLEEN? IT'S MARIE AGAIN... YES... WELL, THOSE PEOPLE ARE ***STILL*** HERE... UHUH... WELL, NO... HE'S ***VERY*** INSISTENT...
HE SAYS CAN YOU ***TELL*** MR. FARRELL THAT THEY DRANK WINE IN BABYLON TOGETHER. THAT'S RIGHT. ***BABYLON.***
SHE'LL TELL HIM, SIR.
Visit

Thank you.
IS THERE A WORD FOR FORGETTING THE NAME OF SOMEONE WHEN YOU WANT TO INTRODUCE THEM TO SOMEONE ELSE AT THE SAME TIME YOU REALIZE YOU'VE FORGOTTEN THE NAME OF THE PERSON YOU'RE INTRODUCING THEM TO AS WELL?
No.

SO FAR THIS HAS BEEN A ROTTEN DAY FOR FARRELL.
LAST NIGHT AN ORGY IN ROME HAD ENDED BADLY: A YOUNG FEMALE PROSTITUTE CHOKED TO DEATH ON HUMAN SEMEN. HER BODY WAS THROWN INTO THE STREET BY AN AIDE TO THE MINISTER OF CULTURE. TWO OF FARRELL'S CHAUFFERS WERE ARRESTED IN THE POLICE ROUND-UP THAT FOLLOWED.
LOOK, I DON'T CARE, LEANDRO. I WANT THEM OUT. TODAY.
CAN WE FLY SOMEONE IN FROM NAPLES?
A LIGHT PLANE CRASHED ON A HIGHWAY IN TRIESTE.
A PASSENGER 747 INEXPLICABLY FAILED TO CRASH OVER TANZANIA.
A MULE TRACK IN PARAGUAY WAS WASHED OUT BY FLOODS.
...I SUPPOSE WE COULD ROUTE IT TO DELHI, KHATMANDU, BANGKOK. BUT I'D STILL RATHER IT WENT BOMBAY-SINGAPORE...
THEN PAY THE BLOODY BRIBE, FOR CHRISSAKES, KARIN. THAT'S WHAT YOU'RE THERE FOR!

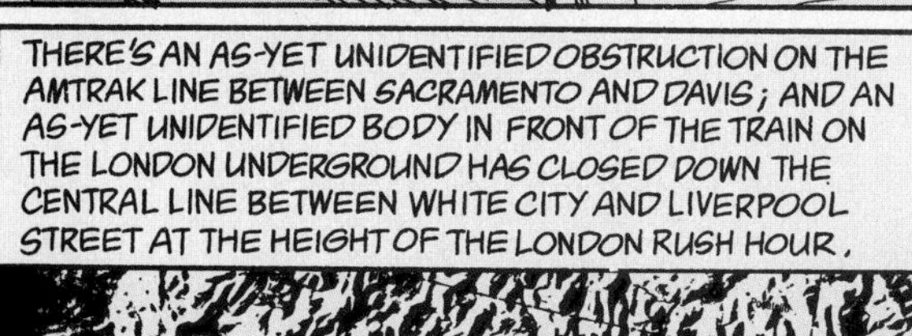
THERE'S AN AS-YET UNIDENTIFIED OBSTRUCTION ON THE AMTRAK LINE BETWEEN SACRAMENTO AND DAVIS; AND AN AS-YET UNIDENTIFIED BODY IN FRONT OF THE TRAIN ON THE LONDON UNDERGROUND HAS CLOSED DOWN THE CENTRAL LINE BETWEEN WHITE CITY AND LIVERPOOL STREET AT THE HEIGHT OF THE LONDON RUSH HOUR.

AISLEEN! WHERE THE HELL'S THE MEMO FROM OSLO?
ON YOUR DESK. UNDER YOUR COFFEE MUG.
OH. YEAH. SORRY.

HIS PERSONAL ASSISTANT TOOK YESTERDAY OFF FOR ROOT-CANAL WORK, AND THE TEMP SEEMS TO HAVE MISFILED FAXES FROM HIS PEOPLE IN SHANGHAI (CHINA), PANAMA CITY (PANAMANIAN REPUBLIC), AND TRUTH OR CONSEQUENCES (NEW MEXICO).
IN ADDITION TO WHICH...
9

IT'S RECEPTION AGAIN, MR. FARRELL. THEY SAY THOSE PEOPLE WON'T GO AWAY.
WELL, TELL THEM TO CALL SECURITY. BODY AND BLOOD, AISLEEN, WHAT DO THEY THINK WE PAY THEM FOR?

MR. FARRELL. THE MAN SAYS THAT YOU HAD A DRINK TOGETHER IN SOME PUB OR SOMETHING.
I DON'T *GO* TO PUBS AND I'M NOT SEEING *ANYBODY* TODAY. THROW THEM *OUT*.
WHERE'S THAT STATUS REPORT ON ON THE BIRMINGHAM CONTRA-FLOW SYSTEM?
IN THE BIRMINGHAM FILE, WHERE IT OUGHT TO BE.
MARIE SEEMED TO THINK MAYBE YOU *OUGHT* TO TALK TO THESE PEOPLE. SHALL I PUT HER ON?
NO.
ON SECOND THOUGHTS, *YEAH*... PUT HER ON.
I'LL BLOODY TELL HER ALL RIGHT.
HULLO? MISTER FARRELL? IT'S MARIE ON RECEPTION.
WHAT THE *HELL* IS GOING ON DOWN THERE?
WELL, THERE ARE THESE TWO PEOPLE HERE, SIR.
THE MAN *SAYS* HE DRANK WINE WITH YOU SOMEWHERE CALLED BABYLON. AND THE LADY...
YES?
SHE'S MAKING LITTLE *FROGS*.
HE SAYS HE'S ON HIS WAY DOWN.
STLE
Good.

LORD MORPHEUS. THIS IS INDEED A PLEASURE.
Pharamond. Good day.
May I present my sister, the Lady Delirium?

INDEED. I AM HONORED. MY HOUSE IS HONORED. TO HAVE TWO OF YOUR ILLUSTRIOUS FAMILY HERE, BENEATH MY ROOF...
WORDS TRULY FAIL ME.
HI.

IN THE CONFERENCE ROOM, I THINK. NOW, HOW CAN I BE OF SERVICE?
I trust you still oversee transportation?
IN MY OWN SMALL WAY, YES.
A LITTLE HERE, A LITTLE THERE. I KEEP BUSY.
Good.
BYE-BYE LITTLE FROGGIES.

My sister and I will be traveling in the waking world. We will be needing transportation.
NO PROBLEM. YOU'LL BE STAYING ON EARTH, THEN? NOTHING OFF-PLANET? OR OFF-PLANE?
This Earth.
WELL, THAT KEEPS EVERYTHING STRAIGHTFORWARD, DOESN'T IT?

MIGHT I ASK THE PURPOSE OF YOUR JOURNEY?
No.
AH.
WELL, WHERE DO YOU WANT TO START, THEN?

Sister? Where should we start?
HERE?
Very good. We are here. Where should we travel to now?

...SOMEWHERE THAT'S NOT HERE?
That was the idea. Yes.

I THINK WE SHOULD GO AND SEE THE PEOPLE ON MY LIST. I WROTE IT MYSELF.
Do you have it with you?
WHAT?
The list.
LIST?
Your list of those who might know our brother's whereabouts.

OH. THAT LIST.
UM. HANG ON. I'LL GO AND GET IT.

You are well Pharamond?
OH YES. KEEPING BUSY. I'M THE LAST OF MY PANTHEON, YOU KNOW.
I know.
I SUPPOSE YOU WOULD DO, WOULDN'T YOU? I WASN'T THINKING.

DIVERSIFICATION. THAT'S THE SECRET. YOU WERE RIGHT ABOUT THAT. I MEAN, THERE'LL ALWAYS BE A NEED FOR TRAVEL.
Yes. For a little while to come.
NEVER THOUGHT YOU'D BE CALLING IN ON THE OFFER, THOUGH. I MEAN, WHEN I SAID, IF YOU EVER NEED MY HELP...

NOT THAT I'M COMPLAINING. I OWE YOU AN AWFUL LOT. I OWE YOU MY LIFE, FOR STARTERS.
Babylon was a long time ago, Pharamond.
I'M STILL GRATEFUL. ANYTHING I CAN DO. AIR, LAND, SEA OR BETWEEN.

HERE. I FOUND IT.
I KNEW IT WAS GOING TO BE IN THE LAST PLACE I LOOKED FOR IT, SO I LOOKED THERE FIRST.
I WROTE DOWN. UM. ALL THE PEOPLE HE USED TO KNOW. THAT I EVER MET. THAT WOULDN'T BE DEAD YET.
I DON'T REMEMBER ALL OF THEM. BUT SOME. SEE?
I WROTE THEM.
SEE?
Second Look
the dancing woman
Yes. I see.

STUMBLING BACK TO WAKEFULNESS, THE DREAM ALREADY FADING INTO NOTHING, JUST FRAGMENTS, LIKE SHAPES SEEN THROUGH THICK MIST; EYES BLEAR AND HEAD AND BODY FEELING THE MUZZY NUMB THAT COMES FROM OVER-SLEEPING...
ETAIN HAD DREAMED OF A HOUSE THAT WAS, IN SOME WAY A POEM, WRITTEN BY A POET WHO HAD KILLED HERSELF FOR LOVE, LONG AGO.
JOY OF COOKING
POP TART
THE COFFEE IN THE PERCOLATOR IS STONE-COLD. SHE POURS HERSELF A CUP-FULL OF DREGS ANYWAY, PUTS IT IN THE MICRO-WAVE, SETS THE LED FOR 70 SECONDS.
AS THE COFFEE GOES AROUND IN THE LITTLE METAL BOX, SHE REALIZES THAT THE POEM IN HER DREAM WAS BOTH BEAUTIFUL AND TRUE, AND THAT IT WAS GENUINELY IMPORTANT. SHE FEELS SLEEPILY PROUD OF HERSELF.
BEEP BEEP BEEP
SHE ADDS CREAM.
THE HOUSE WAS THE POEM. SHE REMEMBERS HOVERING DISEMBODIED ABOUT THE HOUSE'S EXTERIOR, WHILE THE SONOROUS WORDS LICKED AROUND HER IN MARVELLOUS MELLIFLUOUS CADENCES.
FRUIT
THE COFFEE IS FOULLY BITTER, BUT IT SERVES TO DRAG HER FURTHER INTO THE WAKING WORLD.
TRANSITIONS.

SHE IS ABOUT TO FIND A PENCIL AND SCRIBBLE THE POEM DOWN, WHEN IT OCCURS TO HER THAT SHE'S LOST THE WORDS.
SHE DOESN'T EVEN KNOW WHAT IT WAS ABOUT.
OH...

OH WELL, EASY COME, EASY GO.
SHE DOESN'T KNOW WHY SAM COLERIDGE BITCHED SO MUCH ABOUT HIS MAN FROM PORLOCK: HE GOT FIFTY-FIVE KILLER LINES DOWN ON PAPER BEFORE HE GOT DISTRACTED, DIDN'T HE?

AND THE STUFF YOU BRING BACK FROM DREAMS IS FREE.

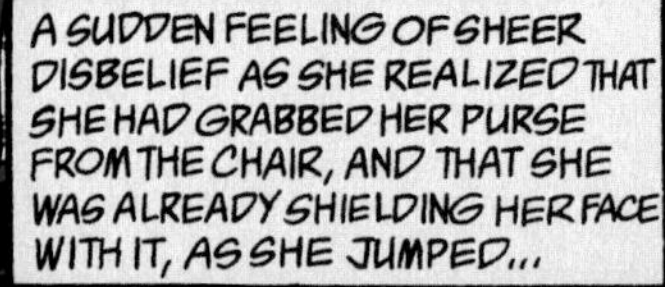
"AND 'MID THIS TUMULT KUBLA HEARD FROM FAR ANCESTRAL VOICES PROPHESYING WAR..."

LATER, ETAIN WAS UNABLE TO CATEGORIZE THE EVENTS THAT FOLLOWED.

CERTAINLY SHE SMELLED GAS. BUT BY THE TIME SHE SMELLED THE GAS SHE WAS ALREADY RUNNING THROUGH THE BEDROOM, TOWARD THE FIRE ESCAPE.

A SUDDEN FEELING OF SHEER DISBELIEF AS SHE REALIZED THAT SHE HAD GRABBED HER PURSE FROM THE CHAIR, AND THAT SHE WAS ALREADY SHIELDING HER FACE WITH IT, AS SHE JUMPED...

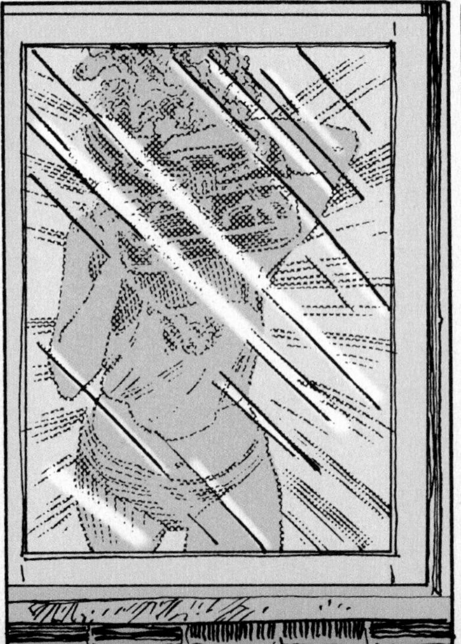

A SHATTERING OF GLASS.

SHE LANDED ON THE FIRE ESCAPE, HER FACE STINGING, HER RIGHT ARM WET WITH BLOOD (THE PAIN WOULD COME LATER), AND OVER THE SIDE, HANG DOWN AS FAR AS SHE COULD--
--AND THEN LETGO.
SMASH DOWN JARRED AND SHAKEN, TO SOLID GROUND, BONES ACHING, SKIN ALL SCRAPED, BLEEDING AND JUST RUN FOR DEAR LIFE AND JUST *RUN*--
--JUST--

SHIT. THAT WAS TOO CLOSE...
ADRENALINE-GIDDY, SHE STUMBLES INTO THE K-MART.
EXIT
HOT BUY
SALE ITEMS
CLOTHES FIRST.
THEN SHOES.
THEN OUT.
16

HUM HUMETTY-HUM. DAH DE DUM...
...DE DUM DUM DOO DOO DE DUM.
I thought I'd find you out here.
WELL? WHAT DO YOU THINK OF IT SO FAR?
I'm not much of an art critic.
I'M NOT ASKING FOR ART CRITICISM, BARNABAS. MERELY FOR A FEW HONEST WORDS OF APPRECIATION.
Honestly? Well, the perspective's shot to Hell, the colors could be better chosen, and the olive tree on the left looks like an overgrown stinging nettle.
HMPH. WHAT THE HELL WOULD YOU KNOW? YOU'RE A DOG.
Did I ever say I wasn't?

AH, WELL, THE LIGHT'S GOING ANYWAY.
I'LL FINISH IT OFF TOMORROW.

THE COLORS COULD BE BETTER CHOSEN MY **FOOT.** ANYWAY-- I THOUGHT DOGS WERE COLOR BLIND.
Yeah? That's a coincidence. I mean, looking at that painting I thought **you** were color blind.

HAHAHAHA
HAHAHAHA!
What's so funny?

YOU KNOW, BARNABAS, THERE **ARE** THOSE WHO CLAIM THAT FOR **UNQUESTIONING** RESPECT AND **ETERNAL** DEVOTION, ALL ONE NEEDS IS A **DOG**.
Hey, schmuck, *Devotion* you've got. *Perjury* isn't in the job description.

Listen! There's something happening in that room round the back.
I CAN'T HEAR IT.
Well, **you** aren't a dog, are you?

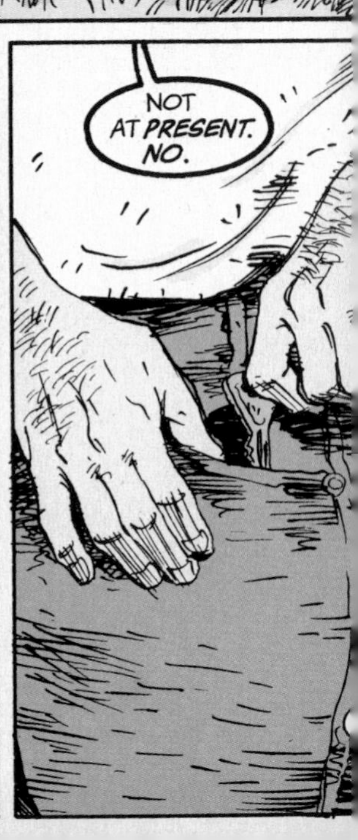
NOT AT **PRESENT. NO.**

What's in here anyway?
I mean, it's been locked as long as I can remember.
I TEND TO THINK OF IT AS THE FAMILY ROOM.
That was what I heard. That bubbling noise. It's that pool.
What is it?
IT'S...
I SUPPOSE YOU COULD CALL IT AN EARLY-WARNING SYSTEM.
I don't like it.
What's it warning you against?
TROUBLE.
Rrrrrr.
BIG TROUBLE.

THIS IS NICE, ISN'T IT?
WELL, I THINK IT'S NICE.
HAVE YOU EVER BEEN IN AN AEROPLANE BEFORE?
No.
I HAVE.
CAUTION! CONTENTS ARE HOT
YOU KNOW THE BEST THING ABOUT AEROPLANES? APART FROM THE PEANUTS IN THE LITTLE SILVER BAGS, I MEAN.
IT'S LOOKING OUT OF THE WINDOWS AT THE CLOUDS, AND THINKING, MAYBE I COULD GO WALKING IN THERE. MAYBE IT'S A SPECIAL PLACE WHERE EVERYTHING'S OKAY.
SOMETIMES I DO GO WALKING IN THE CLOUDS, BUT IT'S JUST COLD AND WET AND EMPTY, BUT WHEN YOU LOOK OUT OF A PLANE IT'S A SPECIAL WORLD...
AND I LIKE THAT.

THAT PERSON. FARRELL-MOND. WHAT WAS HE?
He used to be a God. When we last met, in Babylon, his sacrifices were dwindling, and many of his shrines had already been abandoned.
I merely suggested that he find himself another occupation.
OH. I DIDN'T KNOW YOU COULD STOP BEING A GOD.
You can stop being anything.
WHAT ABOUT, UM. OUR BROTHER?
MOMMY? I HAD A BAD DREAM.
REALLY DAHLING?
I HAD A DREAM THAT I WAS LOOKING FOR YOU AND DADDY, AND I LOOKED IN THE GARDEN BUT YOU WEREN'T THERE, SO I WENT INTO THE WOODS LOOKING FOR YOU, BUT I COULDN'T FIND YOU AND I CALLED OUT BUT NO-BODY WAS THERE.
AND I WAS LOST. AND I WAS SCARED I'D BE LOST FOR EVER.
YOU'RE A SILLY MOUSE. YOU CAN'T GET LOST IN A DREAM. YOU ALWAYS WAKE UP.
I SUPPOSE.
MOMMY'S GOING TO POWDER HER NOSE. ASK THE STEWARDESS IF THERE'S ANYTHING YOU NEED.
21

Child?
YUH?
Your mother was wrong. You can indeed become lost, in dreams. And you may not always find yourself when you wake up.
OH. MY NAME'S CHLOE RUSSELL.
I know.
MY MOMMY CALLS ME HER LITTLE MOUSE.
LAVATORY DO NOT USE DURING TAKE-OFF OR LANDING NO SMOKING
EXCUSE ME. THE OTHER COUPLE IN FIRST CLASS. ARE THEY, UH, ROCK AND ROLL STARS? OR MOVIE STARS? OR SOMETHING? THERE'S SOMETHING VERY FAMILIAR ABOUT BOTH OF THEM.
I MEAN, I KEEP THINKING I KNOW THEM REALLY WELL. ESPECIALLY THE MAN. BUT I KNOW HE'S NO ONE I EVER MET.
IT'S LIKE, WELL, AT THIS PARTY OF RON'S--THAT'S MY EX-HUSBAND'S LAWYER--I SAW THIS GUY I KNEW AS WELL AS I KNEW MY FATHER. SO I SAID HI. HE SAID HI.

THEN I REALIZED I DIDN'T KNOW LIKE, WHO HE WAS. WE TALKED ABOUT OLD MUSICALS AND THE TROUBLE I WAS HAVING WITH MY POOLMAN, AND HE SMILED AND WAS REALLY NICE, BUT LIKE, I STILL DIDN'T KNOW HIS NAME.
YOU FOLLOW ME?
WELL, HEY, I WAS DOING A LOT OF COKE AT THE TIME, THIS WAS TEN YEARS AGO, THAT WAS BEFORE I REALIZED, LIKE YOU HAVE TO BE REALLY OPEN TO THE UNIVERSE, SO THESE DAYS I WON'T EVEN LET CHLOE DRINK DIET COLA, BECAUSE OF THE ASPARTAME. I DON'T TRUST THAT SHIT.
AH...

THE PARTY. I'M SORRY. EVENTUALLY THE GUY GOES AWAY. HALF AN HOUR LATER, I REALIZED. I'D BEEN TALKING TO CHARLTON HESTON.
LAVA
DO NO
DURING
OFF OR
LANDING
I DON'T KNOW. THE MAN IS VERY FAMILIAR.
YOUR DAUGHTER WAS TALKING TO HIM, WHEN YOU WERE IN THE BATHROOM.

DARLING?
DID THAT MAN SAY SOMETHING TO YOU?
YES, MOMMY.
OH. WHAT DID HE SAY?
TRUE THINGS.
"OH. DID HE MENTION HIS NAME?"
"NO. HE PROBBLY HASN'T GOT ONE."
"DON'T BE SILLY, CHLOE-MOUSE. EVERYONE HAS A NAME."
WILL YOU TELL ME SOMETHING?
Perhaps.
WHEN I DREAM, SOMETIMES I REMEMBER HOW TO FLY. YOU JUST LIFT ONE LEG, THEN YOU LIFT THE OTHER LEG, AND YOU'RE NOT STANDING ON ANYTHING, AND YOU CAN FLY.
AND THEN WHEN I WAKE UP I CAN'T REMEMBER HOW TO DO IT ANY MORE.
So?
SO WHAT I WANT TO KNOW IS, WHEN I'M ASLEEP, DO I REALLY REMEMBER HOW TO FLY? AND FORGET HOW WHEN I WAKE UP? OR AM I JUST DREAMING I CAN FLY?
When you dream, sometimes you remember. When you wake, you always forget.
BUT THAT'S NOT FAIR...
No.
HI. I'M RUBY. YOU'LL BE THE FOLKS FARRELL ASKED ME TO TAKE CARE OF. WELCOME TO THE UNITED STATES.
WILL YOU BOTH FOLLOW ME, PLEASE.
FARRELL TRAVEL
THROUGH THAT DOOR. THE ONE WITH NO EXIT ON IT...

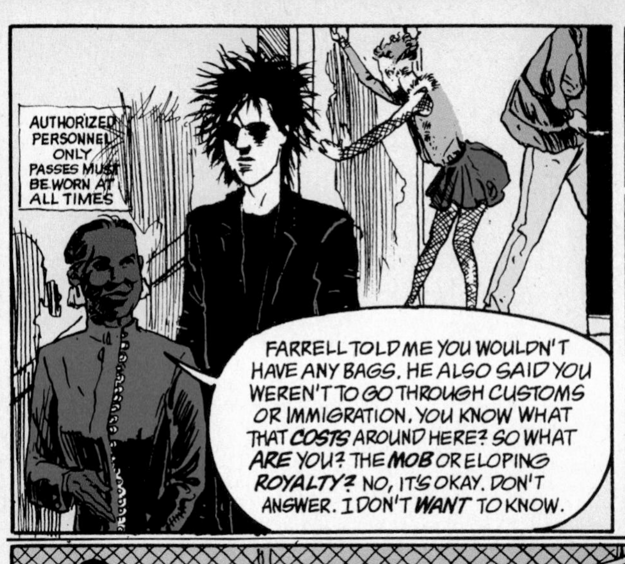
AUTHORIZED PERSONNEL ONLY PASSES MUST BE WORN AT ALL TIMES
FARRELL TOLD ME YOU WOULDN'T HAVE ANY BAGS. HE ALSO SAID YOU WEREN'T TO GO THROUGH CUSTOMS OR IMMIGRATION. YOU KNOW WHAT THAT COSTS AROUND HERE? SO WHAT ARE YOU? THE MOB OR ELOPING ROYALTY? NO, IT'S OKAY. DON'T ANSWER. I DON'T WANT TO KNOW.

WELL, HERE'S THE CAR.
FARRELL SAID YOU'D LIKE SOMETHING CLASSICAL, AND THIS WAS AS CLASSICAL AS WE'VE GOT WITHOUT YANKING SOMETHING FROM A MUSEUM.
IT'S AN ANTIQUE, BUT THEY'VE PROMISED IT'LL RUN FINE.

HERE IT IS.
CAN I DRIVE?
No.
BUT I WANT TO DRIVE. I BET I'D BE REALLY GOOD.
No.
HMPH.

SO. FARRELL FAXED ME THE ITINERARY. YOU SURE ARE GOING TO DO SOME SERIOUS TRAVEL-LING.
Yes.
I WANTED TO BE THE DRIVER.
OKAY. LET'S SEE. FIRST UP WE PAY A VISIT TO THE LAWYER, I GOT IT WRITTEN DOWN HERE SOMEWHERE...
OH YEAH. HERE IT IS. WEIRD NAME.

OKAY, FOLKS. HOLD ON TIGHT. WE'RE OFF TO SEE YOUR MR. CAPAX...
UM. WHAT'S THE NAME OF THE WORD FOR THINGS NOT BEING THE SAME ALWAYS. YOU KNOW. I'M SURE THERE IS ONE. ISN'T THERE?
THERE MUST BE A WORD FOR IT... THE THING THAT LETS YOU KNOW TIME IS HAPPENING. IS THERE A WORD?
BEATS ME, HON.

Change.

OH.
I WAS AFRAID OF THAT.

"Twinkle's a nice word. So's viridian."
The perils of hunting in bed?
chapter 4
A treatise on optics
Departed secrets
A bear and his shadow
The other side of the sky

THE LONG DAY IN THE NORTH LANDS.
THE SUN HAS NOT SET. FOR OVER A MONTH; EVEN NOW, AT MIDNIGHT, IT HANGS PALE AND SILVER AND COLD ABOVE THE HORIZON.
THE MIDNIGHT SUN.
ON THE OTHER SIDE OF THE SKY, THE LIGHTS OF THE BOREALIS FLICKER AND EXPLODE AND SWIRL IN SURGES OF PLASMA, OF RETINAL PURPLE, FIREWORK YELLOW, VDU GREEN.
THIS IS A MID-WINTER DISPLAY, THINKS THE ALDER MAN.
THERE IS SOMETHING DEEPLY UNNATURAL ABOUT SEEING THE NORTHERN LIGHTS IN MIDSUMMER.
THE LAPPS BELIEVE THAT IT IS UNWISE IN ANY WAY TO ATTRACT THE ATTENTION OF THE DANCING NORTHERN LIGHTS, OR THEY WILL CARRY YOU OFF INTO THE SKY, TO BE ONE WITH THEM FOREVER.
THE ALDER MAN IS OLD ENOUGH TO KNOW HOW RARELY THIS HAPPENS. STILL AND ALL, HE IS UNEASY.
HE STAYS AWAKE THROUGH THE NIGHT THAT NEVER COMES, STARING SADLY AT THE LIGHTS IN THE SKY.

IN THE MORNING THE SUN CLIMBS HIGHER INTO THE SKY, AND THE COLOR OF THE SKY TRANSMUTES FROM LEADEN GRAY TO PERFECT CERULEAN BLUE.

DISTURBED DEEP IN HIS BEING, THE ALDER MAN WALKS TWENTY MILES, IN A SLOW CIRCLE, AT A STEADY LOPE, TO CHECK HIS DEATH-TRAPS.
HE MADE THE DEATH-TRAPS HIMSELF.
THEY WERE MADE OF INTERWOVEN THONGS OF REINDEER LEATHER, TIED INTO INTRICATE CAT'S CRADLES, HUNG BY THE ALDER MAN FROM THE BRANCHES OF THE STUNTED TREES.
TO THE NORTH AND EAST AND WEST, THE TRAPS ARE UNTOUCHED.
THE SOUTHERN TRAP, HOWEVER, HAS BEEN TORN APART.
A BIG DEATH IS ON ITS WAY, THEN.
FROM THE SOUTH.
THE ALDER MAN EYES THE SKY. THE SUN HAS PASSED ITS ZENITH, AND THE SHADOWS ARE STREAMING.
PLEASED HE IS THAT THE SHADOWS ARE CLEAR AND CRISP.
CAREFULLY THE ALDER MAN REMOVES HIS CLOTHES, THEN PILES THEM ALL IN A HEAP.
HE PISSES AROUND THEM, IN A WIDE CIRCLE, AND THEY TURN TO STONE.
A MOMENT OF STRETCHING, OF RENDING, BENEATH THE FULL SUN, AND IT IS OVER.
2

HE IS A BEAR, THEN, WITH THE SHADOW OF A MAN.
HE EYES HIS SHADOW, THEN BARES HIS TEETH, LOWERS HIS MUZZLE, AND BEGINS TO CHEW.
TO BITE OFF YOUR SHADOW IS NEITHER EASY NOR PAINLESS. IT DEMANDS A SINGLE-MINDEDNESS THAT IS ALMOST UNKNOWN IN THIS DAY.
STILL, AT THE END, THE HUGE BEAR SNUFFLES CONTENTEDLY, AND STARES AT THE SHADOW ON THE GROUND.
LISTEN TO ME NOW, O MY SHADOW.
FOR THE PRESENT, YOU ARE LEIB-OLMAI, THE ALDER MAN. I AM BUT A NOTHING BEAR, NAMELESS AND WITHOUT ANY MANNER OF INTEREST.
"MY DEATH IS NOW YOUR DEATH, AND MY DOOM YOUR DOOM. YOURS AND YOURS ALONE, O MY SHADOW."

THEN THE BEAR LUMBERS AROUND THE STONE CAIRN, SQUIRTING RANK BEAR PISS AS IT GOES, AND ITS CLOTHES ARE NO LONGER STONES.
ITS SHADOW (WALKING TENDERLY ON FEET THAT STILL FEEL THE POWER AND TEARING AND EDGE OF SHARP BEAR TEETH) PUTS ON THE CLOTHES.
THE BEAR EYES IT CRITICALLY. IT HAS, TO HIS EYES, LITTLE OF HIS MAJESTY; THERE IS NOT FIRE IN ITS EYES.
STILL, IT WOULD SERVE.
GO.
HE WATCHES HIS SHADOW LIMP AWAY, ALREADY FORGETTING THAT IT WAS HIS SHADOW, KNOWING ONLY THAT IT WAS THE ALDER MAN.
AND, FINALLY, THE BEAR WITHOUT A SHADOW FORGETS THAT IT HAD EVER BEEN THE ALDER MAN, THAT IT HAS EVER BEEN ANYTHING OTHER THAN A BEAR.

ON ALL FOURS THE BEAR LUMBERS NORTH, IN THE PALE LIGHT OF THE EVENING SUN.

WHAT ARE YOU LOOKING AT?

YOU'RE LOOKING FOR SOMETHING. AREN'T YOU? I MEAN, THE WAY YOU KEEP LOOKING AT THINGS.
YOU'RE LOOKING FOR... SOME...
WHY DON'T YOU HAVE PROPER EYES? INSTEAD OF THOSE THINGS? EVERYONE ELSE IN THE FAMILY'S GOT PROPER EYES.

UM. EXCEPT DESTINY.
Destiny is blind.

YOU KEEP LOOKING AT THE PEOPLE. ARE YOU LOOKING FOR SOMEONE?
ARE YOU LOOKING FOR OUR BROTHER?
We are both looking for our brother.
EXCUSE ME, FOLKS. THIS IS THE ADDRESS. IT'S THAT HOUSE.

YOU WANT ME TO COME IN WITH YOU?
YES.
No. Wait here, please, Ruby.
BUT...
I would rather we conducted this business privately, sister. If you have no objections.

YEAH?

We are looking for Bernard Capax.
YOU WANT DAD? YOU HAVEN'T HEARD? JESUS.
UH. WON'T YOU COME IN?
I'M DANNY CAPAX.

UH. YOU WERE FRIENDS OF MY FATHER'S?
Not as such.
I MET HIM. AGES AGO.
AGES AND AGES AND AGES.

THAT'S MY MOM. SHE'S BEEN KIND OF OUT OF IT, DAD...
LISTEN. HE DIED YESTERDAY.
I'm sorry.
YEAH...
CAN I GET YOU ANYTHING? A BEER?
No.

MY DAD. I MEAN, I WAS ALWAYS KIND OF DISAPPOINTED IN HIM, YOU KNOW? NOT DIS-APPOINTED. SHIT. WHAT'S THE WORD. EMBARRASSED.
AND NOW I DON'T UNDERSTAND ANYTHING. IT'S JUST--
LOOK. COME DOWN HERE. I'LL SHOW YOU.

I HAD TO COME BACK FROM COLLEGE. MAKE THE ARRANGEMENTS. THIS MORNING.
THE GUY, THE WHATSISNAME, MORTICIAN. KEPT TALKING ABOUT "THE DEPARTED." AS IF DAD HAD JUST HAD TO STEP OUT IN A HURRY...

THEY GAVE US HIS KEYS. I MEAN, SO WE OPENED HIS OFFICE DOWN HERE. WE OPENED HIS FILING CABINETS.
THE FUNERAL'S TOMORROW. JESUS. MY DAD. HE WAS SKINNY. HE HAD A DUMB MOUSTACHE, AND A PONY TAIL, SO HE'D LOOK YOUNGER, I SUPPOSE. HE WAS A LAWYER.

I MEAN, MY FATHER WAS THE MOST BORING MAN I EVER MET.
I LIKED HIM OKAY. HE WAS MY DAD. YOU KNOW. BUT I THOUGHT I KNEW HIM.

AND LOOK AT THIS SHIT. LOOK AT IT. JESUS. I MEAN, MY FATHER. DAD. GOOD OL' BERNIE CAPAX.
YOU KNOW WHAT THESE ARE? KRUGERRANDS. GOLD KRUGERRANDS. TWO HUNDRED OF THEM. LOOK.

ONE BAG OF BROWN POWDER. MY GUESS IS SMACK. ONE BAG OF WHITE POWDER. I TASTED IT AND IT MADE MY TONGUE GO ALL NUMB, SO I FIGURE IT'S PROBABLY COCAINE.
I NEVER DID DRUGS. DAD USED TO COME DOWN REALLY HEAVY ON US. HE DIDN'T EVEN LIKE MOM DRINKING. YOU KNOW?

GUNS AND KNIVES ARE IN THE TOP DRAWER.

NEXT DRAWER DOWN IS FILLED WITH BLANK PASSPORTS. HERE--YOU WANT ONE? AMERICAN, FRENCH, BRITISH, SOUTH AFRICAN, TAKE YOUR FREAKIN' PICK.
JESUS.
I MEAN, HE WAS MY DAD. HE WAS A SWEET GUY BUT HE WAS SO DULL. YOU KNOW?
BIRTH CERTIFICATES, VARIOUS NAMES AND DATES. CREDIT CARDS, DITTO. I MEAN, THIS IS LIKE A SPY MOVIE OR MISSION IMPOSSIBLE OR SOMETHING.
HOW DO WE EXPLAIN IT TO THE IRS?
SHOULD WE TELL THE POLICE ANYTHING? OR THE FBI?

THERE'S A PICASSO IN THE BOTTOM DRAWER. AND A MATISSE. AND SOMETHING I THINK MAY BE A DA VINCI FREAKING PENCIL DRAWING. WHATATHEYCALLEMS. CARTOON.
THERE'S OTHER STUFF...
I MEAN, WHO THE HELL WAS HE, HUH?
MY FATHER. WHO WAS HE?

CAN I HAVE THIS?
THAT? YEAH. SURE. WHATEVER.

How did he die?
HA...YEAH. I'VE BEEN DRINKING SINCE BEFORE BREAKFAST, AND I'M NORMALLY A ONE-BEER GUY. AND MOM'S JUST WALKING AROUND LIKE SOMEONE SHOT HER IN THE BRAIN. YOU KNOW?

How did your father die?
A BUILDING FELL ON HIM. ISN'T THAT...I FORGET THE WORD FOR IT.
IRONIC? DUMB? BIZARRE?
THERE WAS SOME DEMOLITION WORK GOING ON, AND BAM! BYE-BYE DADDY...

...WHOEVER YOU WERE.

LISTEN. I COULDN'T HELP OVERHEARING YOU EARLIER. YOU SAID DESTINY WAS BLIND. WELL, DIDN'T YOU MEAN LOVE? IT'S LOVE IS BLIND. THAT'S THE SAYING, ISN'T IT?

he subject is one
find entirely lack-
ng in interest.

YEAH. SO. HOW WAS YOUR LAWYER?
Dead.
HAHAHA. CUTE. THAT'S LIKE THE JOKE, ISN'T IT? WHAT HAVE YOU GOT IF YOU'VE GOT A DOZEN LAWYERS BURIED UP TO THEIR NECKS IN CATSHIT?

NOT ENOUGH CATSHIT. TADAA. ENOUGH WITH THE JOKES. HOW WAS HE REALLY?
REALLY DEAD.

OH.
SORRY. AHH. WHERE DO YOU WANT TO GO NOW, THEN?

Sister? Whom do we see next?
ETAIN. OF THE SECOND THING. UM. LOOK.

THAT'S THE ONE IN OHIO? GOING TO BE A LONG DRIVE. FOURTEEN, FIFTEEN HOURS AT LEAST.
I FIGURE WE'LL STOP IN A MOTEL TONIGHT, START AGAIN IN THE MORNING WHEN WE'RE FRESH. IT'S ALL ON FARRELL'S PLATINUM CARD, SO MONEY'S NO PROBLEM.

You wish to break our journey? Why?
WELL, SO WE CAN SLEEP, SHIT, SHOWER. WHY DO YOU THINK?
No.

LOOK, MISTER HIGH AND MIGHTY, I DON'T KNOW WHO YOU ARE AND I DON'T CARE, BUT IF YOU THINK I'M DRIVING ALL NIGHT FOR YOU OR ANYONE ELSE, YOU'RE OUT OF YOUR MIND.

HERE. YOU WANT TO CALL FARRELL? YOU WANT ME TO?
SHIT!
WHAT DO YOU THINK, LADY, HUH?

I THINK YOU'RE VERY NICE. I THINK TWINKLE'S A NICE WORD. SO'S VIRIDIAN. I MET A LADY ONCE WHO HAD AN IMAGINARY FISH.

GREAT. OKAY. LET ME PUT IT THIS WAY. WE STOP SOMEWHERE FOR THE NIGHT, OR I STOP THE CAR HERE, AND I QUIT, AND YOU CAN DRIVE ALL NIGHT TO OHIO OR ANCHORAGE OR TIMBUKTU IF YOU WANT TO, WITHOUT ME.

As you will. It makes little difference to me.

ARE YOU SAYING YOU DON'T CARE?
at is what I am
aying. Yes.

YOU'RE A SCARY SON OF A BITCH, MISTER. CUTE AS HELL, BUT SCARY.
LET'S GO TO A MOTEL.

WHAT ABOUT THE LAWYER. SHOULDN'T WE SEE HIM?
He's dead.

OH YES. I FORGOT.
9

OKAY. I'VE GOT US THREE ADJOINING ROOMS. WOULD YOU PEOPLE LIKE TO GO DOWN AND EAT FIRST OR JUST ORDER ROOM SERVICE?

I have no wish to eat.
OKAY. **WHATEVER**. JUST RING ROOM-SERVICE IF YOU CHANGE YOUR MIND.
I'VE GOT YOUR KEY-CARDS HERE. YOU KNOW HOW TO OPERATE THEM?

Which is my room?
110
THEY'RE **ALL** THE **SAME**. PICK ONE.

Very well. I will take this one.
Good night to you both.
HEY, **WAIT** A MINUTE...

...YOU FORGOT YOUR KEY-CARD.
I DON'T THINK HE **LIKES** KEYS ANY MORE. LEAVE HIM.

HERE. THIS ONE'S YOURS. DO YOU KNOW HOW TO WORK THEM?
KEYS? **SURE**. I FIGURED **THAT** OUT **AGES** AGO. I'M NOT **STUPID** OR ANYTHING.

WELL, I'LL SEE YOU IN THE MORNING, THEN. GOODNIGHT.

111
111
111
FOUR: THE OTHER SIDE OF THE SKY—A BEAR AND HIS SHADOW—DEPARTED SECRETS—"TWINKLE'S A NICE WORD. SO'S VIRIDIAN." THREE KEYS—A TREATISE ON OPTICS—THE PERILS OF SMOKING IN BED?

HER NAME IS RUBY ELISABETH DeLONGE.
SHE WAS BORN IN JAMAICA IN 1962.
SHE SPEAKS ELEVEN LANGUAGES. SHE'S BEEN WORKING FOR FARRELL FOR SEVEN YEARS NOW, AND SHE KNOWS WHAT SHE WANTS.

SHE WANTS TO BE RICH. NOT MERELY WEALTHY, BUT RICH LIKE FARRELL, LIKE A TINY HANDFUL OF OTHERS SHE'S MET OVER THE LAST FEW YEARS.

THE PEOPLE WHO ARE RICH ENOUGH THAT THEIR NAMES WILL NEVER WIND UP ON ANY LIST OF THE HUNDRED WEALTHIEST PEOPLE; THEIR NAMES AND FACES QUITE UNKNOWN TO THE PRESS OR THE WORLD...

MONEY.
THAT'S ALL RUBY WANTS.
* * * *
YOUR FREE VIEWING TIME IS OVER PRESS PAY BUTTON TO CONTINUE WATCHING YOUR MOVIE CHOICE
* * * *

WAKE-UP CALL FOR 7:00 AM. THAT'S RIGHT.
RUBY DeLONGE IS, IN NO PARTICULAR ORDER, A PRACTICING CATHOLIC, AN EXCELLENT COOK, A MEDIOCRE CELLIST, A SPECIALIST IN BOTH ARMED AND UNARMED COMBAT, THREE WEEKS AWAY FROM HER THIRTIETH BIRTHDAY, AND A VIRGIN.

IT MAY BE UNFASHIONABLE TO BE A VIRGIN, BUT RUBY DOESN'T CARE. SHE WANTS A WHITE WEDDING; AND SHE WANTS IT TO MEAN SOMETHING.
THERE WAS A GUY SHE LIKED, A FEW YEARS BACK. LIKED HIM AN AWFUL LOT; BUT HE FAILED A ROUTINE CREDIT CHECK.
PITY, REALLY.

SOMETIMES SHE STILL MISSES HIM.
AND SHE WANTS TO BE ***SO*** GODDAMNED RICH...
AND SHE WANTS SOMEONE TO LOVE...
AND SHE WANTS TO BE HAPPY...

TOMORROW SHE'LL BE BACK ON THE ROAD, DRIVING FARRELL'S PALE CRAZIES OFF TO THEIR NEXT LUNATIC DESTINATION.
TIRED. SHE'S TIRED.
DESTINY IS BLIND?
ONE CIGARETTE. A GIRL NEEDS HER NICOTINE FIX, AND SHE'S ALREADY CUT DOWN TO FIVE A DAY.

SHE DRAWS THE BLUE SMOKE DEEP INTO HER LUNGS, FEELS HER HEAD GO SWIMMY AND HER INSIDES RELAX.
SHE'S GOT TO GIVE IT UP. SHE REALLY MUST. THESE THINGS ARE GOING TO KILL HER.
IT'S NOT DESTINY. IT'S LOVE.

112
SHE WAS RIGHT. HE WAS WRONG.

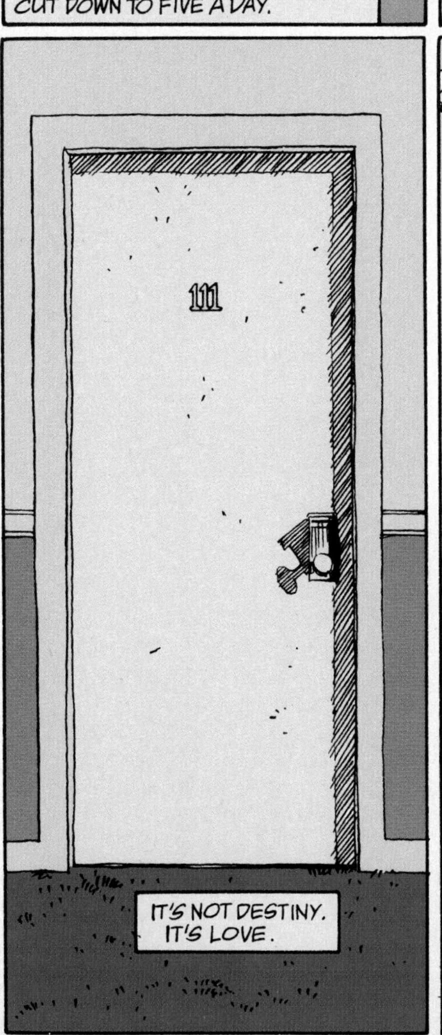
111
IT'S NOT DESTINY. IT'S LOVE.

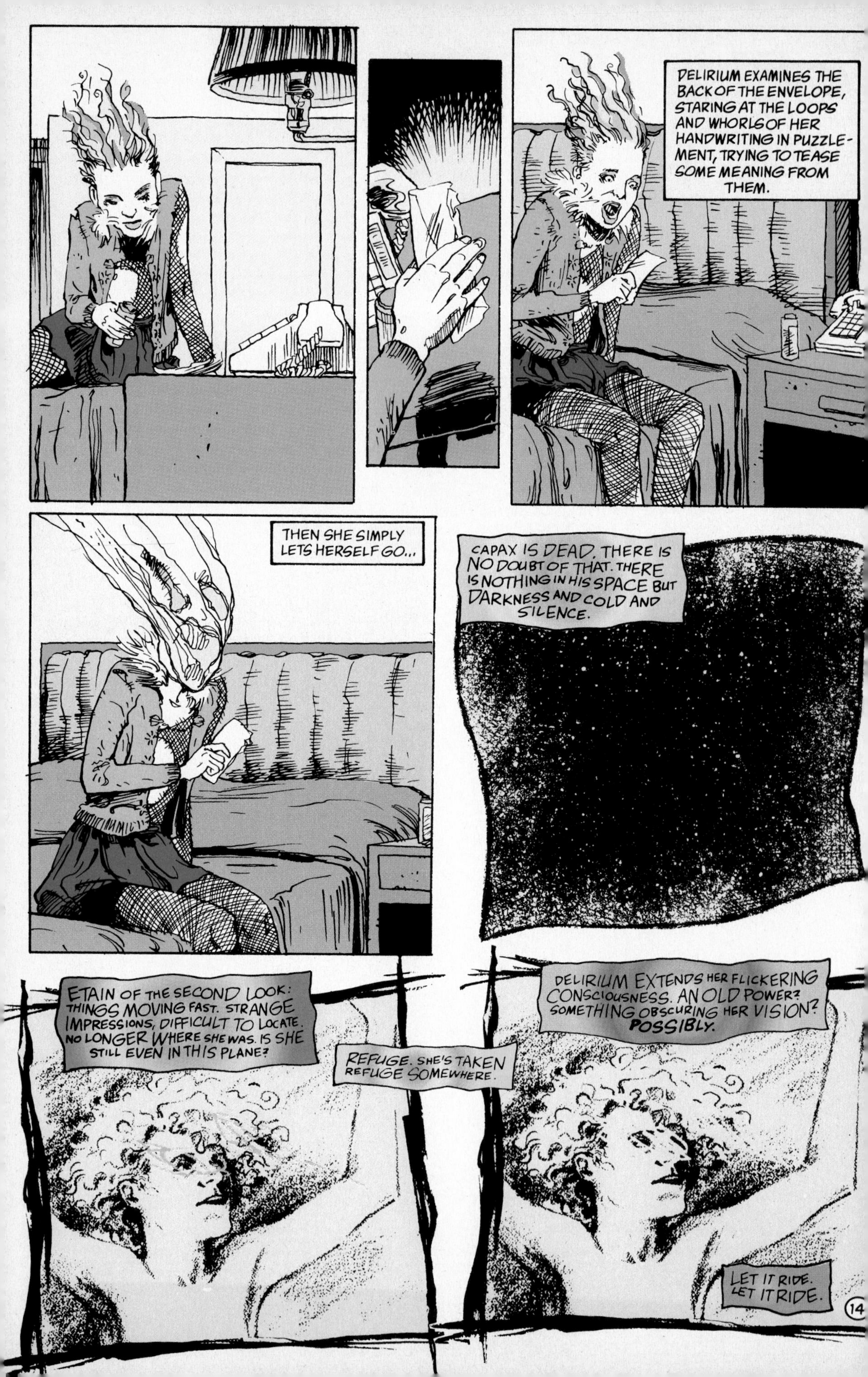
DELIRIUM EXAMINES THE BACK OF THE ENVELOPE, STARING AT THE LOOPS AND WHORLS OF HER HANDWRITING IN PUZZLEMENT, TRYING TO TEASE SOME MEANING FROM THEM.
THEN SHE SIMPLY LETS HERSELF GO...
CAPAX IS DEAD. THERE IS NO DOUBT OF THAT. THERE IS NOTHING IN HIS SPACE BUT DARKNESS AND COLD AND SILENCE.
ETAIN OF THE SECOND LOOK: THINGS MOVING FAST. STRANGE IMPRESSIONS, DIFFICULT TO LOCATE. NO LONGER WHERE SHE WAS. IS SHE STILL EVEN IN THIS PLANE?
REFUGE. SHE'S TAKEN REFUGE SOMEWHERE.
DELIRIUM EXTENDS HER FLICKERING CONSCIOUSNESS. AN OLD POWER? SOMETHING OBSCURING HER VISION? POSSIBLY.
LET IT RIDE. LET IT RIDE.

LIEB-OLMAI: THE ALDER MAN. SHE KNOWS THE FEEL OF HIM...
AN IMPRESSION OF COLD AND--SOMETHING INSUBSTANTIAL, HARD TO TOUCH... AND IT'S GONE...
THE DANCING WOMAN AND...
YES.
CONTACT.
CHRIST, TIFFANY. WHAT THE HELL HAVE YOU BEEN DOING?
NOTHING. HAVEN'T DONE NOTHING. PROBLY LIKE FLU OR SOMETHING...
GONNA BE SICK AGAIN.
OOKAY. IT'S OOKAY. YOU JUST LET IT OUT, HON. YOU LET IT HAPPEN.
JEEZ, ISHTAR, CAN'T YOU MAKE HER THROW UP IN THE JOHN? IT STINKS IN HERE. HOW'M I SUPPOSED TO PSYCH MYSELF SEXY IN A ROOM STINKS OF PUKE?
LEAVE HER ALONE, NANCY.
FIVE MINUTES, GIRLS. LAST NUMBER OF THEIR SET'S JUST STARTING.
WHAT'S THE CROWD LIKE?
SO-SO. IT'S STILL EARLY.
HMPH. I CHECKED IT OUT EARLIER. MOSTLY COLLEGE KIDS. THEY ALWAYS GET GRABBY AND THEY'RE ALWAYS CHEAP.
OKAY. NEXT SET'S ISHTAR, VENICE, MAI LAI, TIFFANY AND LINDI...
ROGER? TIFFANY'S GOING TO HAVE TO SKIP THIS SET. SHE'S REALLY SICK.
WELL, I'M NOT FORCING HER ON. BUT HEY, NO DANCING, NO-DOLLARS. YOU GOT THAT, TIFFANY?
VENICE
MAI LAI
TIFFANY
LINDI
ISHTAR... I GOTTA GO UP. I'LL BE FINE.
GET OUT OF HERE, ROGER...
YOU'RE THE DANCING LADY, AREN'T YOU? YOU'RE REALLY PRETTY.
HUH? TIFFANY?
WE'LL SEE YOU SOO-OOON...

Lucien?
How do things go in my absence?
ALL GOES WELL, MY LORD.
Ah. No... difficulties?
NO, LORD. NO DIFFICULTIES WHATSOEVER.
Ah.
Good. Well, should there be any reason to call me, do not hesitate...
OF COURSE, LORD.
AND YOUR QUEST, MY LORD? ARE YOU NEAR TO FINDING YOUR BROTHER?
I have no desire to find my brother. His whereabouts are unimportant to me.
I travel for the sake of travelling, and that is all.
However...
Yes.
Lucien. Perhaps you should make enquiries. It occurs to me that it is possible that certain forces might be acting counter to our interests in this matter.
If this is the case, I would know who. And I will know why.
I'LL PUT SOMETHING ONTO IT IMMEDIATELY, LORD.
I...
IT MAY NOT BE MY PLACE TO SAY THIS, AND, WELL, I ONLY MET YOUR BROTHER ON A HANDFUL OF OCCASIONS. HOWEVER, I LIKED HIM ENORMOUSLY. AND I ALSO RESPECTED HIM.
I HOPE YOU DO FIND HIM...
My brother abandoned his responsibilities.
In retrospect, I suspect he told me that that was what he intended to do. But I did not listen, Lucien, nor did I hear.
Enough. We will speak again soon.

SIR.
Sir. You wished to talk to me.
'TIS SO, MY BROTHER. WILL YOU WALK A WHILE?
If that is what you wish.

You are familiar with the Corinthian?
INDEED. RARE IT IS TO SEE A NIGHTMARE ABROAD IN DAYLIGHT. GOOD DAY TO YE, CORINTHIAN.
AND TO YOU, GREAT LORD.

SO: YOU ACCOMPANY YOUR LORD THIS DAY?
ON HIS SUFFERANCE. I HAD A YEARNING UPON ME TO WALK THE EARTH, THAT MY LORD MORPHEUS WAS GOOD ENOUGH TO GRANT.
'TIS GOOD. MYSELF, I FIND I SPEND AN EVER-INCREASING AMOUNT OF TIME IN THIS MORTAL WORLD. THIS PROMISCUOUS RABBLE: IT SPEAKS TO ME.

Sir?

LET ME GO, YOU ROGUE. I SHALL HAVE YOU IN THE PILLORY FOR THIS, WHERE ROTTEN EGGS ARE PLENTY.
Sir? You have something of mine.

SOMETHING OF YOURS? YOU'RE A LYING CORPSE-WHITE NINNY-HAMMER, A WORM-PICKER AND A SNAIL-CATCHER. HOLD YOUR TONGUE, SIR, OR I'LL WHET MY NEEDLE AND SEW YOUR LIPS TOGETHER?
IF THE EYES ARE THE WINDOWS OF THE SOUL, THEN YOUR SOUL IS BLACK AS THE DEVIL'S ARSE-HOLE--

Enough.

You are Dickon Hawksthorne.
YOU KNOW ME?
Aye. After my fashion.
Tell me, Master Hawksthorne, was it wise to return from transportation? When they find you out, you'll swing for it.
THAT'S A LIE!

It is rare that I tell fortunes. But Tyburn tree haunts your dreams, Master Hawksthorne, and it will continue so to do, until you are hung there in chains, without benefit of clergy.

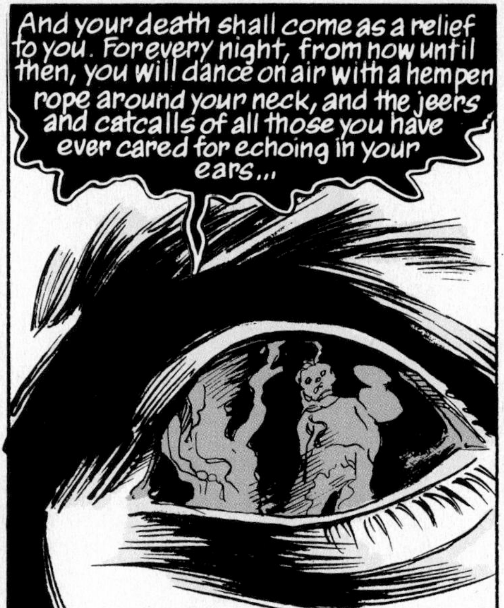

And your death shall come as a relief to you. For every night, from now until then, you will dance on air with a hempen rope around your neck, and the jeers and catcalls of all those you have ever cared for echoing in your ears...

HERE--TAKE YOUR DAMNED STONE, YOU WIGHT! I WILL HAVE NONE OF IT!

YOU COULD SIMPLY HAVE TAKEN IT BACK FROM HIM. YOU DID NOT NEED TO DO THAT.
I do not tell you how to conduct your affairs, brother.
I must confess I see no reason for you to tell me how to conduct mine.

MY AFFAIRS.
YES.
I HAVE GIVEN MUCH THOUGHT TO MY AFFAIRS IN RECENT YEARS.
TIMES ARE CHANGING, MY BROTHER.

...AND THIS IS WHAT THE INVISIBLE COLLEGE HAS BECOME. HAVE YOU BEEN HERE BEFORE?
I do not believe so.
THEY ARE USING REASON AS A TOOL.
REASON.
IT IS NO MORE RELIABLE A TOOL THAN INSTINCT, MYTH OR DREAM.
BUT IT HAS THE POTENTIAL TO BE FAR MORE DANGEROUS, FOR THEM.
THEY ARE EXPLORING AND CREATING, DEFINING AND DISSECTING...
So I see.
...WHEN I AM KING, DILLY DILLY, YOU SHALL BE QUEEN. LAVENDER'S BLUE, DILLY DILLY...
OH! MY HEART, GENTLEMEN, I DID NOT HEAR YOU COME IN.
No.
BUT I PRESUME YOU ARE HERE TO EXAMINE MY PRIZE, GOOD SIRS. IS HE NOT FINE?
THIS IS A SPECIMEN OF HOMO SYLVESTRIS, ORAN OATAN AS HE IS CALLED, BY THE NATIVES. THE WILD MAN OF THE WOODS.
HE WAS BROUGHT ALIVE TO THIS COUNTRY FROM THE JUNGLES OF DARK BORNEO, AND I PAID THE CAPTAIN OF THE SHIP TWENTY-FIVE GUINEAS FOR HIM.
I HAVE DISSECTED HIM WITH MUCH CARE, FOR DISPLAY TO THE SOCIETY. LET ME FIRST DRAW YOUR ATTENTION TO THE ORGANS OF GENERATION--
Enough. I think perhaps you had better recollect urgent business in another room.
BUT FORGIVE ME: IT HAS JUST SWEPT INTO MY MIND THAT I NEED A CERTAIN VOLUME THAT I MUST HAVE MISLAID IN AN ADJACENT ROOM.
GENTLEMEN, I MUST LEAVE YOU, FOR THE NONCE. PLEASE--TOUCH NOTHING.

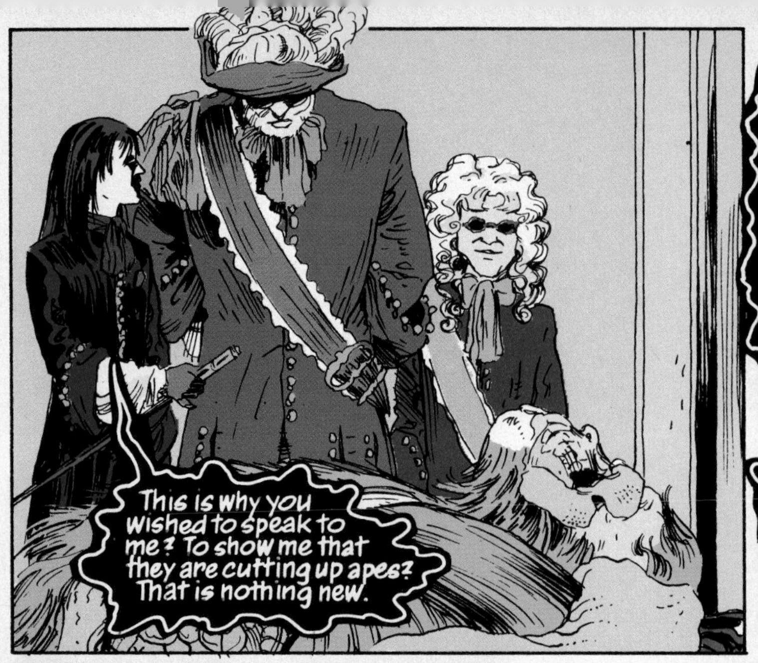
This is why you wished to speak to me? To show me that they are cutting up apes? That is nothing new.

Do they think that they can impale the soul of it on their knives? That if they cut deep enough they can extract its dreams, naked and writhing and screaming, from its head?
Reason is a flawed tool at best, my brother.

ONE OF THEM HAS PRISMED THE SUN'S RAYS INTO BEAMS OF DISCRETE COLOR.
A pretty phenomenon, indeed.

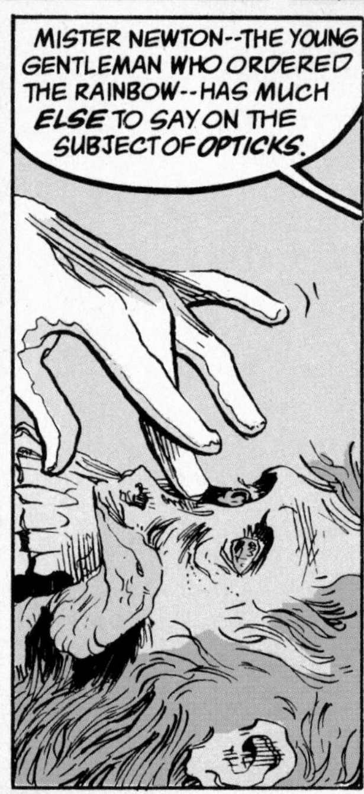
MISTER NEWTON--THE YOUNG GENTLEMAN WHO ORDERED THE RAINBOW--HAS MUCH ELSE TO SAY ON THE SUBJECT OF OPTICKS.

"ARE NOT LIGHT AND GROSS BODIES INTRACONVERTIBLE?"
HE HAS ALREADY POSED THAT QUESTION; ALTHOUGH AT PRESENT IT IS BUT AN IDLE NOTION, AND I DOUBT HE WILL RETURN TO IT. HE HAS TOO MANY OTHER THINGS TO OCCUPY HIS MIND.

I confess, sir, I fail to understand you...
THE RELATIONSHIP BETWEEN MATTER AND LIGHT; THE TRANSFORMATION, ONE TO THE OTHER.

I HAVE BEEN HERE BEFORE. AFTER A WHILE CERTAIN IDEAS BECOME INEVITABLE.

This is your territory, brother, not mine.
So they begin to reorganize their lives on principles of reason. Well, what of that? It does not affect my domain; and it will do little to yours that will not change once more.
As you say, you have been here before. In many times, in many worlds.
AEON AFTER AEON. FROM THE DAWN DAYS WHEN TIME WAS FRESH-MINTED. AND FOR HOW MUCH LONGER?
As long as they need us.
ARE NOT LIGHT AND GROSS BODIES INTRACONVERTIBLE? ALAS, THEY ARE. AND FROM THAT FOLLOWS THE FLAMES...
THE BIG BANG. THE LOUD EXPLOSIONS.

SIR! MY ORAN OATAN! WHERE ARE HIS EYES? DID YOU OBSERVE?
WHAT HAPPENED TO HIS EYES?

EYES?
I SEE NO EYES.

AYE. THEN FOLLOWS MY TIME, BROTHER. THE AGE OF FIRE AND FLAME...

HELLO?
ANYONE IN THERE?

OVER HERE, FELLA! QUICKLY!
Your pardon. I was remembering.
MOVE! C'MON YOU NUMB-NUT SON OF A BITCH! THE WHOLE PLACE IS GOING UP!
MOVE!
Ruby.

OUT THROUGH THE FIRE EXIT, BACK THERE. LEADS ONTO THE PARKING LOT. MOVE IT.
Hmm.
Before I leave, do you have any idea how the fire started?

OU PEOPLE. YOU PEOPLE ARE JUST GONNA KILL ME, YOU KNOW THAT?
YEAH. WE THINK WE KNOW.

LADY IN THE ROOM NEXT TO YOURS, SMOKING IN BED, FALLS ASLEEP, CIGARETTE FALLS ONTO THE BED. WHOOMPF.
IT WAS JUST LUCKY THE NIGHT PORTER SAW THE SMOKE COMING UNDER THE DOOR, AND CALLED US WHEN HE DID.

My sister. Have you seen her?
She would probably have appeared to be a young woman with rather wild hair...

THERE WAS ONLY ONE OTHER PERSON ON THIS WING -- SHE'S ALREADY OUT IN THE PARKING LOT.
LOOK, I HATE TO DISTURB YOU, AND ONLY IF IT'S NOT TOO MUCH TROUBLE, BUT WILL YOU KINDLY GET THE HELL OUT OF HERE, OR AM I GONNA HAVETA BUST YOU IN THE MOUTH AND CARRY YOU OUT MYSELF?

That will not be necessary. I can find my own way out.
And thank you. You have been most helpful.

Ruby is dead, my sister. They tell me that the fire began in her room.
This may of course have been an accident.
However, she was assigned to guard us, and to take us from place to place, and thus we had responsibility for her.
We failed her.
As I say, it might be simple accident that Ruby's room was where the fire started.
As it might be coincidence that our first quarry chose yesterday to be hit by a falling building.
Reason was never an important part of my dominion. But certain conclusions become inescapable.
Do you understand what I am trying to tell you?

RUBY'S DEAD?
Yes.
OH.
OH WOW.
THAT MEANS I GET TO DRIVE.
To Be Continued

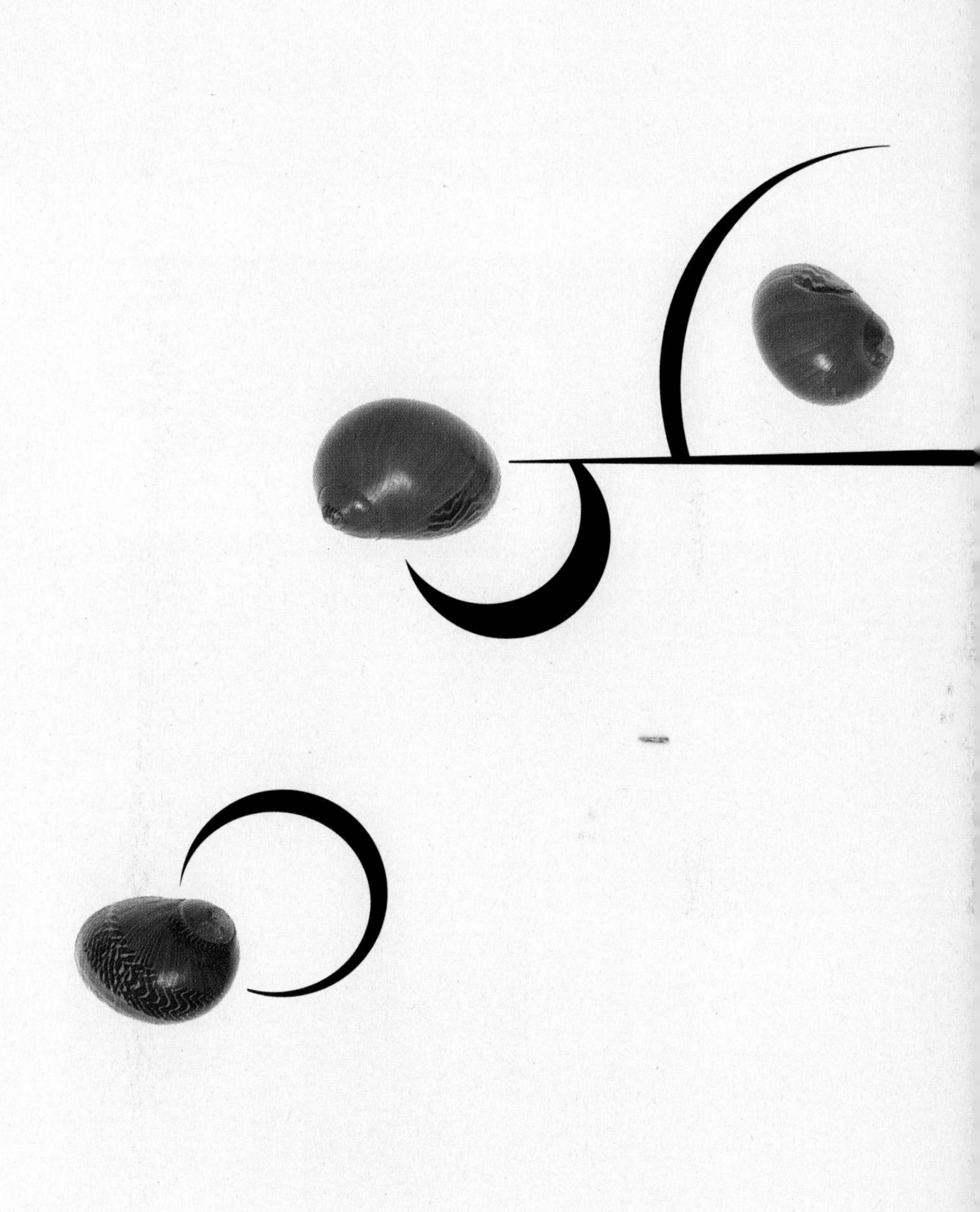

The things we do to be loved

her hands do not go to the moon

the driving instructor

Tiffany Watches I

chapter 5

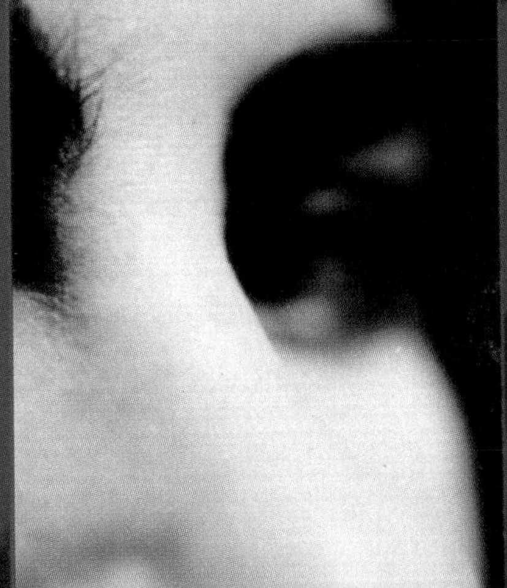

white knights and/or pond-scum

Are Dalmations flowers?

Nancy displays her erudition

Wham Bam thank you Ma'am

Tiffany Watches II

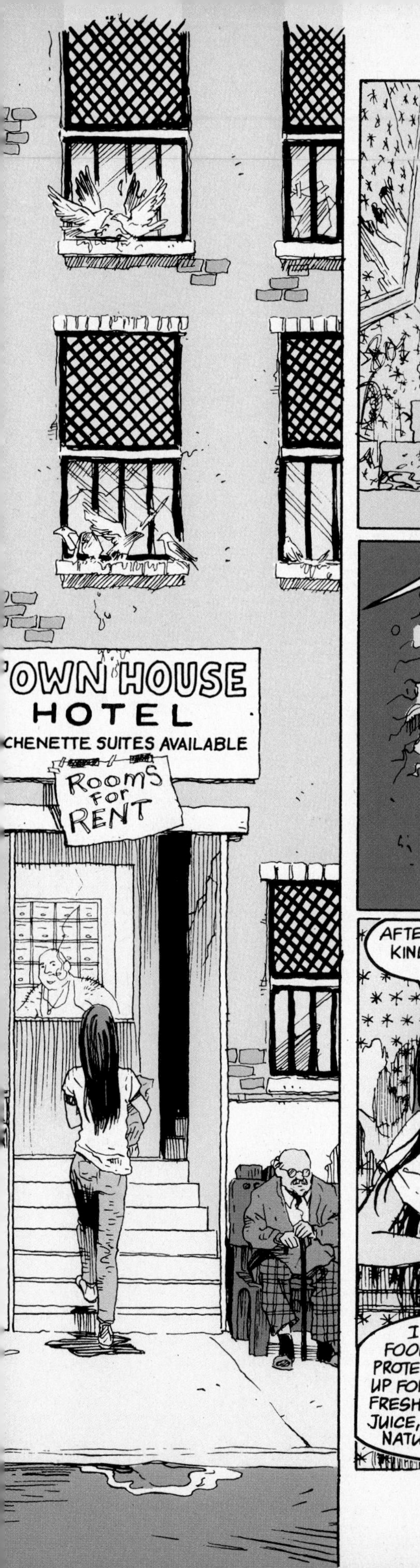

OWN HOUSE
HOTEL
CHENETTE SUITES AVAILABLE
Rooms for RENT

RAPATAP

HEY, TIFFANY.
UH. HI, ISHTAR.
RoxyBlue

AFTER LAST NIGHT, I WAS KIND OF **WORRIED** ABOUT YOU.
I BROUGHT YOU SOME FOOD. BREAD. MILK. EGGS. PROTEIN POWDER IF YOU AREN'T UP FOR SOLID STUFF. AND FRESH-SQUEEZED ORANGE JUICE, **BRIMMING** WITH MOTHER NATURE'S OWN VITAMIN C.

OH.
NOW YOU SAY, "GEE, THAT'S AWFUL NICE OF YOU, ISHTAR. WHY DON'T YOU COME IN?"
YEAH. **SORRY.** YEAH. I WASN'T THINKING. COME IN.
I'M SORRY.

ISHTAR? DO YOU THINK I'M ATTRACTIVE?
SURE, TIFF. WHAT'S NOT TO LIKE?
OH.
YOU GOT ANY CLEAN PLATES AROUND, OR DO I HAVE TO WASH UP FOR YOU TOO?

I'M NOT HUNGRY.

I'LL MAKE YOU SOME BREAKFAST. YOU'LL BE HUNGRY WHEN YOU SMELL IT. HOW'D YOU WANT YOUR EGGS?
UNFERTILIZED. THAT'S A JOKE.

HEY, ISHTAR? D'I EVER TELL YOU ABOUT THIS GIRL I MET WHEN I WAS DANCING IN PORTLAND? SHE WAS A DANCER, AND SHE WAS SHOOTING UP, AND THE MANAGEMENT TOLD HER THAT SHE HAD TO GET OFF OR GET OUT BECAUSE THE NEEDLE MARKS WERE GROSSING PEOPLE OUT.
SO YOU KNOW WHAT SHE DID?

SCRAMBLED EGGS AND TOAST. THAT'S PROTEIN AND CARBOS. OKAY?
NO. WHAT DID SHE DO?

SHE STARTED SHOOTING UP IN HER EYES.
NOT INTO THE EYEBALL. INTO THE RED STUFF UNDERNEATH. CAN YOU IMAGINE DOING THAT?
STICKING A NEEDLE STRAIGHT IN, UNDER THERE? CAN YOU IMAGINE?
THE THINGS WE DO TO BE LOVED...

SHIT. I *HATE* NEEDLES.
SO WHAT HAPPENED TO HER?

I DON'T KNOW. PROBABLY WOUND UP IN A LANDFILL SOMEWHERE.
YOU DON'T DO THAT SHIT FOR LIFE-EXPECTANCY. YOU KNOW?

HERE YOU GO. EAT IT UP.
I'M NOT *HUNGRY*, ISHTAR.
YOU'VE GOT TO WORK TONIGHT, TIFF.
ONCE YOU GET SOME FOOD INTO YOU, YOU'LL BE *FINE*.

MWHRAOOLLPHH...

YOU REALLY *WEREN'T* HUNGRY, WERE YOU?
OKAY. LET'S CLEAN YOU UP AND TRY THE PROTEIN POWDER.

BZUUM. BZUUM. BRRRR. BZUUUUUUUM!

I'M GOOD AT THIS, AREN'T I? I'M REALLY GOOD. I KNEW I'D BE GOOD AT DRIVING. BZUUM. BZUUM.
DREAM? LOOK AT ME! LOOK AT ME DRIVING!
I see you, Delirium.

Are you certain that we are going the correct way?
SURE. I THINK...
YOU KNOW, IF THIS CAR HAD GREAT BIG RUNNY LEGS LIKE A CENTIPEDE IT COULD RUN VERY FAST AND WE'D GET THERE QUICKER. CAN I...?
No.

I let you drive.
WHEEE-OOOO-WHEEE-OOO
YOU NEVER LET ME DO ANYTHING.
HONNK!
HONNK!
HONNK!

WHY IS THAT CAR MAKING THAT NOISE, WHOO-OOP, WHOO-EE-OOP, AND FLASHING ITS LIGHTS AT US?
I have no idea. Perhaps the driver wishes to talk with you.
OH. NEAT. OKAY. LET'S STOP AND SAY HI.

YOU. OUT OF THE CAR, AND KEEP YOUR HANDS WHERE I CAN SEE THEM.
YOU MEAN NOT MAKE MY HANDS GO TO THE MOON OR ANYWHERE?
I. AM NOT. IN THE MOOD. FOR JOKES. OUT.

WHAT THE SAM HILL'S THE IDEA? I'VE BEEN TRYING TO GET YOU TO PULL OVER FOR FIVE MILES, NOW. YOU'VE BEEN DRIVING ALL OVER THE ROAD, YOU'VE DRIVEN THROUGH EVERY RED LIGHT -- LISTEN, YOU BETTER HAVE A GOOD ATTORNEY, KID, BECAUSE YOUR ASS IS GREEN AND GROWING.
LET'S SEE YOUR DRIVER'S LICENSE.
HUH?

HAVE YOU GOT A DRIVER'S LICENSE?
I'M A VERY GOOD DRIVER.
STATE HIGHWAY PATROL
YOU'RE THE SINGLE WORST DRIVER I'VE SEEN IN EIGHT YEARS ON HIGHWAY PATROL, LADY. AND RIGHT NOW YOU ARE IN IT UP TO YOUR EARS.

I THINK YOU'RE NASTY TO ME, NOW.
I THINK YOU'LL HAVE INVISIBLE INSECTS ALL OVER YOU NOW FOR ALL YOUR LIFE AND FOR EVER AND ALWAYS.

LISTEN, KID...
JESUS!
GET OFF ME!
OFF!
OW!
SHIT! GETTEMOFFAMEEE! SHIT!

Was that really entirely necessary?
I DON'T TELL YOU HOW TO, UM. WHAT YOU DO. DO IT. YOU KNOW.
YOU'VE DONE LOTS WORSE THAN THAT. ANYWAY. LOTS AND LOTS AND LOTS AND LOTS AND LOTS.

I DON'T WANT TO DRIVE ANYMORE. LET'S JUST GO PWOOF AND BE THERE. I CAN GO THROUGH TIFFANY'S HEAD. SHE'S THIS GIRL. I KNOW HOW.
PWOOF.

I do not think so, sister. We began this journey in the waking world. We shall finish it in the waking world. However...
Hmm.
Yes.
MATTHEW?

BOSS? IS THAT YOU?
I am afraid so.
Matthew. When you were a man, were you able to drive a motor vehicle?

COULD I? HEY, I KILLED MYSELF DRUNK DRIVING, DIDN'T I? I MEAN, THE FIRST TIME.
I am not convinced that is any recommendation. However...

This is my sister, The Lady Delirium.
Delirium, this is Matthew. He will advise you on the protocol of vehicle management.

YEAH? YOU'RE DELIRIUM? I'VE HEARD ABOUT YOU.
Y'KNOW, YOU'RE THE FIRST ONE OF THE BOSS'S FAMILY I'VE EVER MET. EXCEPT FOR THE FOXY CHICK WITH ALL THE HAIR, OF COURSE.

REALLY? YOU'RE THE UM. ONE TWO THREE FOUR FIVE SIX SIX AND A HALF SEVEN EIGHT NINE. THE ONE WHO CAME BACK AGAIN AFTER HE WAS A MAN AGAIN. ELEVENTH OF DREAM'S RAVENS I'VE EVER MET.
SOMEONE ONCE BROUGHT ME A FLOWER, CLANDESTINELY. THAT MEANS I DON'T KNOW WHO IT WAS.
AND I NEVER SAW THE FLOWER, EITHER. MAYBE THEY NEVER BROUGHT IT AT ALL.
I DON'T KNOW.

UH. RIGHT.
...HEY-- WHAT'S WITH HIM?
He is troubled by delusory insects.
BUGS. YEAH. I BEEN THERE.
SO WHAT'S THE DEAL?

The deal?
Delirium will drive. You will advise her.
I am sure you will find the experience one of great interest and variety.

HOW'D I LOOK?
MUCH BETTER.
HEY, WHEN YOU'RE UP, YOU'RE UP. Y'KNOW? WATCH OUT, WORLD, HERE COMES TIFFANY CALHOUN.
snf
MADONNA BLONDE AMBITION

WHY'D YOU PICK ISHTAR?
WHAT?
AS A NAME? I MEAN, IT WAS A LOUSY MOVIE.
IT GOES WAY BACK. WHY'D YOU PICK TIFFANY?

YOU REALLY WANT TO KNOW? OKAY.
MY MOM HAD A TIFFANY WATCH. IT WAS THE ONLY PRETTY THING SHE HAD. SHE KEPT IT IN THIS BOX BY HER BED. IF I WAS REALLY GOOD SHE'D LET ME TRY IT ON.
I'D WEAR IT IN FRONT OF A MIRROR. WHEN I WAS LITTLE.

WHEN I LEFT HOME IT WAS THE ONLY THING I TOOK AWAY WITH ME.
SHE GAVE IT TO YOU?
SHIT, NO. ARE YOU KIDDING? MY MOM LOVED THAT WATCH.
MADONNA BLONDE

WHAT WAS YOUR NAME BEFORE IT WAS TIFFANY CALHOUN?
IT'S A REALLY SHITTY NAME. YOU DON'T WANT TO KNOW.
SURE I DO.
ALVA. ALVA ELLEN RASMUSSEN. YICKY, HUH?

I WAS FIFTEEN WHEN I LEFT HOME. AND MY MOM SAID, YOU DON'T KNOW SHIT, ALVA. YOU'LL STARVE.
SOMETHING ELSE SHE WAS WRONG ABOUT. I MAY NOT KNOW SHIT, BUT I CAN DANCE.
MADONNA BLONDE AMBITION

ISH? WHY DON'T YOU DANCE AS GOOD AS YOU CAN? YOU'RE A REALLY GOOD DANCER. I MEAN, NOT JUST GOOD. REALLY GOOD. BUT MOSTLY YOU DON'T SHOW IT. IT'S LIKE YOU'RE COVERING IT UP.
THAT'S WHAT IT'S LIKE, HUH?
MADONNA BLONDE AMBITION
ME, I DANCE AS WELL AS I CAN. I'M AN OKAY DANCER, AND I'M CUTE ENOUGH THAT NO ONE CARES THAT I'LL NEVER BE A GREAT DANCER.
ROOMS FOR RENT
YOU'RE DIFFERENT. I MEAN THAT WIGGLY THING YOU DID WITH YOUR HANDS LAST NIGHT. ON LIKE A VIRGIN. WHAT WAS THAT?
YOU MEAN THIS?
YEAH.
IT'S CALLED THE BUTTERFLY CALL.
WISH I WAS AS GOOD AS YOU. WHY DON'T YOU DANCE AS GOOD AS YOU CAN?
BECAUSE THEY DON'T COME TO SEE THAT.
MADONNA BLONDE AMBITION
THEY COME TO SEE TITS AND THEY COME TO SEE ASS AND LEGS AND MAYBE A PRETTY FACE AND A GOOD HEAD OF HAIR WOULD BE NICE. BUT THEY DON'T COME TO SEE US DANCE.
AND THEY DON'T WANT TO SEE ME DANCING FOR REAL.
8
WHY NOT?
THEY JUST DON'T. REALLY.
WHAT TIME IS IT? ROGER'LL KILL ME IF I'M LATE AGAIN.
FIVE THIRTY. HEY, I THOUGHT YOU HAD A TIFFANY WATCH.
I DID HAVE. BUT I ALSO HAD A BOYFRIEND NAMED SEAN. ONE DAY I WOKE UP AND DIDN'T HAVE EITHER.
WELL, SHITS HAPPEN.
SAY THAT AGAIN. LET'S TAKE MY CAR.
MADONNA BLONDE

Ramirez Fresh Food
GROCER
295
ISHTAR? YOU KNOW WHAT I WORRY ABOUT?
WHAT IF ALL MEN ARE SHITS. I MEAN, I'VE NEVER MET A GUY WHO DIDN'T COME ON LIKE A KNIGHT ON A WHITE HORSE, AND WHO DIDN'T TURN OUT TO BE POND SCUM.
FIRST WEEK--THAT'S GREAT. WE REALLY PARTY, Y'KNOW. GET REALLY SMASHED AND GO PLACES AND THEN GO HOME AND VA-VA-VOOM. EVERYTHING'S GREAT.
SECOND WEEK, HE STARTS BORROWING MONEY AND TELLING ME HOW DUMB I AM.
THEN IT JUST GOES ON LIKE THAT TILL I TAKE OFF FOR A NEW CITY, OR HE FINDS SOMEONE WITH MORE CASH AND BIGGER TITS. AND HE ALWAYS LOVES TO TELL ME HOW GODDAMNED STUPID I AM.
I OUGHTTA TELL THEM, IF IT'S BRAINS YOU'RE AFTER, DRILL A HOLE IN MY HEAD AND STICK YOUR GODDAMNED WEENIE IN THAT.
HAH!
AND EVERY TIME I SWEAR THAT'S IT.
I SAY TO MYSELF, FROM NOW ON, I'M A GAL ON MY OWN.
I GOT SOME BUCKS AND SOME BLOW AND A VIBRATOR-- WHAT DO I NEED SOME GUY MAKING ME FEEL LIKE I'M STUPID FOR?
THEN SOONER OR LATER SOME GUY COMES OVER AND SAYS HI, AND THE WHOLE STINKING THING STARTS OVER.
NOTHING EVER GODDAMN CHANGES.
A GOOD MAN IS HARD TO FIND, HUH?
HEY-- I USED TO HAVE THIS SHIRT. IT SAID, "A HARD MAN IS GOOD TO FIND." FUNNY, HUH?
SO DID YOU EVER FIND A GOOD ONE?
A GOOD MAN?
YEAH.
HMM...
ONE. BUT THAT WAS A LONG TIME AGO.
IN THE END WE SPLIT UP. FIGHTS ABOUT HIS FAMILY AND HIS JOB. YOU KNOW HOW IT GOES.
WE WERE AN ITEM FOR A LONG TIME. I WISH I KNEW WHAT HE WAS DOING NOW.
UHN.
HEY! THAT WAS WEIRD.
WHAT WAS?
SUDDENLY I JUST GOT THIS KIND OF MYSTICAL VISION. THERE WAS THIS SORTA BIG BLACK BIRD SHOUTING AT ME.
REALLY? COOL. WHAT WAS IT SAYING?

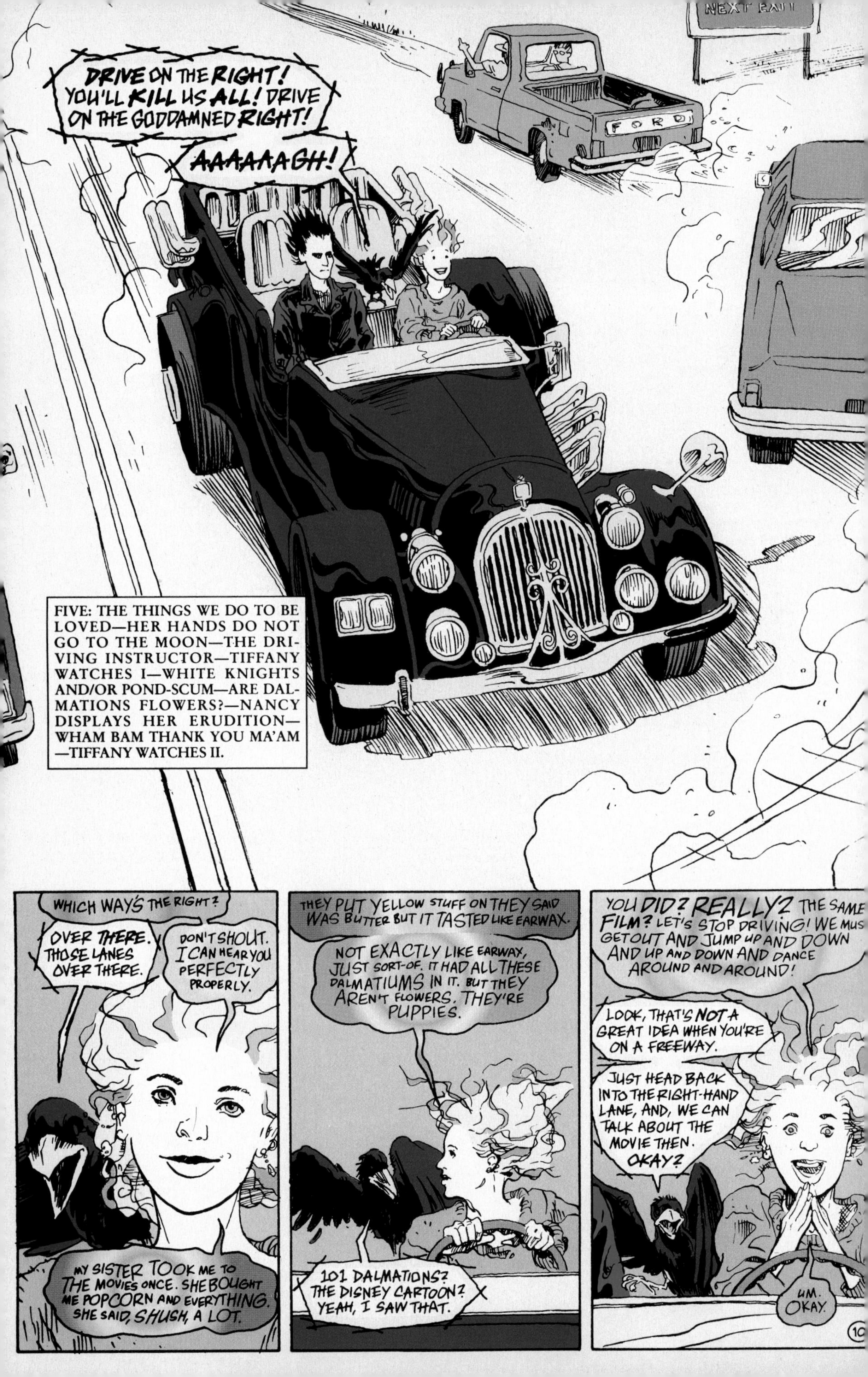
NEXT EXIT
FORD
DRIVE ON THE RIGHT! YOU'LL KILL US ALL! DRIVE ON THE GODDAMNED RIGHT!
AAAAAAAGH!
FIVE: THE THINGS WE DO TO BE LOVED—HER HANDS DO NOT GO TO THE MOON—THE DRIVING INSTRUCTOR—TIFFANY WATCHES I—WHITE KNIGHTS AND/OR POND-SCUM—ARE DALMATIONS FLOWERS?—NANCY DISPLAYS HER ERUDITION—WHAM BAM THANK YOU MA'AM—TIFFANY WATCHES II.
WHICH WAY'S THE RIGHT?
OVER THERE. THOSE LANES OVER THERE.
DON'T SHOUT. I CAN HEAR YOU PERFECTLY PROPERLY.
MY SISTER TOOK ME TO THE MOVIES ONCE. SHE BOUGHT ME POPCORN AND EVERYTHING. SHE SAID, SHUSH, A LOT.
THEY PUT YELLOW STUFF ON THEY SAID WAS BUTTER BUT IT TASTED LIKE EARWAX.
NOT EXACTLY LIKE EARWAX, JUST SORT-OF. IT HAD ALL THESE DALMATIUMS IN IT. BUT THEY AREN'T FLOWERS. THEY'RE PUPPIES.
101 DALMATIONS? THE DISNEY CARTOON? YEAH, I SAW THAT.
YOU DID? REALLY? THE SAME FILM? LET'S STOP DRIVING! WE MUS GET OUT AND JUMP UP AND DOWN AND UP AND DOWN AND DANCE AROUND AND AROUND!
LOOK, THAT'S NOT A GREAT IDEA WHEN YOU'RE ON A FREEWAY.
JUST HEAD BACK INTO THE RIGHT-HAND LANE, AND, WE CAN TALK ABOUT THE MOVIE THEN. OKAY?
UM. OKAY.

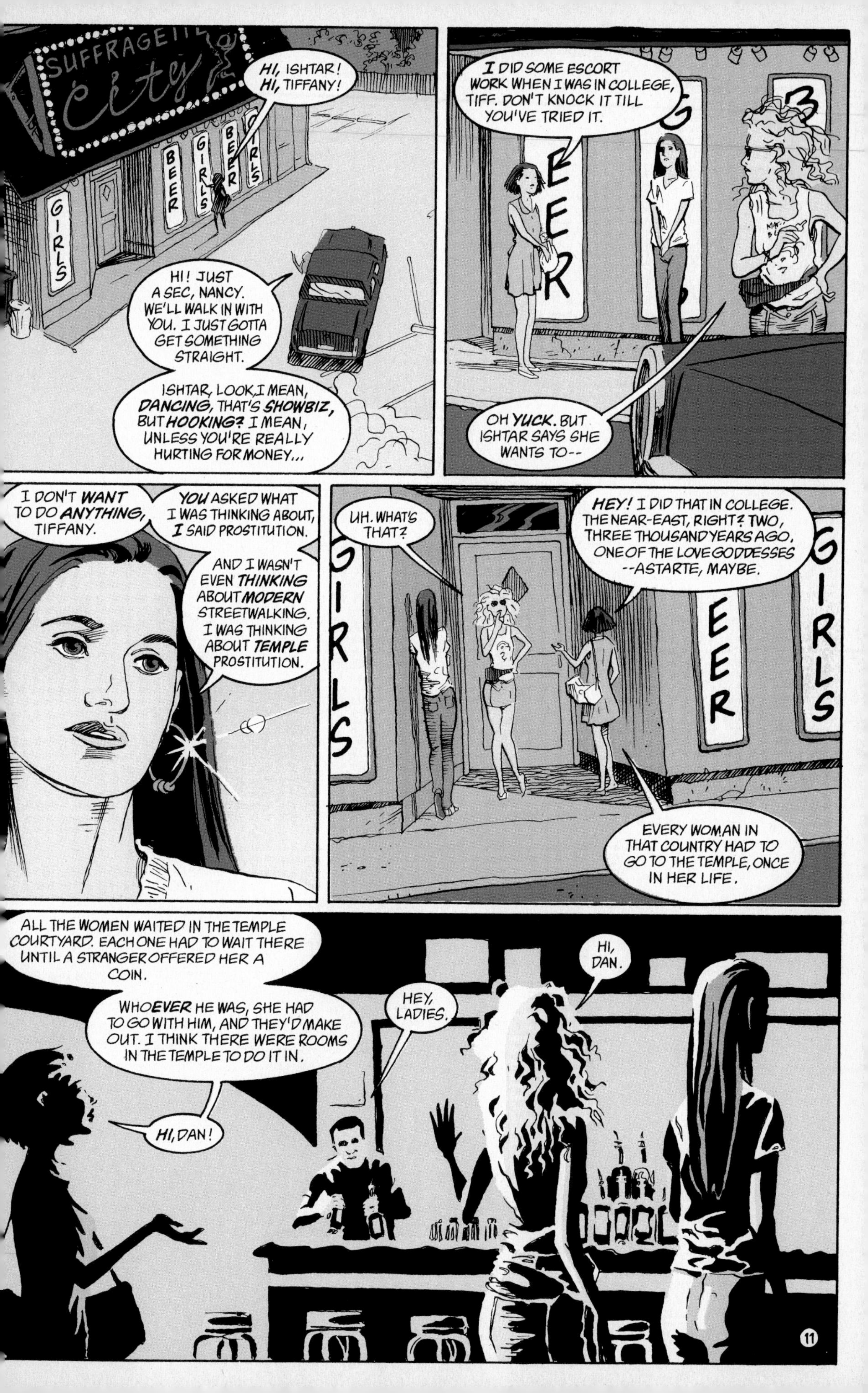
SUFFRAGETTE city
BEER GIRLS BEER GIRLS
GIRLS
HI, ISHTAR! HI, TIFFANY!
HI! JUST A SEC, NANCY. WE'LL WALK IN WITH YOU. I JUST GOTTA GET SOMETHING STRAIGHT.
ISHTAR, LOOK, I MEAN, DANCING, THAT'S SHOWBIZ, BUT HOOKING? I MEAN, UNLESS YOU'RE REALLY HURTING FOR MONEY...
I DID SOME ESCORT WORK WHEN I WAS IN COLLEGE, TIFF. DON'T KNOCK IT TILL YOU'VE TRIED IT.
OH YUCK. BUT ISHTAR SAYS SHE WANTS TO--
I DON'T WANT TO DO ANYTHING, TIFFANY.
YOU ASKED WHAT I WAS THINKING ABOUT, I SAID PROSTITUTION.
AND I WASN'T EVEN THINKING ABOUT MODERN STREETWALKING. I WAS THINKING ABOUT TEMPLE PROSTITUTION.
UH. WHAT'S THAT?
HEY! I DID THAT IN COLLEGE. THE NEAR-EAST, RIGHT? TWO, THREE THOUSAND YEARS AGO. ONE OF THE LOVE GODDESSES --ASTARTE, MAYBE.
EVERY WOMAN IN THAT COUNTRY HAD TO GO TO THE TEMPLE, ONCE IN HER LIFE.
ALL THE WOMEN WAITED IN THE TEMPLE COURTYARD. EACH ONE HAD TO WAIT THERE UNTIL A STRANGER OFFERED HER A COIN.
WHOEVER HE WAS, SHE HAD TO GO WITH HIM, AND THEY'D MAKE OUT. I THINK THERE WERE ROOMS IN THE TEMPLE TO DO IT IN.
HI, DAN!
HEY, LADIES.
HI, DAN.

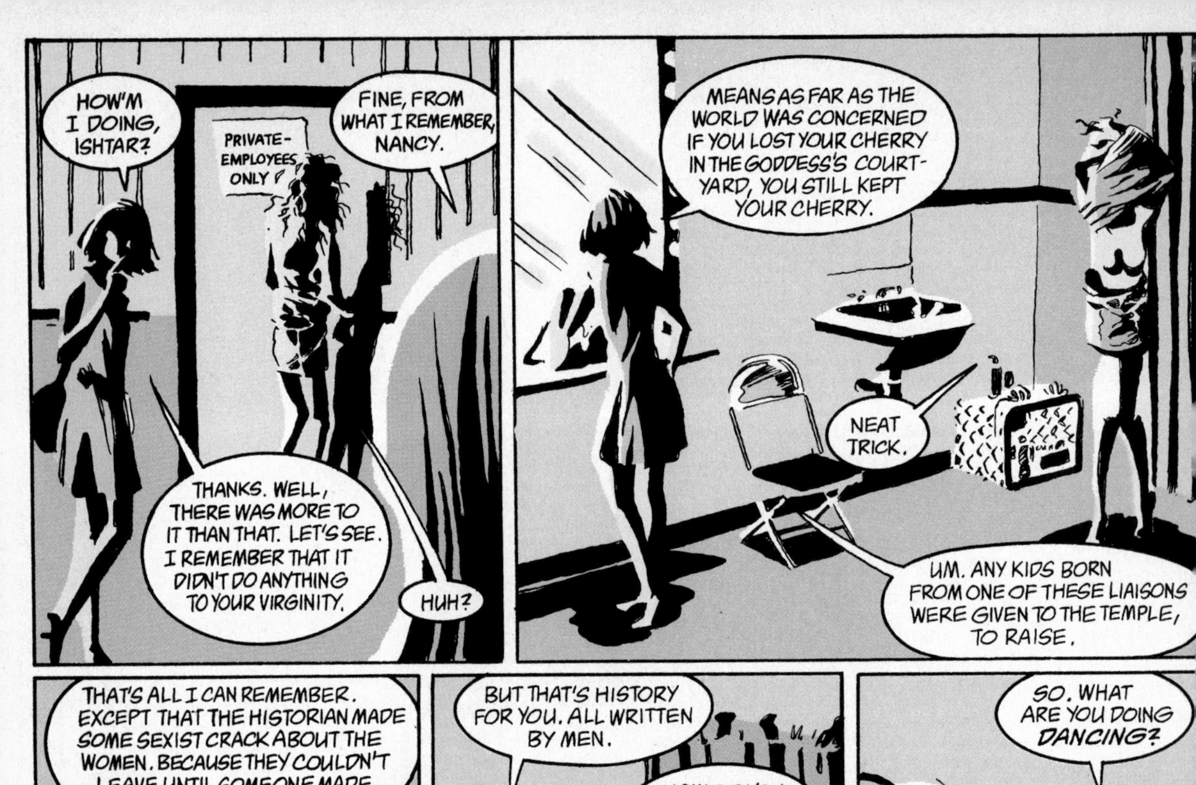
HOW'M I DOING, ISHTAR?
PRIVATE- EMPLOYEES ONLY
FINE, FROM WHAT I REMEMBER, NANCY.
THANKS. WELL, THERE WAS MORE TO IT THAN THAT. LET'S SEE. I REMEMBER THAT IT DIDN'T DO ANYTHING TO YOUR VIRGINITY.
HUH?
MEANS AS FAR AS THE WORLD WAS CONCERNED IF YOU LOST YOUR CHERRY IN THE GODDESS'S COURT-YARD, YOU STILL KEPT YOUR CHERRY.
NEAT TRICK.
UM. ANY KIDS BORN FROM ONE OF THESE LIAISONS WERE GIVEN TO THE TEMPLE, TO RAISE.

THAT'S ALL I CAN REMEMBER. EXCEPT THAT THE HISTORIAN MADE SOME SEXIST CRACK ABOUT THE WOMEN. BECAUSE THEY COULDN'T LEAVE UNTIL SOMEONE MADE LOVE TO THEM.
HE SAID THE GOOD-LOOKING ONES GOT OFF EARLY, BUT THE ROUGHER-LOOKING ONES SOME-TIMES WAITED IN THE TEMPLE COURTYARD FOR MONTHS.

BUT THAT'S HISTORY FOR YOU. ALL WRITTEN BY MEN.
HOW DO YOU KNOW ALL THIS STUFF, NANCY?
TIFFANY, I GOT A MASTERS IN WOMEN'S STUDIES.

SO. WHAT ARE YOU DOING DANCING?
THE MONEY'S GOOD, THE HOURS SUIT ME, A
I GET A ROOMFUL OF MEN MAKING ME FEEL WANTED, AND PAYING FOR THE PRIVILEGE.
AND WHEN I GET OLD AND MY BOOBS START TO SAG, I'LL WRITE A BOOK ABOUT IT AND GO ON DONAHUE.

"I LIKE OPRAH BETTER."
"YEAH, WELL. I'LL GO ON OPRAH, TOO."
"OH GOOD. SO WAS THAT WHAT YOU WERE THINKING OF, ISHTAR?"
"YES. THE TEMPLE COURTYARD, AND THE WOMEN WAITING. ONCE IN EACH OF THEIR LIVES..."

AFTER A WHILE IT BEGAN TO DECAY.
BUT IT WAS THE MOST SIGNIFICANT OF ALL THE RITUALS--A TERRIFYING EXPERIENCE FOR BOTH THE WOMEN AND THE MEN, WHERE THEY GAVE THEM-SELVES TO LUST AND THE UNKNOWN.

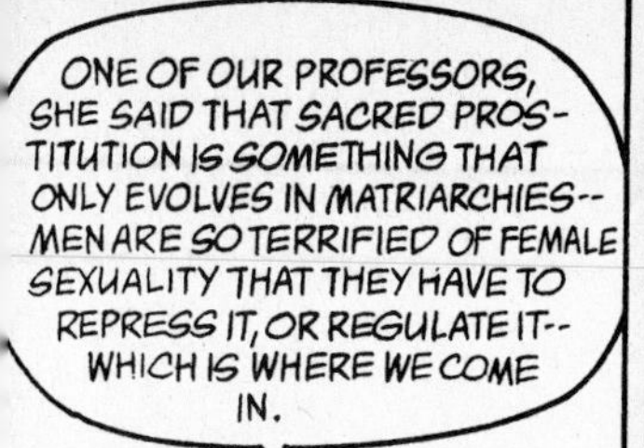

ONE OF OUR PROFESSORS, SHE SAID THAT SACRED PROSTITUTION IS SOMETHING THAT ONLY EVOLVES IN MATRIARCHIES-- MEN ARE SO TERRIFIED OF FEMALE SEXUALITY THAT THEY HAVE TO REPRESS IT, OR REGULATE IT-- WHICH IS WHERE WE COME IN.
YOU'RE GOING TO GO ON OPRAH AND SAY ALL THIS?
ONE DAY.

WHAT'S A--A MATRIARCHY?
A SOCIETY RUN BY WOMEN.
YOU MEAN LIKE THE GIRL SCOUTS?
NOPE. NOTHING LIKE THAT.

OH. SO WHAT HAPPENED TO THE TEMPLES? I MEAN, ARE THESE PLACES STILL THERE?
NO, TIFF. THEY'VE BEEN RUBBLE FOR TWO THOUSAND YEARS.
MAKES YOU FEEL SORRY FOR THE GODS AND GODDESSES, DOESN'T IT? AFTER THEIR TEMPLES FALL APART. I WONDER WHAT HAPPENS TO THEM?

SOME OF THEM DIE. SOME OF THEM CHANGE, AND SOME OF THEM JUST KEEP GOING. MAYBE SOME EVEN GET JOBS AS DANCERS.

OH SURE. "ON DONAHUE TONIGHT--ANCIENT GODS AND GODDESSES WITH JOBS IN THE SEX INDUSTRY!"
DON'T SAY THAT.
WHAT?
SEX INDUSTRY. MAYBE YOU'RE IN THE SEX INDUSTRY, NANCY. THE REST OF US ARE IN SHOWBIZ.

BUT THEN, I WOULDN'T EXPECT ANYTHING MORE OF SOMEONE WHO CALLS HERSELF AFTER A DRINK WHEN THEY DANCE.
DUMB, TIFFANY. MAI LAI IS... NOT A DRINK.
DON'T CALL ME DUMB. AND DON'T FRIGGING PATRONIZE ME. OKAY?
COOL IT, TIFFANY. COOL IT.

ISHTAR TAKES TO THE CATWALK FOR HER FIRST SET OF THE EVENING AT 7:30 PM.

SHE SMILES AT THE MEN, SIZING THEM UP, AND THEN BEGINS TO DANCE TO "I HEARD IT THROUGH THE GRAPEVINE."

UH HUH I GUESS YOU'RE WONDERIN' HOW I KNEW...

SHE'S WORRIED ABOUT TIFFANY. BUT YOU CAN'T LIVE THEIR LIVES FOR THEM. IT'S LIKE FALLING IN LOVE WITH A KITTEN: ONE DAY YOU'LL HAVE TO PUT AN OLD CAT TO SLEEP...

A SWEATY HAND FUMBLES THE FIRST DOLLAR OF THE EVENING INTO HER GARTER BELT. SHE REWARDS HIM WITH A SMILE.

WITH SOME OTHER GUY YOU KNEW BEFORE...

HER FEET MOVE, HER HANDS MOVE, HER BODY MOVES, AUTOMATICALLY.

SHE FINDS HERSELF THINKING ONCE MORE ABOUT THE WOMEN IN THE TEMPLE COURTYARD. THERE IS A MAGIC GENERATED BY MONEY GIVEN FOR LUST.

ONCE ON A TIME, SHE COULD USE THAT MAGIC, DRAW IT TO HER. CREATE AN ASPECT, TAKE THE POWER TO HERSELF.

NOW, SHE USES A SHADOW OF IT TO SURVIVE.

EVEN A LITTLE WORSHIP IS BETTER THAN NOTHING.

TIFFANY'S FOUND AN EARLY DRUNK, AND SHE'S MILKING HIM FOR ALL HE'S WORTH.

IT'S A QUIET NIGHT. BUT IT'S EARLY YET.

ISHTAR SHAKES HER HAIR, AND SMILES, AND RELAXES INTO THE MUSIC.

AND SHE DANCES.

AND SHE DANCES.

AND SHE DANCES.

AND I'M JUST ABOUT TO LOSE MY MIND, HONEY HONEY...

WHY'VE YOU STOPPED THIS TIME? MORE INTERESTING ROCKS?

WE'RE HERE. THIS IS WHERE THE DANCING LADY IS.

SUFFRAGETTE City

BEER GIRL BEER GIRL

HUH? WHAT KIND OF A PLACE...?

ISHTAR BECOMES AWARE OF SOMETHING HAPPENING NEAR THE DOOR.

A THUDDING BASS SIGNALS THE START OF *UNDER PRESSURE*. IT'S NOT A SONG SHE LIKES TO DANCE TO.

SHE FEELS SWEAT BEGINNING TO RUN DOWN HER SPINE.

HER HAIR FALLS INTO HER EYES, AND SHE FLICKS IT AWAY.

UNDER PRESSURE...

UNDER PRESSURE...

YOU'RE NOT TAKING THAT BIRD IN THERE.
HE'S NOT A BIRD. HIS NAME'S... UM...
MATTHEW.
WELL, MAYBE HE IS A BIRD, NOW I THINK ABOUT IT. BUT HE'S A NICE BIRD.

LISTEN, GIRLIE. YOU WOULDN'T LIKE IT IN THERE, OKAY? IT'S NOT FOR GIRLS, YOU GET ME? I DON'T WANT YOU MAKING THE CUSTOMERS UNCOMFORTABLE.
I'M A FRIEND OF TIFFANY'S.
SHE GETS OFF WORK AT 1:00. COME BACK AND SEE HER THEN.

BUT I WANT TO SEE THE DANCING.
SEE THAT SIGN? THE MANAGEMENT RESERVES THE RIGHT TO REFUSE ADMISSION? WELL, THAT'S ME, AND THAT'S WHAT I'M DOING. NOW GET OUT. AND TAKE YOUR BIRD WITH YOU.

Excuse me.
If you reflect for a moment, it will occur to you that we are three adult males, dressed and attired in conformity with local standards, and you are only too pleased to invite us into your establishment.

YOU ALL HAVE A GREAT NIGHT NOW, Y'HEAR?
I DID THAT. WHAT YOU JUST DID. I DID THAT IN THE BEGINNING.

LOOK! THAT'S TIFFANY.
SHE LOOKS SMALLER FROM OUTSIDE HER HEAD.

ISHTAR FEELS THEM ENTER: A CHILL WIND THAT TOUCHES HER. SHE STEALS A HASTY GLANCE, AND FALTERS.
HEY! SKINNY! I GOT A NICE DOLLAR FOR YOU! OVER HERE!
IT HAS BEEN A VERY LONG TIME; AND SHE HAS MET A GREAT MANY PEOPLE. BUT THERE ARE SOME PEOPLE YOU NEVER FORGET.

HEY!
WHEREYAGOIN'?
OW!

ISHTAR? WHAT THE BLAZES DO YOU THINK YOU'RE DOING? YOU CAN'T JUST RUN OFF...
OUT OF MY WAY, ROGER.

ISHTAR? HEY, AREN'T YOU MEANT TO BE ON NOW?
YOU LOOK LIKE YOU'VE SEEN A GHOST.
YOU OKAY?

HEY, BUD. YOU CAN'T GO IN THERE.
PRIVATE-
EMPLOYEES
ONLY
HEY, WAS IT YOU THAT UPSET ISHTAR LIKE THAT? 'CUZ I'M TELLING YOU...

No.
You are not telling me anything. You will, however, remove your hand from my arm.
I will talk to the lady Ishtar, and I will talk to her in private. Now. Do you understand me?

ALL OF YOU GIRLS--OUT OF HERE, **NOW!**
BUT ROGER...
JUST-- JUST CLEAROUT. YOU--YOU CAN WAIT IN MY OFFICE, OKAY?
NOT **YOU**, ISHTAR. YOU STAY.

Hello, Belili.
ISHTAR.
As you will. It has been a long time.

It is strange. My sister spoke of a Dancing Woman, who knew my brother. It never occurred to me that it would be you.
DELIRIUM? OF COURSE... SHE SPOKE TO ME LAST NIGHT. THROUGH TIFFANY. I DID NOT REALIZE THAT IT WAS HER.

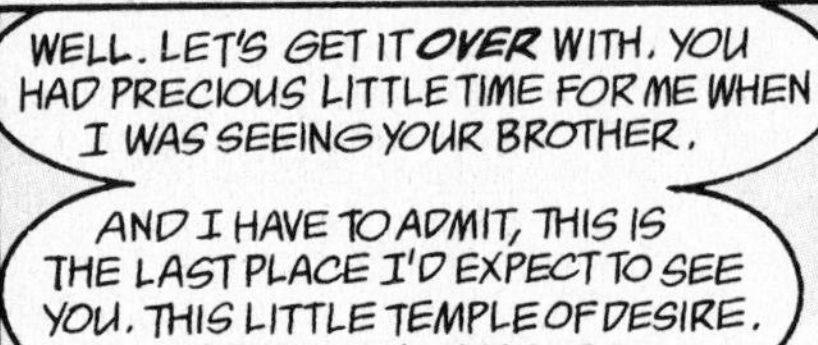

WELL. LET'S GET IT **OVER** WITH. YOU HAD PRECIOUS LITTLE TIME FOR ME WHEN I WAS SEEING YOUR BROTHER.
AND I HAVE TO ADMIT, THIS IS THE LAST PLACE I'D EXPECT TO SEE YOU. THIS LITTLE TEMPLE OF DESIRE. WHAT BRINGS YOU HERE?

You do, Astarte.
ISHTAR.

THE LAST TIME I SAW YOU WAS TWO THOUSAND YEARS AGO. YOU TOLD ME YOU THOUGHT I WAS A BAD INFLUENCE ON YOUR BROTHER. **REMEMBER?**
AND THEN YOU ACTED LIKE I WASN'T THERE, WHENEVER I WAS WITH HIM.
I remember. I have not changed my opinions.
YOU REALLY DON'T **LIKE** WOMEN, DO YOU?

Ishtar, I have no desire to quarrel further with you.
THEN WHY ARE YOU HERE?
I have a question for you, and I have a warning.
IF YOU'RE TRYING TO *THREATEN* ME...
No threats.
OKAY. SHOOT.

The question is this: my sister and I seek our brother, your former lover; have you any clue as to his present whereabouts?
I HAVEN'T SEEN HIM IN CENTURIES.
That is not a direct answer.
I DON'T KNOW *WHERE* HE IS. IS THAT DIRECT ENOUGH FOR YOU?

It may have to be.
YOU COULD SACRIFICE A BLACK LAMB TO ME, IF YOU LIKE. BUT THIS IS ALL THE TEMPLE I'VE GOT, AND WE'RE KIND OF SHORT ON ORACLES.
You have my sympathies.

SPARE ME. WHAT'S THE WARNING, THEN?
That you may be in some form of danger. I do not know what, and I am unsure as to why. However, the fact remains as I have stated it.
WHY, *THANK* YOU, DREAM LORD. IS THAT ALL?
Yes.

I LOVED YOUR BROTHER. I REALLY DID.
You were goddess of Love. I would expect nothing less of you.

Good night.

HER NAME'S TIFFANY. I WENT INSIDE HER ALREADY. YOU SHOULD GIVE HER LOTS OF DOLLARS. OODLES AND OODLES OF THEM.

Delirium, we are leaving.
YOU ALREADY SPOKE TO HER? WITHOUT ME?
Yes.

AND YOU KNOW? WHERE HE IS?
I know where we are going next.
OKAY...

Matthew.
UH. BOSS. LOOK, HOW ABOUT TEN MORE MINUTES?
No.
AW...

ISHTAR? WHAT'S GOING ON? WHO WAS THAT GUY? ARE YOU IN SOME KIND OF TROUBLE? ARE YOU OKAY?
NO. SURE. I DON'T KNOW.
I'M GOING TO DANCE NOW, ROGER.
PRIVATE-EMPLOYEES ONLY
YOU'VE NEVER REALLY SEEN ME DANCE, ROGER. I MEAN IT. THE LAST TIME I DANCED, THEY HAD TEMPLES TO ME. FIFTY PRIESTESSES IN EACH TEMPLE. YOU KNOW THAT?

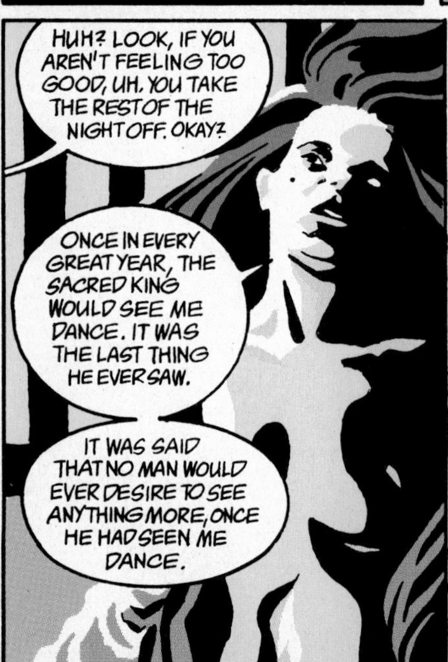
HUH? LOOK, IF YOU AREN'T FEELING TOO GOOD, UH, YOU TAKE THE REST OF THE NIGHT OFF. OKAY?
ONCE IN EVERY GREAT YEAR, THE SACRED KING WOULD SEE ME DANCE. IT WAS THE LAST THING HE EVER SAW.
IT WAS SAID THAT NO MAN WOULD EVER DESIRE TO SEE ANYTHING MORE, ONCE HE HAD SEEN ME DANCE.

STOP TALKING LIKE THAT, ISH. YOU'RE SCARING ME. COME INTO MY OFFICE, I'LL FIX YOU A DRINK...
I KNOW HOW GODS BEGIN, ROGER. WE START AS DREAMS. THEN WE WALK OUT OF DREAMS INTO THE LAND.
WE ARE WORSHIPPED AND LOVED, AND TAKE POWER TO OURSELVES.
AND THEN ONE DAY THERE'S NO ONE LEFT TO WORSHIP US.

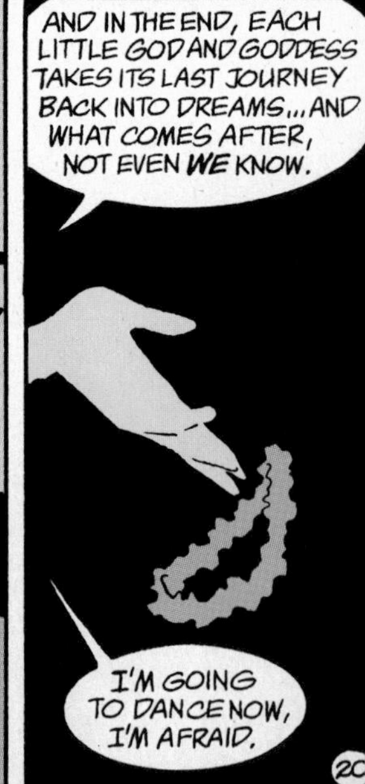
AND IN THE END, EACH LITTLE GOD AND GODDESS TAKES ITS LAST JOURNEY BACK INTO DREAMS... AND WHAT COMES AFTER, NOT EVEN WE KNOW.
I'M GOING TO DANCE NOW, I'M AFRAID.

ISHTAR? WHAT'S HAPPENING?
WHAT'RE YOU DOING?

THE MUSIC BEGINS. A LOW, MENACING BASS. ISHTAR NODS IN APPROVAL.
CALLING SISTER MIDNIGHT. I'M AN IDIOT FOR YOU...
AND SHE BEGINS HER LAST DANCE.

CALLING SISTER MIDNIGHT...
WHAT'S GOING ON? WON'T SOMEBODY TELL ME WHAT'S GOING ON?
PLEASE?
SOMEBODY?
WHAT CAN I DO ABOUT MY DREAMS?

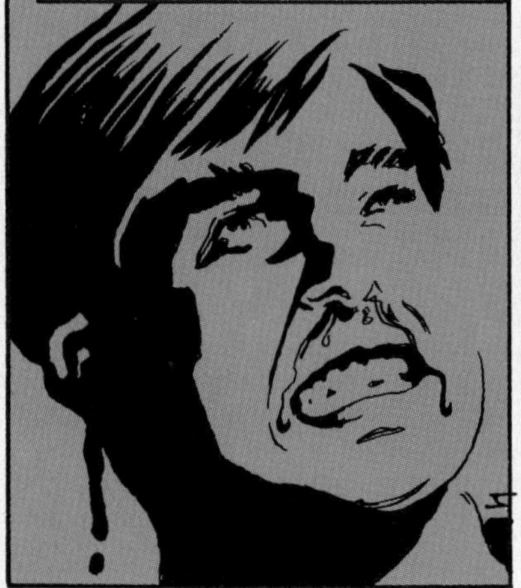
JAY MUSGRAVE FEELS THE BLOOD BURST FROM HIS EARS. THERE IS PAIN, TRUE, BUT HE SCARCELY NOTICES IT...

MURRAY BROWN FEELS A SUDDEN TIGHTNESS IN HIS CHEST. HIS HEAD FALLS ON A PILE OF BEER-SODDEN DOLLAR BILLS, AND HE GASPS FOR BREATH WHILE HE STARES, AND REJOICES.

AND SHEP CAYCE, WHO HASN'T HAD AN ERECTION IN A DOZEN YEARS, IS EJACULATING, VIOLENTLY-- AGAIN, AND AGAIN, AND AGAIN: AND NOW HE'S COMING BLOOD, AND HE DOESN'T CARE...

AND TIFFANY RUNS.

AND ISHTAR DANCES...

SUFFRAGETTE
city
BEER
GIRLS
BEER
GIRLS

AHH.
AHH.
AHH.
"AND I ONLY AM ESCAPED ALONE TO TELL THEE..." NOT THAT THEY'LL BELIEVE YOU, OF COURSE.

AH, TIFFANY. CONSOLE YOURSELF: YOU CAN'T BE THAT DUMB. AT LEAST YOU GOT OUT OF THERE BEFORE SHE WENT CRITICAL...
HUH?

YOU KNOW, SHE STILL REALLY LOVED HIM. EVEN AS SHE WENT, HE WAS ALL SHE WAS THINKING OF. I COULD FEEL IT.
POOR THING.
HE WAS THE ONLY ONE SHE EVER LOVED WHO WASN'T ALL USED UP IN THIRTY, FORTY YEARS.
SNF

HERE YOU GO, TIFFANY. DON'T EVER LET IT BE SAID THAT I NEVER DID ANYTHING FOR YOU.
YOU KNOW ME? DO I KNOW YOU?
I TRIED TO TELL THEM, TIFFANY. THEY WOULDN'T LISTEN.
IF THEY WERE SMART, THEY'D NEVER HAVE STIRRED IT ALL UP. BUT THEN, SOME PEOPLE AREN'T BRIGHT ENOUGH TO COME IN OUT OF THE RAIN.

HEY, MISTER? WHERE'D YOU GO?
HELLO?

HELLO?

The trouble with mortals
The parting of the ways
"have you got anything with a happy ending?"
chapter 6
Dreamings of meetings of dreaming
The trouble with gods
Life isn't pleasant, petrified
Mervyn sets him straight
Tempus Frangit.

Scritch
Scritch
Scritch
Scritch
Scritch

Scriiiitch

I'D? BUYED? CRIED? DIED? HM? DRIED? EYE'D? FRIED...? HMM... FUH-FUH-FUH-FUH...
AHA! I HAVE IT!

Scritch
Scritch
Scritch
Scritch

THERE. IT'S FINISHED. ARE YOU READY FOR THIS, BARNABAS?
As I'll ever be.

AHEM.
I CALL THIS BASILISK AND COCKATRICE: A MORAL POEM.

I DREAMED I SAW A BASILISK THAT BASKED UPON A ROCKY SHORE I LOOKED UPON THE BASILISK...

WITH EYES OF STONE I LOOKED NO MORE.

I DREAMED I SAW A COCKATRICE A-CHEWING ON A PIECE OF BONE I GAZED UPON THE COCKATRICE...
ONE CANNOT GAZE WITH EYES OF STONE.

TO LOOK UPON A BASILISK IS REALLY NEVER WORTH THE RISK TO GAZE UPON A COCKATRICE IS PERMANENT AND NEVER NICE.

FOR IT CAN NEVER BE DENIED LIFE ISN'T PLEASANT, PETRIFIED.

Is that it?

IT IS INDEED.
Ah. Well, at least it wasn't long.
I TAKE IT YOU WEREN'T OVERLY IMPRESSED, THEN.

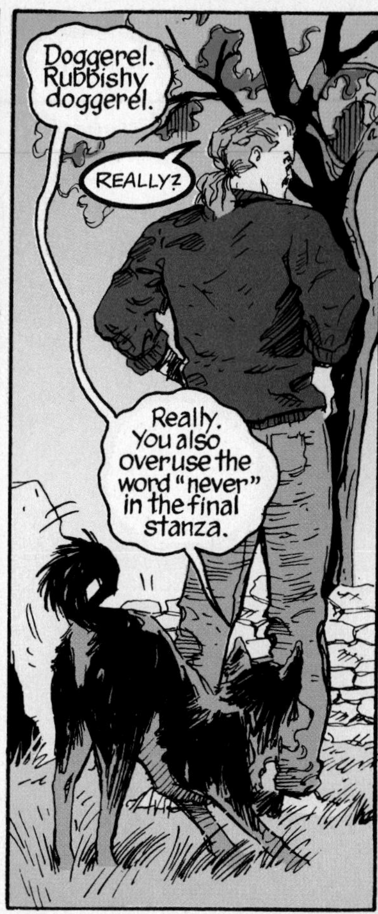
Doggerel. Rubbishy doggerel.
REALLY?
Really. You also overuse the word "never" in the final stanza.

WELL, YOU'D KNOW. EH? DOGGEREL? EH?
Spare me. So, what remarkable feats are we going to accomplish today?
THE USUAL. I'M GOING TO WORK ON A PAINTING. YOU'RE GOING TO SIT IN THE SUN, SCRATCH FOR FLEAS, ROMP ABOUT, EAT AND SLEEP.

MAYBE YOU'LL GAZE UP AT ME ADORINGLY FROM TIME TO TIME, MY FAITHFUL HOUND.
Hmph. In your dreams.
I DON'T DREAM. WOULDN'T DO TO GIVE TOO MUCH AWAY. ESPECIALLY NOT NOW.

I don't see what you're so worried about.
NO? AH, BARNABAS, THAT'S BECAUSE YOU NEVER MET MY FAMILY.

WHAT DO YOU MEAN, YOU DON'T WANT TO GO WITH ME ANY MORE?

I mean exactly what I say, sister. I have gone as far with you as I will go.

BUT YOU SAID. YOU TOLD ME. YOU SAID YOU KNEW WHERE WE WERE GOING TO GO NEXT.
YOU SAID.

And I meant what I said. I know exactly where we are going to go. I will go back to my realm, Delirium, and you will go back to yours.

BUT OUR BROTHER. WE'RE LOOKING FOR HIM. WE HAVE TO KEEP LOOKING.

We do not have to do anything, Delirium.
All we have done thus far is bring death and damage to those we seek.
No more.

YOU NEVER LIKED ME. I THOUGHT THAT YOU LIKED ME MAYBE IN THE END, AND YOU WOULDN'T BE HORRID THIS TIME AND THAT YOU WERE MY FRIEND AND EVERYTHING.
AND I THOUGHT WE COULD FIND HIM AND MAKE EVERYTHING OKAY AGAIN. I THOUGHT WE WERE FRIENDS.

Friends, my sister? I thought we were family.
And we have gone as far together as we will go. Farewell.

OKAY.
WELL.
I SEE. IT'S LIKE THAT.

WELL, I'LL BE BACK IN MY REALM THEN.
IF YOU WANT ME.

IF ANYONE WANTS ME.

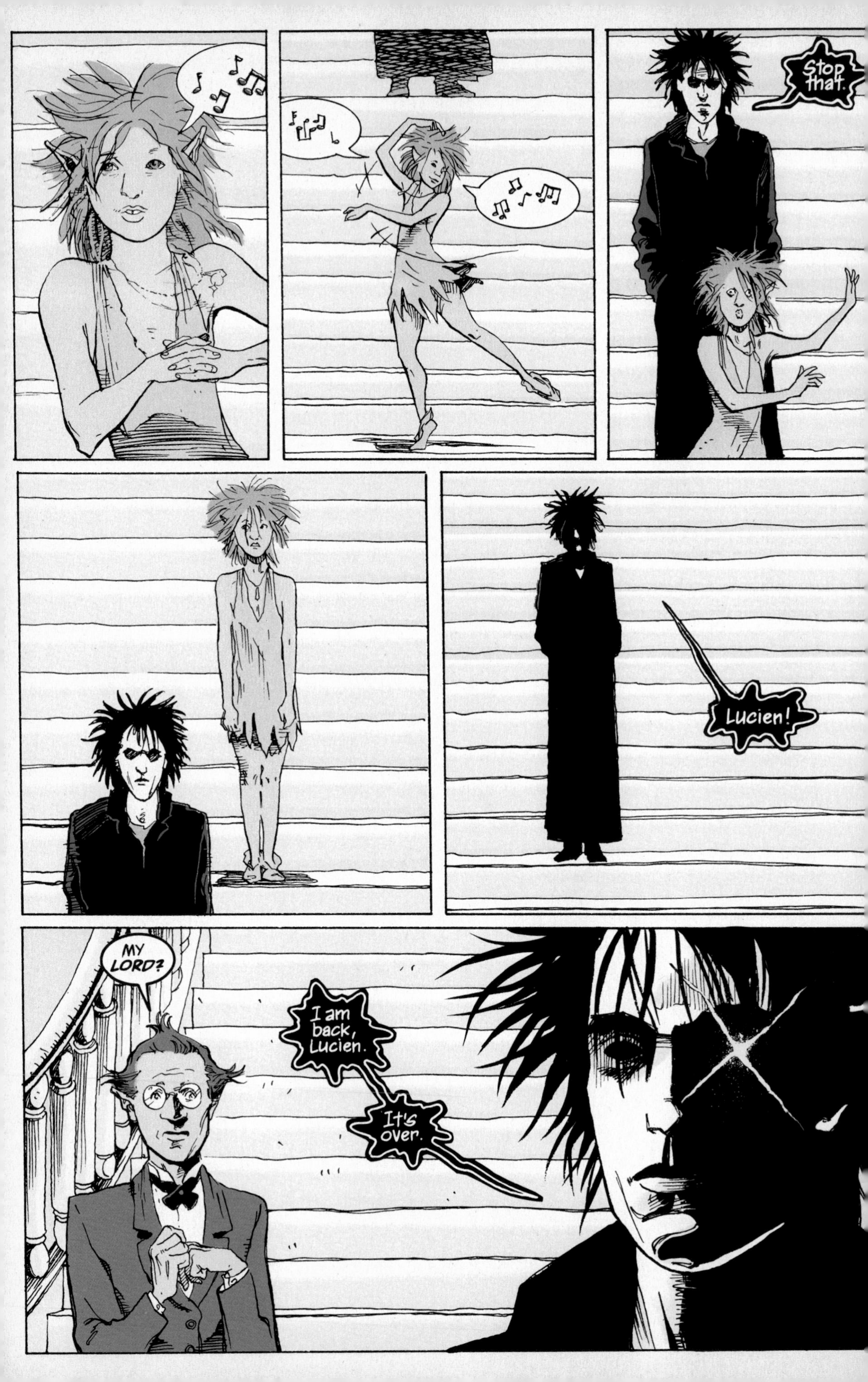
Stop that.
Lucien!
MY LORD?
I am back, Lucien.
It's over.

SIX: LIFE ISN'T PLEASANT, PETRIFIED — THE PARTING OF THE WAYS — THE TROUBLE WITH MORTALS — DREAMINGS OF MEETING OR MEETINGS OF DREAMING? — THE TROUBLE WITH GODS — MERVYN SETS HIM STRAIGHT — "HAVE YOU GOT ANYTHING WITH A HAPPY ENDING?" — TEMPUS FRANGIT.

Pharamond?

LORD MORPHEUS? IS THAT YOU?
Yes, it is.
AND HOW DO YOUR TRAVELS GO?
I am no longer travelling in the waking world.

NO? AH. WELL, I TRUST YOUR JOURNEY WAS PRODUCTIVE.
It was... interesting.
I am afraid when I curtailed our journeying, your car was left behind.
NO PROBLEM. I'LL SEND A TEAM OUT TO PICK IT UP.

Pharamond?
I have an apology to make to you. The woman, Ruby. She is dead.
There was a fire... I am... convinced.., that she was killed, directly, or indirectly, because she was aiding my sister in our quest.

RUBY'S DEAD?
Yes.
AH ME. THAT'S THE TROUBLE WITH MORTALS. THEY DO THAT. NOT TO WORRY, EH?

Pharamond...?
YES, LORD MORPHEUS.
Do you not regret Ruby's death?
I TRY NOT TO LET MYSELF GET OVERLY FOND OF THEM. IT ONLY LEADS TO SORROW.
AND YOU?
I knew her but briefly.

SO. YOU'VE FINISHED WITH YOUR QUEST, THEN?
Finished? Perhaps. I no longer require your aid, however.
IF THERE'S ANYTHING I CAN DO...
If there is, I will let you know. Fare well.

THE THRONE ROOM, WHEREVER IT HAPPENS TO BE, IS LOCATED AT THE PRECISE HEART OF THE DREAMING.

AND THE LORD OF DREAMS, WHO CREATED THIS PLACE FROM FORMLESS TUMULT LONG AGO, MENTALLY CLOSES AND SECURELY FASTENS EACH AND EVERY DOOR BETWEEN THE THRONE ROOM AND TO THE CASTLE OUTSIDE, TO THE WAKING WORLD, TO THE DREAMING.
THERE ARE MANY DOORS TO THE CENTER, SOME OF THEM OBVIOUS, SOME OF THEM LESS SO, AND THE PROCESS TAKES SOME TIME.
STILL, HE IS PATIENT. WHEN CIRCUMSTANCES DEMAND, HE CAN BE METICULOUS.
AND, IN THE END, HE IS ALONE IN HIS THRONE ROOM. ALL DOORS TO THE OUTSIDE ARE CLOSED. NO ONE OUTSIDE THE ROOM WOULD EVEN BE ABLE TO FIND IT.

ASSURED OF HIS PRIVACY, HE BEGINS TO CONJURE AND CREATE.

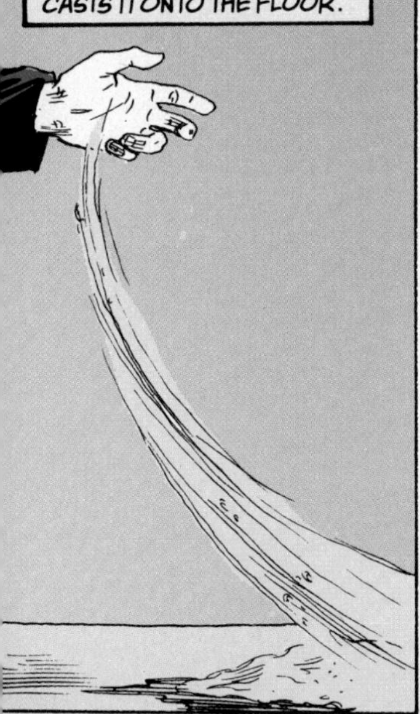
THE SAND TUMBLES LIKE DUST FROM HIS HAND, AND A LOW WIND SEIZES IT AND CASTS IT ONTO THE FLOOR.

HUGE DUNES RISE, THEN, GOLDEN AND UMBER. THE SKY ABOVE IS VAST AND VIOLET, A SKY OF OLDER DAYS.

PRESENTLY THE MOON RISES.

I walk across the dreaming sands under the pale moon: through the dreams of countries and cities, past dreams of places long gone and times beyond recall.

Ghost cats prowl the shadows and hills, the desert gullies and ravines.

At the edge of the desert is the City of Bubastis.
The City is Bubastis as she never was, save in the dreams of a long-dead builder; and in the dreams of a blind child dead four thousand years, who had never seen the city she lived in all her short life; and in the dreams of the goddess of that place.

The dreams of Bast.

HELLO, DREAM.
My Lady Bast.

IT IS STRANGE TO SEE YOU. TODAY I FOUND MYSELF THINKING OF YOU. I FORGET EXACTLY WHY.
TELL ME--AM I SIMPLY DREAMING THAT WE ARE MEETING? OR ARE WE ACTUALLY MEETING-- ALBEIT IN A DREAM?

We are meeting.
YES. BUT THEN PERHAPS I AM SIMPLY DREAMING OF YOU, DREAMING THAT YOU SAID THAT.
Perhaps.

YOU ALWAYS KNOW MORE THAN YOU SAY, OLD FRIEND. NO, IT'S YOU. THERE'S NO ONE ELSE WHO HAS QUITE YOUR WAY WITH WORDS.
DID YOU MAKE THIS PLACE? MRR?
I brought it about, yes. It was a place I knew you cared for.
WHY... YOU SWEETHEART.

YES. MY POOR LOST CITY.
AND MY PEOPLE. COME HERE, MY DARLING.
THE WRETCHED THING.
THESE ARE THE GHOSTS OF THOSE OF MY FOLK WHO WERE EMBALMED, THAT THEY WOULD LIVE FOREVER IN THE WORLD BEYOND

BUT THEIR PHYSICAL FORMS WERE EXHUMED, OVER A HUNDRED YEARS AGO, GROUND UP AND USED TO FERTILIZE THE LAND.
NOW THEY ARE ONLY MEMORIES, SLOWLY FADING FROM THE LAND AND THE WORLD. DREAMS OF GHOST CATS, AND CATS OF GHOST DREAMS...
SSS. I KNOW HOW THEY FEEL.

DO YOU WISH TO STROKE HER?
I have no wish to--
I'M TEASING YOU, OLD FRIEND. HM. WELL, IF THIS IS ONE OF YOUR DREAMS, CAN YOU SHAPE US SOMEWHERE TO SIT?
Certainly.

MRRRRRR...
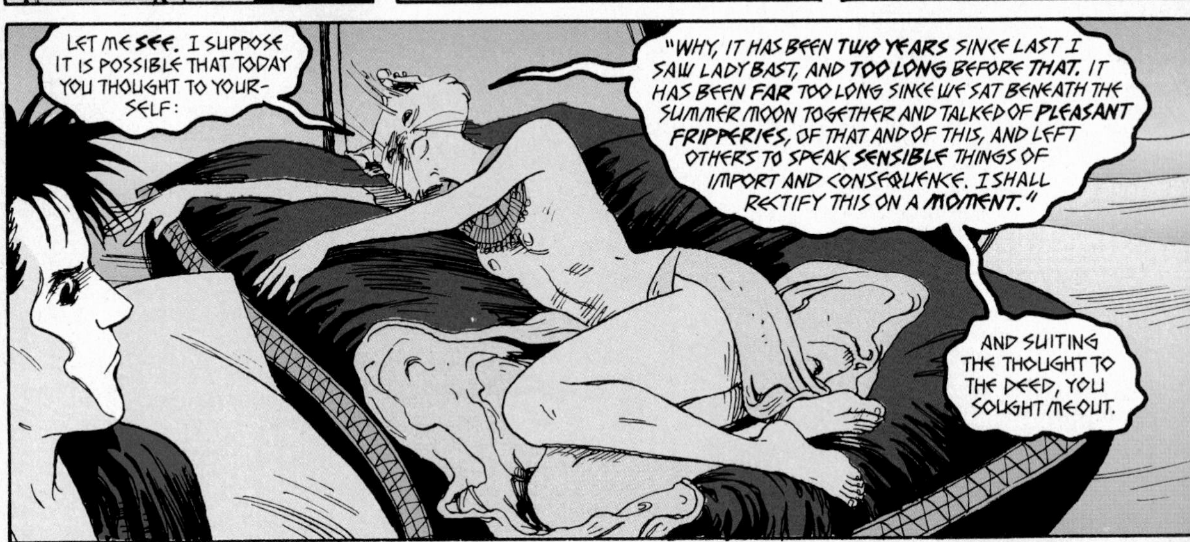
LET ME SEE. I SUPPOSE IT IS POSSIBLE THAT TODAY YOU THOUGHT TO YOURSELF:
"WHY, IT HAS BEEN TWO YEARS SINCE LAST I SAW LADY BAST, AND TOO LONG BEFORE THAT. IT HAS BEEN FAR TOO LONG SINCE WE SAT BENEATH THE SUMMER MOON TOGETHER AND TALKED OF PLEASANT FRIPPERIES, OF THAT AND OF THIS, AND LEFT OTHERS TO SPEAK SENSIBLE THINGS OF IMPORT AND CONSEQUENCE. I SHALL RECTIFY THIS ON A MOMENT."
AND SUITING THE THOUGHT TO THE DEED, YOU SOUGHT ME OUT.

BUT THEN, THAT IS NO LONGER YOUR WAY.
SO IT SEEMS TO ME MORE LIKELY THAT YOU HAVE COME TO ME TO TALK OF SENSIBLE THINGS. MRR?
You are most perceptive, my Lady Bast.

OH DREAM. I DO LOVE YOU, YOU KNOW. YOU MAKE ME LAUGH. WHY WEREN'T WE EVER LOVERS?
Perhaps you know me too well, my lady.
SEE? YOU'RE SO FUNNY.

WELL? WHAT'S THE PROBLEM?

My brother. When last we met, you told me that you knew where he was to be found.
MRRR? DID I?
Bast.
PERHAPS I DID.

I need to know, Bast.
AND WHAT WOULD YOU GIVE ME, IF I TOLD YOU? WOULD YOU RUN WITH ME, IN THE NIGHT, UNDER THE MOON? WOULD YOU BE MY TOM?

You would ask that of me?

NO. NO I WOULDN'T. CALM YOURSELF. SO YOU WANT TO KNOW WHERE TO FIND DESTRUCTION?
I CANNOT HELP YOU.

But you said--
I KNOW WHAT I SAID. I WAS THERE, AFTER ALL. AND I WAS LYING.
You were--?
NOT TELLING THE EXACT TRUTH. HAD YOU WISHED TO TAKE THE MATTER FURTHER I WOULD HAVE HAD TO ADMIT THAT I DID NOT KNOW YOUR BROTHER'S CURRENT LOCATION. HE HAS NEVER BEEN FOND OF MY FOLK, AFTER ALL.

I see.

SO, WHAT NOW? ARE YOU GOING TO LEAVE ME, JUST AS MY DREAM BECOMES INTERESTING?
I don't know.
AH, THAT IS UNLIKE YOU. WHAT'S WRONG?

WHY DIDN'T YOU COME TO ME IN REALITY? WHY DO YOU COME TO ME IN MY DREAMS?
DREAM-KING? WHAT IS GOING ON?
I need to find my brother.
YOU WANT TO FIND HIM. WHY?

I do not want to. But... I am much afraid I need to.
Perhaps I should not have come here.

I LAST HEARD TELL OF YOUR BROTHER SIXTY YEARS AGO, IN PARIS. HIS COMPANION SAVAGED ONE OF MY PEOPLE. BUT I HAVE HEARD NOTHING SINCE. HE IS WELL HIDDEN.
MRRR.
TO FIND HIDDEN THINGS YOU NEED AN ORACLE.
WHY NOT TALK TO THE SPHINX?

I need no riddles. And there are no oracles who can tell me of my family, if my family do not wish it.
NONE?

You have been most helpful, my lady, and for that I thank you.
DREAM...?

BAST WAKES UP ON THE FLOOR OF HER SLEEPING PLACE.
HER DREAM FADES AS SHE WAKES. SHE REMEMBERS LITTLE OF IT. THERE WAS SOMEBODY SHE REALLY LIKED, SOMEBODY IN DIFFICULTY...
SHE COULDN'T HELP THEM.

THE DREAM COLORS HER MOOD. UNABLE TO SHAKE HER DEPRESSION, BAST PADS SILENTLY THROUGH THE VASTY HALLS OF HER TEMPLE, LOOKING FOR FOOD.
WHEN SHE FINDS IT SHE HAS NOT EVEN THE HEART TO PLAY.

SHE IS UNCOMFORTABLY AWARE OF THE ACHE IN HER SHOULDER JOINTS; AND THE RODENT'S BLOOD LACKS SAVOR AND TASTE.
HER EARS PRICK FORWARD: SOMEONE IS PRAYING TO HER. A YOUNG HUMAN FEMALE WHOSE CAT-COMPANION WAS RECENTLY HIT BY A CAR.

THE CAT IS BEYOND RECOVERY, AND BAST SENDS IT AN EASY DEATH.
THE EFFORT TIRES HER.
SHE REMEMBERS WHEN THE PRAYERS AND OFFERINGS SWARMED AROUND HER AT ALL TIMES, UNCOUNTABLE, WHEN SHE WOULD PICK AND CHOOSE BETWEEN THEM, SELECTING PRAYERS ON MERIT OR ON WHIM, ACCEPTING OR REJECTING OFFERINGS...

SHE IS BEGINNING TO BE SCARED OF DREAMS.
BAST IS GETTING OLD.

HEY, LOOSH? IT'S ME, MERV. LEMME IN.
the Library of Dreams
The Management cannot be held responsible for anything lost or found within.
Signed
Lucien
Chief Librarian
YOU'RE LATE, MERVYN.
HEY, I'M A BUSY GUY, OKAY?

WHERE DO YOU WANT IT?
OH. UM. OVER THERE, PLEASE.
I HEAR THE BOSS CAME BACK.
YES. HE DID.

DON'T TELL ME--HE COMES BACK AND LOCKS HIMSELF IN HIS THRONE ROOM.
I'VE BEEN HERE BEFORE, YOU'VE BEEN HERE BEFORE, HELL, WE'VE ALL BEEN HERE BEFORE.
NEXT THING YOU KNOW, HE'S GONNA BE MOONING AROUND AGAIN--MOON MOON MOON.

HEY, YOU ASK ME, I MEAN, OKAY, HE'S OUR BOSS. YOU KNOW, RIGHT OR WRONG. BUT THE GUY'S A FLAKE.
THE DEATH OF KAI LUNG
Ernest Bramah
CHANTICLEER'S DANCE Hope Mirrlees
THE LAST VOYAGE OF LEMUEL GULLIVER Swift
THE EMPEROR OVER THE SEA C.S. Lewis
IAN AND ANN'S BOOK OF DAYS

BUT I BEEN THINKING ABOUT THIS--YOU WORK WITH YOUR HANDS, YOU GOT A LOT OF TIME FOR THINKING--AND WHAT I FIGURE IS THIS. IT'S NOT HIS FAULT. Y'KNOW? IT'S LIKE, YOU HANG OUT WITH POETS AND THOSE GUYS, YOU'RE BOUND TA GO A LITTLE FLAKY.

HE OUGHTA HANG OUT WITH GUYS LIKE ME. THE SALT-A THE EARTH. REAL EVERYDAY JOES. Y'KNOW? WE'D SET HIM STRAIGHT.

I MEAN, LOOK AT YOU--
phhhhht!
--YOU'RE A BOOK-PUSHER. I MEAN, HEY, NUTHIN' AGAINST BOOKS, BUT SEEMS TO ME THAT THESE DAYS YOU'RE PRACTICALLY RUNNING THIS PLACE.

THE OLD DAYS, A HUNDRED YEARS WOULD GO BY AND HE WOULDN'TA SAID MAYBE A DOZEN WORDS TO YOU--

But then, when I was held captive, and the castle crumbled, Lucien stayed here, and did his duty as best he saw it, while the rest of you fled. Who else here can make that claim?
You, Mervyn? What did you do while I was imprisoned?

I, UH. BIT A THIS. BIT A THAT. I DROVE A BUS...
And would you care to explain exactly in what way I am... what was your word? Flaky?
UH.
Well? I thought I heard you say you were going to set me straight.
HEHH. UH.

Lucien demonstrated loyalty and faith. I see nothing strange about placing my trust in him.
HEY. I'M WITH YOU, BOSS.
I am pleased to hear it. Now if you will excuse us...
YEAH. SURE. NO PROBLEM.
YOU KNOW ME, BOSS. OL' MERV PUMPKINHEAD, WHAT A KIDDER!

Lucien, when we last spoke...
AH YES, LORD. YOU WISHED ENQUIRIES TO BE MADE CONCERNING CERTAIN FORCES ACTING CONTRARY TO YOUR INTERESTS ON YOUR JOURNEYING.

And you have investigated, and found nothing.
HOW DID YOU KNOW?
I know.

MY LORD, THERE IS SOMETHING ELSE I THOUGHT I SHOULD INFORM YOU OF, WITHOUT DELAY.
IT IS, OF COURSE, PERFECTLY POSSIBLE THAT YOU KNOW ALL ABOUT IT ALREADY, HOWEVER...
Yes?
THERE IS SOMETHING HAPPENING, MY LORD. IN YOUR GALLERY.

I see.

IT HAPPENED THIS MORNING. IT JUST WENT BLACK.
I THOUGHT YOU SHOULD KNOW.

You were right, Lucien.

My sister? I stand in my gallery, and I hold your sigil. We should talk.
Will you come to me?

HELLO, LUCIEN.
HOW'S THE LIBRARY?
MY LADY. ALL GOES WELL. I THANK YOU FOR ASKING.
OH GOOD. I HAVE TO COME AND BORROW SOME BOOKS FROM YOU. I DON'T HAVE ANYTHING TO READ.

My sister...?
I'M NOT TALKING TO YOU.
LUCIEN, HAVE YOU GOT ANY THING WITH A HAPPY ENDING? AND NICE PEOPLE IN IT? OR FUNNY ANIMALS?
I... UH... MY LADY... WHATEVER YOU, ERM... ANYTHING YOU NEED... I... UH...

You are not talking to me?
THAT'S NOT NICE, SENDING HIM AWAY LIKE THAT. HE WAS GOING TO FIND ME A BOOK.
And why are you not talking to me?

Well, my sister?
BECAUSE I'M MAD AT YOU. THAT'S WHY I'M NOT TALKING TO YOU.

?

WHAT DID YOU DO TO DELIRIUM?
I beg your pardon?
WHAT HAVE YOU DONE TO HER? SHE'S CLOSED OFF HER REALM. YOU'VE SEEN HER SIGIL.

IT'S BLACK. WHAT DID YOU DO?
DREEEAM?
I did nothing to her.
I merely curtailed our journeyings.

DREAM...?
DREAM...
I was trying to protect her...
I called you... as soon as I saw it... I called you...
HMPH.
WELL, YOU BETTER DO SOMETHING ABOUT IT.

Such as?
YOU KNOW WHAT SHE'S LIKE. SHE'S NOT EXACTLY STABLE. SHE'S ONLY A KID. GO AND TALK TO HER.
...Why me?
YOU UPSET HER. YOU SORT IT OUT.

But she's closed her realm... She will not want visitors.
OF COURSE SHE DOESN'T WANT VISITORS. SHE'S IN A SNIT.
BUT YOU CAN STILL GO TO HER REALM. GO AND TALK HER OUT OF IT.
But--

I'M NOT HAVING HER GOING THE SAME WAY DESTRUCTION DID...

Very well. I will talk to her. Is that all?
YES. I SUPPOSE IT IS.

LOOK, DREAM. I KNOW THAT THINGS HAVEN'T BEEN EASY ON YOU RECENTLY.
AND I HEARD YOUR LATEST FLAME BURNT OUT, AND I KNOW THAT THAT ALWAYS LEAVES YOU IN A ROTTEN MOOD. BUT YOU SHOULDN'T HAVE TAKEN IT OUT ON DELIRIUM.
But I didn't...

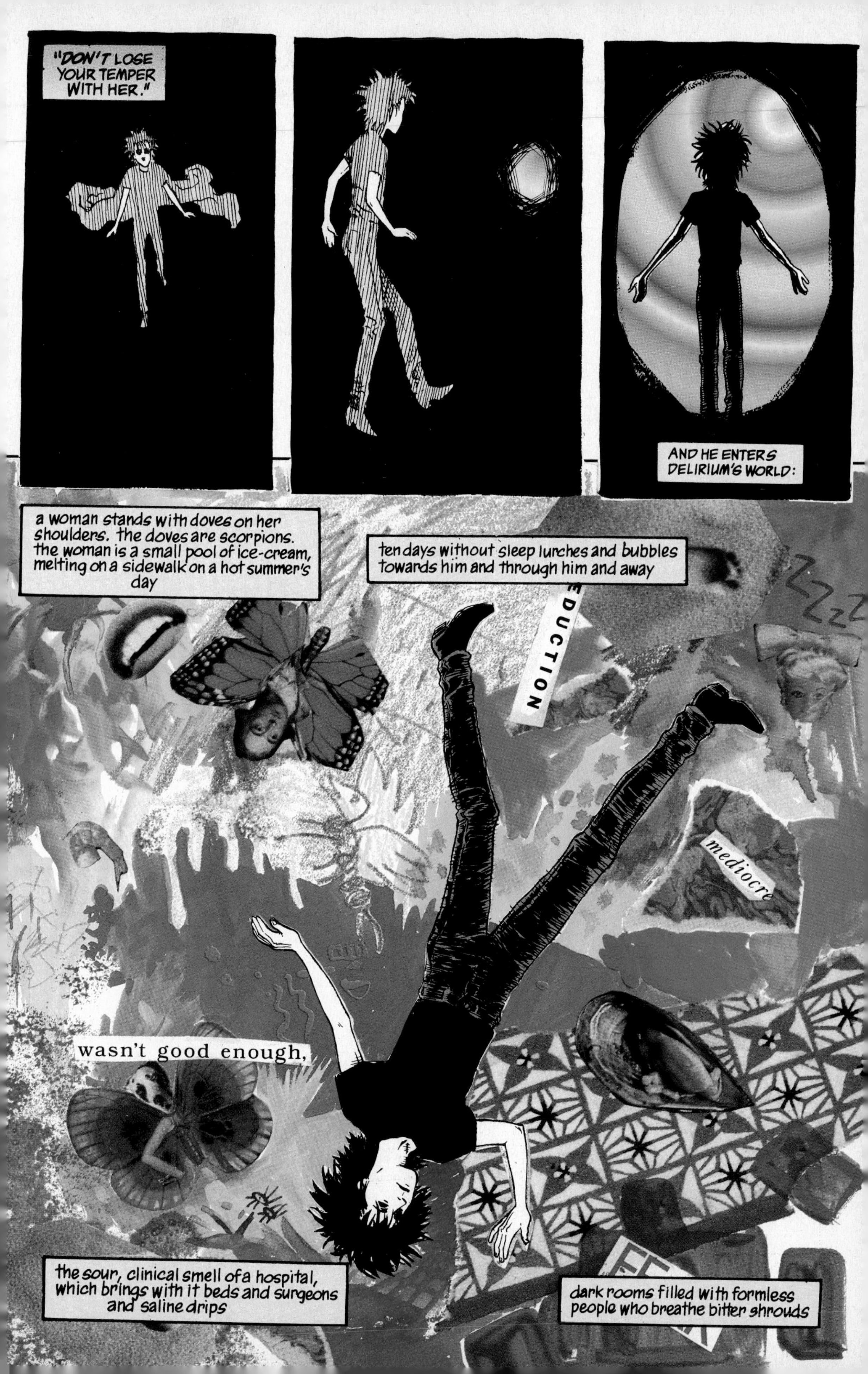
"DON'T LOSE YOUR TEMPER WITH HER."
AND HE ENTERS DELIRIUM'S WORLD:
a woman stands with doves on her shoulders. the doves are scorpions. the woman is a small pool of ice-cream, melting on a sidewalk on a hot summer's day
ten days without sleep lurches and bubbles towards him and through him and away
EDUCTION
mediocre
wasn't good enough,
the sour, clinical smell of a hospital, which brings with it beds and surgeons and saline drips
dark rooms filled with formless people who breathe bitter shrouds

unripe mind apples tumble screaming through the sky, and the stars gasp in brief flashes of pain and time
putrid the sea heaves in slow, glutinous waves that stink and shudder and fetal shapes that bob and gleam and wail
I feel her presence, and slowly I move toward her,
the sea is a princess who had a dance very unusual. the alien is an alien. the dance is an alley where the babies die...
(put the gun in your mouth put the gun in your mouth put the gun in your mouth)
toward the center of her realm.
Tempus Frangit
My sister? Do you hear me?
My sister?
You...you have a remarkable sundial.
IT'S STOPPED.
22

I DON'T LUHLUHLIKE IT AT ALL. IT'S STOPPED. IT'S NOT GOING ANY MORE. I HATE IT.

AND I HATE YOU.
I SHOULD NEVER HAVE TRUSTED YOU.

IF YOU WEREN'T MY BROTHER I'D MAKE IT SO YOU COULD NEVER GET OUT OF MY WORLD. SO WHEN YOU THOUGHT YOU WERE OUT OF MY WORLD YOU'D JUST BE FURTHER IN.
MAYBE I WILL. HAVE YOU EVER GONE MAD, DREAM?
I COULD DO THAT. I COULD DO IT IF I WANTED. YOU AREN'T EVEN WEARING YOUR HELM.

Hush, little sister.
GO. AWAY.

If that is what you wish, then I will go away. But first, if I may, I would talk with you.
I... I wish to apologize.

I travelled with you through the waking world because I hoped ... foolishly perhaps, on reflection ... to encounter a young lady with whom I had earlier had a ... parting of the ways. She had returned to the waking world, and travelling with you gave me an excuse...
I was not seeking our brother.
When I realized that our quest was having repercussions, I deemed it sensible to call it off.
I did not do this with ill-will, my sister, but because I felt that travelling further could only have worsened matters.
Since then I have thought about this, and have made a further enquiry on my own.
If you are willing to travel with me... I would resume our journey together.
UM. DREAM? DO YOU LIKE ME?
Yes... I suppose I must do, Delirium. You entertain me. And it distresses me to see you troubled.
REALLY?
Really.
WELL... I LIKE YOU TOO, I THINK. WHEN YOU DON'T TEASE ME.
SO LET'S GO AND FIND HIM PROPERLY THIS TIME.
READY OR NOT. HERE WE COME.
To Be Continued

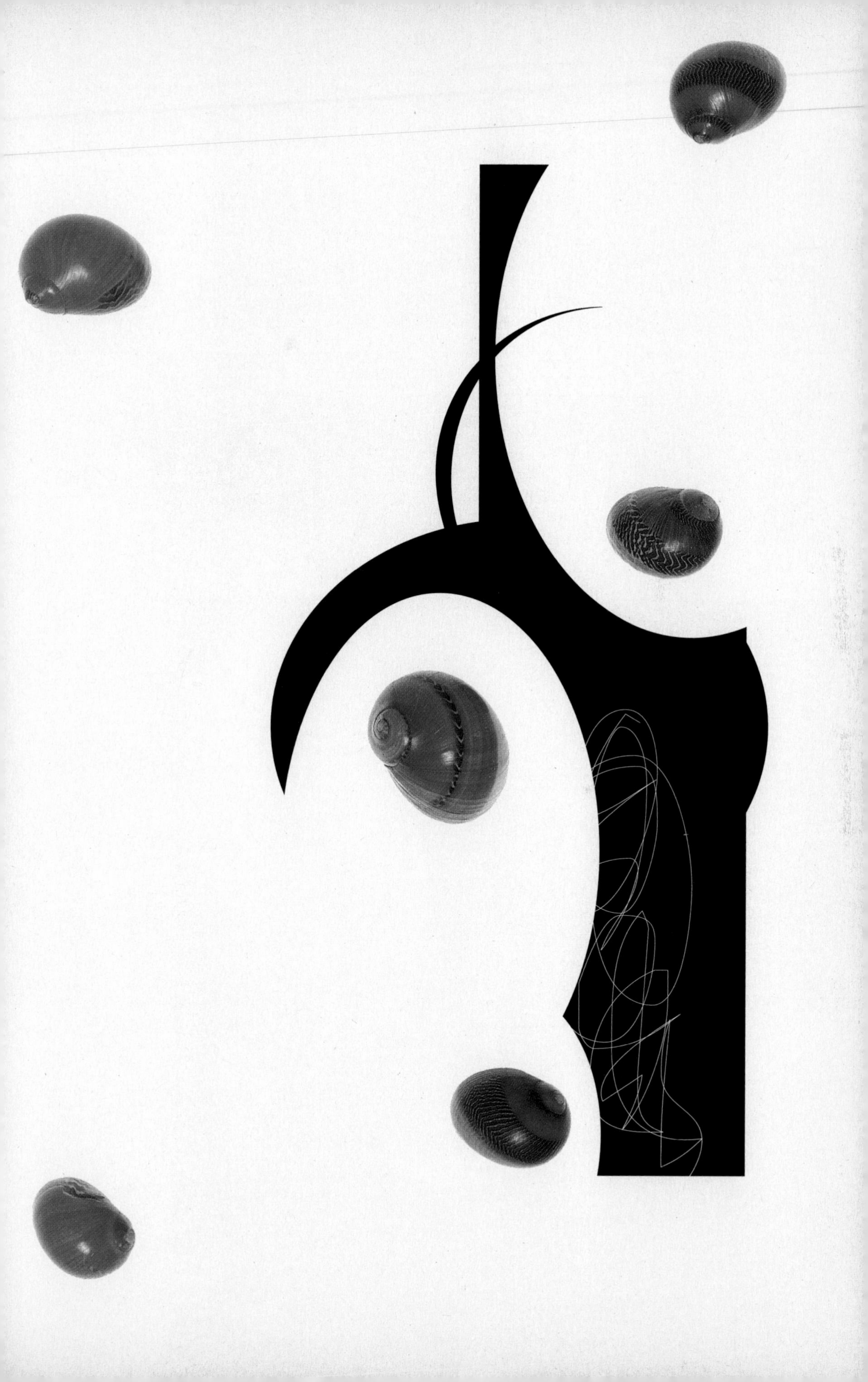

An unlikely growth

The other side of the coin

"My envelope isn't any good anymore"

Cooking considered as one of the fine arts

chapter 7

Cherries are counted and a bargain is made

Life as a glass of bitter wine

Where all mazes meet

Well? Where have you been?
DOWN TO THE VILLAGE. GETTING SOME PROVISIONS IN.
Uh...did you happen to get any salami?
POSSIBLY.
Any chocolate?
OH, I DOUBT IT.
What did you get all that food for?
HAS IT EVER OCCURRED TO YOU, BARNABAS, THAT COOKING IS ONE OF THE FINE ARTS?
Not that I recall, no.
IT IS. ONE TAKES RAW MATERIALS--
--AND ONE TRANSFORMS THEM, BY THE SIMPLE APPLICATION OF A KNIFE, SOME HEAT, SOME JUDICIOUS MIXING, INTO SOMETHING MIRACULOUSLY OTHER.

You've never cooked anything as long as I've known you.
HAVEN'T I?
No.

Am I going to get any of this heavenly repast, once it's complete?
THAT DEPENDS ON HOW IT TURNS OUT.
This is another one of your ideas, isn't it? Like that thing you left in the garden.

THING? THING?
BARNABAS, THAT THING IS A SCULPTURE.
What of? A big rock with holes in it?
HAAA! HAHAHAHA HAHAHA!

I'LL TELL YOU WHAT, BARNABAS.
THE HAMMER AND CHISEL ARE OUTSIDE IN THE HALL. THERE'S ANOTHER MARBLE BLOCK UPSTAIRS. WHY DON'T YOU DO YOUR OWN SCULPTURE, AND I'LL LAUGH AT WHAT YOU MAKE?

Hmph. Leaving aside the issue of hands, I have no desire to ruin a perfectly good piece of marble. Dogs have more sense. We don't make fools of ourselves like you do.
OF COURSE YOU DON'T.

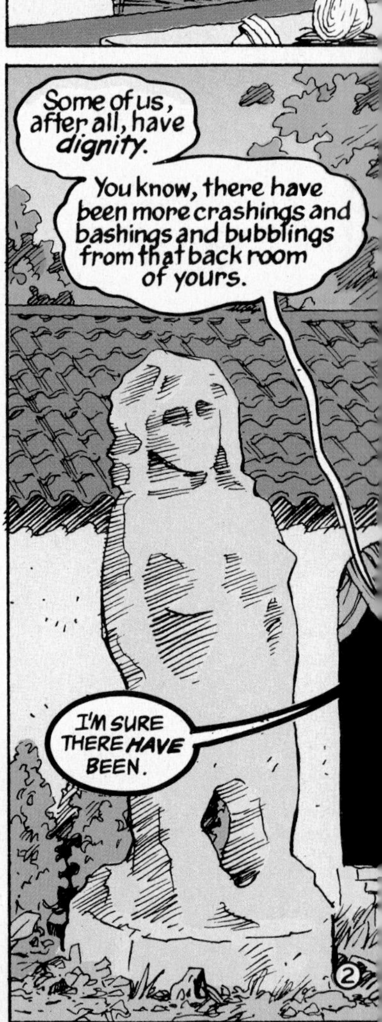
Some of us, after all, have dignity.
You know, there have been more crashings and bashings and bubblings from that back room of yours.
I'M SURE THERE HAVE BEEN.
2

NOW, WHAT COULD I HAVE BEEN THINKING OF? I DID BUY SOME CHOCOLATE AFTER ALL.
Really?

OKAY... SIT!

NOW BEG!

HERE YOU GO!

Good chocolate.
Hey, that was fun. Can we do it again? Please?
Come on. Please?

LEAVE ME TO COOK, BARNABAS.
A CULINARY ARTIST NEEDS GENIUS, INSPIRATION, AND A DOG-FREE KITCHEN.
So you'll settle for one out of three, huh?
Hee! He-he-he-he-heh!

BARNABAS...

HAA! HAHAHAHAHAHA! HAHAHA!

I'M COLD. I HATE BEING NOWHERE. LET'S GO SOMEWHERE INSTEAD.
Very well.

BUT I DON'T KNOW WHERE ETAIN IS. AND THE ALDER MAN'S GONE TO BE NO ONE FOR A BIT. HE WON'T TALK TO US.
AND THE OTHERS ARE SORT OF DEAD.
MY ENVELOPE ISN'T ANY GOOD ANY MORE.

There are places to look. We will find him.
Let us leave this place. We shall seek answers. We may also seek questions.
OH.
4

DREAM? I WISH YOU'D TELL ME WHAT WAS GOING ON.
DON'T TREAT ME LIKE I DON'T MATTER. YOU MUSTN'T DO THAT ANY MORE.
...very well.

This is a family matter. We shall take it to the family.
ALL OF THEM? YOU'RE GOING TO CALL A MEETING?
No.
THEN WHO? DESIRE SAID NO. AND DESPAIR TOLD ME, NO, I WON'T HELP YOU. SHE SAID IT.

Our elder brother.
DESTINY? OH. OKAY. ARE WE GOING TO YOUR GALLERY?
We will walk there.
BUT WE'LL NEED A THING. WITH ALL THE WIGGLY THINGIES COMING OUT OF IT.
UM.
A LABYRINTH.

Yes. Would you like to find one? Or shall I?
CAN I? REALLY?
Certainly.

DELIRIUM CLOSES HER MISMATCHED EYES.

A WHISPER, A FLUTTER, AND SILENCE FALLS ONCE MORE, BETWEEN THE WORLDS.

AROUND THEM CHILDREN RUN AND SHOUT AND ADULTS WALK. NO ONE SEES THEM, NO ONE TOUCHES THEM.
NO ONE KNOWS THAT THEY ARE EVEN THERE AT ALL.
SEVEN: COOKING CONSIDERED AS ONE OF THE FINE ARTS—"MY ENVELOPE ISN'T ANY GOOD ANYMORE"—WHERE ALL MAZES MEET—THE OTHER SIDE OF THE COIN—LIFE AS A GLASS OF BITTER WINE—CHERRIES ARE COUNTED, AND A BARGAIN IS MADE—AN UNLIKELY GROWTH.
Beer
Beer
Funnel
-A- WHIRL!

If you go in you may never come
OUT!
IS THIS. UM. OKAY?
Don't go in if you're in a hurry!
This is perfectly satisfactory, my sister.
Look it's
WHICH
OH. GOOD.

ALL LABYRINTHS ARE ONE LABYRINTH. ALL MAZES MEET IN THE CENTER.
THERE IS A PORTION OF SPACE THAT ALL LABYRINTHS SHARE, A SPACE COMMON TO EVERY PLACE IN WHICH PATHS FORK AND JOIN AND DIVERGE ONCE MORE.

TURN.
RIGHT.
LEFT.
LEFT.
TURN.

ONE BY ONE THE OTHER MAZE-WALKERS VANISH.

SLOWLY THE HIGH WOODEN WALLS BEGIN TO CHANGE THEIR SHAPE, TO SPREAD OUT AND CHANGE, TO BRANCH AND DIVERGE.

THE WALLS BECOME HEDGES.
ODD ITEMS OF STATUARY BEGIN TO APPEAR.
RIGHT.
LEFT.
RIGHT AGAIN.

THEY STEP INTO A PATCH OF MIST: ABOVE THEM CARRION BIRDS CAW AND SHRIEK, AND THEN ARE SILENT FOREVER.

BRIEFLY, IT IS NIGHT; THEN DAWN BEGINS TO LIGHTEN THE SKY.
THEY CROSS A RIVER: THEIR FEET TRIP-TRAP ACROSS THE LITTLE WOODEN BRIDGE.
THEY KEEP WALKING.

AN OLD RED SUN HANGS LOW IN THE GRAY SKY.
THIS IS NOT EARTH. THIS IS NOT NOW. THIS IS DESTINY'S GARDEN, THAT IS A PLACE TO ITSELF, AND EXISTS IN ITS OWN TIME.
PATHS CONNECT AND DIVERGE IN THIS PLACE.
DREAM RESPECTS HIS BROTHER, BUT THE GARDEN OF DESTINY DISTURBS HIM.
IT IS USUAL, HOWEVER, FOR THE ENDLESS TO FEEL UNCOMFORTABLE IN EACH OTHER'S REALMS; ONLY DEATH TRAVELS WHERESOEVER SHE MUST, WITHOUT MISGIVING.
THE GARDEN OF DESTINY. LOOK BEHIND YOU: SHADOW-PLAYS OF MEMORY ARE FOREVER BEING ENACTED, ON PATHS YOU WALKED TOO LONG AGO.
DREAM? LOOK.
IS THAT ME?
Yes. It IS you. You, a very long time ago.
Yes. You were.
I WAS VERY PRETTY.
I... REMEMBER THAT DAY: DANCING MEN CAME TO ME FROM A FAR WORLD, BRINGING TRIBUTE, OF BIRDS AND FLOWERS AND FINE GEMS. THEY WERE GRATEFUL FOR... FOR WHAT?
Happiness, perhaps?
MM. SOMETHING LIKE THAT.

YES. YOU TWO ARRIVE HERE NOW.
WELCOME TO MY GARDEN.

It is good to know that we were expected, my brother.
I take it you also know why we are here.
INDEED.

Well? Will you assist us? Will you offer us advice?
CERTAINLY.
REALLY? OH... WOW...

Give me your advice, my brother.
VERY WELL: FORGET THIS FOOLISHNESS. DROP IT. GO HOME.
OUR BROTHER TOLD US THAT HE WAS LEAVING US. HE ADVISED US TO LEAVE HIM BE. UNTIL NOW YOU HAVE BEEN CONTENT TO RESPECT HIS WISHES; DO LIKEWISE IN THE TIME TO COME.

I cannot do that, my brother, as you well know.

I KNOW.
AND I AM SORRY.
8

Will you tell us where to find him?
I AM DESTINY. I AM WHAT MUST HAPPEN, WILL IT OR NO. AND I AM YOUR BROTHER.
IF I COULD LIVE YOUR LIFE FOR YOU, I WOULD. BUT THAT IS NOT WITHIN MY POWER.

Life, Brother? A strange way of describing our existence.
Is there naught else you can tell me?

NOTHING YOU WOULD WANT TO HEAR.
SHE DOES NOT LOVE YOU, AND, TRULY, SHE NEVER DID. SHE WILL NOT CHANGE HER MIND, NO MATTER HOW LONG NOR HOW DEEPLY YOU WISH THAT THIS WERE THE CASE.

YOU WILL SEE HER BUT ONE MORE TIME, LONG AFTER ALL THIS IS OVER, AND THE OUTCOME OF THAT MEETING WILL NOT BE SATISFACTORY FOR EITHER OF YOU.

I did not wish to be told that.
YOU ASKED ME TO TELL YOU WHAT YOU NEEDED TO KNOW; NOT WHAT YOU WISHED TO HEAR.

WELL AND ALL: AND WHILE YOU ARE PRINCE OF THOSE SYMBOLS AND SHAPES THAT MEAN OTHER THAN THEY SEEM, OF METAPHOR AND OF ALLUSION, MY DOMINION IS THAT WHICH IS, OF ACTIONS AND CONSEQUENCES AND PATHS.
BUT I CAN NEITHER LIVE YOUR LIFE FOR YOU, NOR SHOULDER YOUR RESPONSIBILITIES.

You will not tell me where our brother is to be found?
I MAY TELL YOU ONLY WHAT OTHERS HAVE TOLD YOU: YOU NEED AN ORACLE.
There are no Oracles who can tell of our family.

YOU THOUGHT OF ONE, WHEN YOU SPOKE TO THE CAT-GODDESS, DID YOU NOT?
THERE IS, AFTER ALL, AN ORACLE WHO IS OF THE FAMILY.

No...
GOOD. THAT IS A FAR MORE SENSIBLE ATTITUDE.

DREAM? WHAT'S HE SAYING?

WHAT DID YOU TELL HIM?
SURELY THAT IS HIS AFFAIR, NOT YOURS.

DO YOU KNOW WHY I STOPPED BEING DELIGHT, MY BROTHER?

I DO.
THERE ARE THINGS NOT IN YOUR BOOK. THERE ARE PATHS OUTSIDE THIS GARDEN. YOU WOULD DO WELL TO REMEMBER THAT.

IT IS... REFRESHING... TO SEE YOU SO COLLECTED.
STICK IT. COINS HAVE TWO SIDES. DESTRUCTION TOLD US THAT, WHEN HE TOLD US HE WAS LEAVING. BUT I KNEW IT ALREADY. YOU DID TOO.

DREAM? WHAT DID HE TELL YOU?
Delirium?

IT'S STILL ME.
But...?
IF YOU'RE GOING TO FALL APART, THEN ONE OF US HAS TO KEEP THIS THING GOING.

PLEASE GET UP.
I DON'T KNOW HOW MUCH LONGER I CAN BE LIKE THIS.
IT HURTS VERY MUCHLY.
Your eyes are the same color.
SO? I CAN DO THAT. I CAN DO THAT IF I HAVE TO.

Well, my sister. Shall we continue on our way?
YES.
PLEASE.

WHERE ARE WE GOING NOW?
To seek an Oracle.

DESTINY STANDS AND WATCHES HIS SISTER AND BROTHER AS THEY VANISH FROM HIS GARDEN. A LOW WIND COMES UP AND STIRS THE CORNERS OF THE PAGES OF HIS BOOK, THEN GUSTS, SUDDENLY.
THE WIND LIFTS THE PAGES OF THE BOOK, FLIPS AND TURNS THEM, RETURNING HIM TO A CHAPTER HE READ LAST ALMOST 300 YEARS BEFORE.
IN DESTINY'S GARDEN IT IS ALWAYS NOW.
FLIP.
IN THE GREAT HALL OF THE CITADEL OF DESTINY, DESTRUCTION HAS GATHERED THE FAMILY TOGETHER.
DESTINY'S SERVANTS FLIT AND FLAP AMONG THEM, BRINGING WINES AND FRUIT FROM HIS GARDEN.
DESTRUCTION TELLS THEM HE IS LEAVING. THAT THEY ARE NOT TO FOLLOW HIM. THAT THEY MUST NO LONGER CONSIDER HIM ONE OF THEM.
EACH SIBLING REACTS IN ITS FASHION: DESTINY WATCHES DESTINY (WITH, PERHAPS, SOME SMALL APPROVAL) APPEAR CALM AND UNSURPRISED;
DEATH SAYS NOTHING;
DREAM BLUSTERS;
DESIRE SMIRKS, AS IF DESIRE CHERISHES ELEGANT SECRETS BEHIND ITS TAWNY EYES; DESPAIR PLEADS WITH HIM TO RECONSIDER; AND DELIRIUM...
DELIRIUM, LIKE DEATH, SAYS NOTHING. SHE SIPS THE WINE OF DESTINY, AND MAKES A SUDDEN FACE, AS IF IT HAS UNEXPECTEDLY BECOME QUITE BITTER. BUT THE WINE OF DESTINY IS VERY FINE.
FLIP. FLUTTER. FLIP.

THE DREAM-KING IS RETURNING, IN TRIUMPH OF A KIND, FROM A FAR GALAXY, TIRED BEYOND RECKONING AND TRIED BEYOND ALL ENDURANCE.
HIS TRIUMPH IS SHORT-LIVED: FROM THE DARKNESS OLD VOICES CALL TO HIM, AND HE AWAKES IN A GLASS PRISON IN A DEEP CELLAR.
FLIP. FLUTTER. FLIP.
ALL TIMES ARE NOW. THE PAGES TURN, THOUGH NO HAND TOUCHES THEM, AND DESTINY MAKES NO EFFORT TO PREVENT THEM FROM TURNING.
BY THE YANGTZE RIVER, DEATH SPENDS HER DAY MORTAL WALKING UNDER THE HOT SUN WITH A YOUNG OX DROVER, WHO TELLS THE LITTLE PEASANT GIRL HIS GRAND SCHEMES AND PLANS.
AT NIGHTFALL HER HANDS SEEK HIS, AND THEY SIT AND WAIT BY THE VAST SLOW RIVER, HAND IN HAND BENEATH THE MYRIAD STARS...
THE PAGES TURN AND GUST AND TURN, FIRST ONE WAY, THEN ANOTHER.
THERE IS BLOOD ON THE THRONE OF THE DREAM KING. THE CORINTHIAN STANDS BEHIND IT, TREMBLING -- RED, WET, TEARS DRIBBLING FROM HIS MOUTHS. THE DREAM KING LOOKS UP, SLOWLY, AND SPEAKS TO HIM. HE IS DRESSED ENTIRELY IN WHITE.
DESTINY REACHES FOR THE BOOK. HIS LEAN FINGERS CALM THE NERVOUS PAGES AND FIND HIS PLACE ONCE MORE.
HE READS: IT WAS LATE AFTERNOON WHEN THEY REACHED THE ISLAND.

IT WAS LATE AFTERNOON WHEN THEY REACHED THE ISLAND, AND THE WARM AIR SMELLED OF PINE NEEDLES AND THE SEA.
SO. THIS ORACLE.
IS THIS SOMEONE YOU KNOW?
Yes.
IS IT SOMEONE I KNOW, TOO?
Yes.
OH.
IS IT SOMEBODY VERY OLD?
No.
HAVE YOU EVER SPENT DAYS AND DAYS AND DAYS MAKING UP FLAVORS OF ICE CREAM THAT NO ONE'S EVER EATEN BEFORE?
LIKE CHICKEN AND TELEPHONE ICE CREAM?
No.
WHY DON'T YOU WANT TO SEE THS PERSON?
Because I gave my word I would not.
WHO DID YOU GIVE YOUR WORD TO?
To myself.
OH.
YOU TWO!
STAY WHERE YOU ARE.

HOW DID YOU GET UP HERE?
We walked.
YOU COULD NOT HAVE WALKED HERE.
Nevertheless, we walked.
BUT I'M A REALLY GOOD DRIVER.

NO LIES. IF YOU'D CLIMBED THE CLIFF THEN I'D KNOW ABOUT IT. NOW, HOW DID YOU GET UP HERE? THE TRUTH THIS TIME.
I do not lie.
WAIT HERE. STAY VERY STILL. ONE FALSE MOVE, AND I WILL SHOOT YOU.

HELLO? FATHER? COME IN.
WE HAVE PEOPLE UP HERE. TWO OF THEM. A MAN AND A WOMAN.
THEY WILL NOT TELL ME.
I DON'T THINK SO.
YES. I'LL WAIT HERE.

WHAT'S A FALSE MOVE? IS IT VERY DIFFERENT FROM A REAL ONE?

GREEN MOUSE ICE CREAM WAS THE WORST. I DIDN'T LIKE THAT AT ALL.

HEH...
WHO ARE YOU? EH? HOW DID YOU GET UP HERE?
We walked the path.
16

THERE IS NO PATH THAT LEADS UP HERE.
There are a number of paths that lead to this place.
I have been avoiding them for some small while, now.

WE STARTED OUT IN A MAZE PLACE AND THEN WE WENT TO MY BROTHER'S GARDEN AND THEN WE CAME HERE AND IT WAS ONE PATH.

I have come here to speak to my son. Please lead me to him.
YOUR SON?
I believe he is here.

ANDROS. WHAT TONGUE DO YOU HEAR WHEN THEY TALK?
THEY ARE SPEAKING GREEK, KRIS.
HM. AND YOU, SON?
THEY SPEAK GREEK, PAPA.
AND I HEAR THEM SPEAKING ENGLISH.

You hear what you need to hear. Now, take me to my son.
ARE YOU APOLLO?
I am your charge's father. Take me to him.

ANDROS?
OUR LORD TALKED TO ME THIS MORNING. HE WARNED ME THAT TODAY MIGHT PROVE AN UNUSUAL DAY.
HE DID NOT SAY HOW UNUSUAL.

SHALL I SHOW YOU IN?
That...
That will not be necessary.

I have... no desire to do this, my sister.

I KNOW.
I'M SORRY.

TINKER... TAILOR... SOLDIER... SAILOR... RICH MAN... POOR MAN... BEGGAR-MAN...
HMM. MORE CHERRIES...

ELF-LORD... IVY... VINEGAR... TOAD... VIRGIN... PILGRIM... KANGAROO...
LADY JOHANNA CONSTANTINE born 1760 died 1859

We have spoken. It is done.
LADY JOHANNA CONSTANTINE born 1760 died 1859

YOU TALKED TO HIM?
Indeed. As he talked to me.

DID HE TELL YOU?
Where our brother is?
Yes. he told me.

DID... IT. UM. I DON'T KNOW. COST YOU ANYTHING?
It cost me a great deal. But no. Not directly. Not now.
But... I... owe my son a boon. In return.
ARE YOU OKAY?
YOU'RE SHIVERING.

I find that difficult to believe, my sister. I am in perfectly fine spirits.
After all, the penultimate step of our quest has been concluded.
AND NOBODY ELSE GOT KILLED OR EXPLODED OR ANYTHING.
As you say.

LADY JOHANNA CONSTANTINE born 1760 died 1859 "Be to her Virtues very Kind. Be to her faults a little Blind."
IS IT A LONG WAY TO WHERE OUR BROTHER IS?

No. Not far.
LADY JOHANNA CONSTANTINE born 1760 died 1859 "Be to her Virtues very Kind. Be to her faults a little Blind."

Thank you, Kris.

HULLO, DOGGY. YOU'RE A VERY NICE DOGGY, AREN'T YOU? YES, YOU ARE. THE CHERRY STONES SAY I'M GOING TO BE A KANGAROO WHEN I GROW UP.
WHAT'S YOUR NAME, THEN?

HIS NAME'S BARNABAS.

WELL, COME UP HERE THEN, YOU TWO. WHERE I CAN SEE YOU PROPERLY.
23

AH, LET ME LOOK AT YOU, LASS.
PRETTY AS EVER YOU WERE, BY MY TROTH, AND YES, I DO BELIEVE YOU'VE GROWN.
MAYBE.
AND YOU, MY BROTHER. YOU ALSO SEEM DIFFERENT. PERHAPS YOU TOO HAVE GROWN.
It is not likely.
NO? STRANGER THINGS HAVE HAPPENED.

AH, AND LET US REPAIR INSIDE. IT GETS CHILL HERE, OF A SUDDEN, WHEN THE SUN GOES DOWN.
YOU MUST HAVE TRAVELLED A LONG WAY.
TO BE HONEST, I WAS EXPECTING YOU TO ARRIVE A LITTLE EARLIER.
BUT NO MATTER. THE DOLMADES MAY BE A TRIFLE COOL, BUT THEY'LL BE NONE THE WORSE FOR THAT, EH?
You were expecting us?
I'M AFRAID SO.
NOW, I AM SURE WE HAVE MUCH TO DISCUSS.
SO, PLEASE: TAKE A SEAT.
I'VE MADE DINNER.
To Be Continued

Brains A heart A ride in a balloon
chapter 8
Dinner something
Journey's end

EIGHT: JOURNEY'S END—BRAINS, A HEART, A RIDE IN A BALLOON—DINNER—SOMETHING NEW—THE ILLUSION OF PERMANENCE—A WREATH OF BRIGHT STARS—ECHOES OF DARKNESS—UP. OUT.
WELL, HELP YOURSELVES TO ANYTHING ON THE TABLE. PLEASE. IT'S HERE TO BE EATEN.
SO.

SO.
I EXPECT YOU'RE ALL WONDERING WHY I CALLED YOU HERE THIS EVENING.

You... called us here?

WELL, NO. NOT REALLY. THAT WAS MORE IN THE WAY OF A JOKE, I SUPPOSE. TO SET YOU AT YOUR EASE.
I MEAN, I KNEW YOU WERE COMING. THAT WAS WHY I MADE DINNER...
RETSINA, ANYBODY?

TRY SOME OF THE LITTLE MEATBALLS. I'M RATHER PLEASED WITH THE WAY THEY CAME OUT...
You... created all this?
NOT THE RAW INGREDIENTS. I PURCHASED THEM DOWN AT THE VILLAGE. BUT I TURNED THEM INTO THE MEAL ON THE TABLE.

He grew the herbs himself, though. In the garden.
He planted the seeds and everything came up. Except the basil.
AND THE CHIVES.
And the chives.

BUT THAT WAS BECAUSE SOMEBODY DECIDED THAT THE CHIVE PATCH WAS AN IDEAL LOCATION FOR BONE-BURYING.
And somebody said he wouldn't keep going on about a perfectly understandable mistake that anyone could have made.

My brother. We are together here on family business.
I confess I do not feel it to be entirely appropriate for your associate to be presen

NO?
AND DO YOU ALSO FEEL THE SAME WAY ABOUT BARNABAS, MY SISTER?

BARNABAS?
Me.

I MET YOU ON THE HILL, DIDN'T I, DOGGIE? WHEN I WAS COMING HERE? WASN'T THAT YOU? AND NOT ANOTHER DOGGIE?
Ah, yes. You must have grown on a particularly penetrating and incisive branch of the family tree.
OH! I LIKE YOU! YOU MUSTN'T MAKE THE DOGGIE GO AWAY, DREAM.

Very well: if it is silent, then it may stay.
Although it may repeat nothing it hears in this place, neither to man nor animal nor any other kind of creature.

SKRITCH

NEVER MIND, BARNABAS. IT'LL DO YOU GOOD TO SIT AND LISTEN, FOR A WHILE.
HAVE SOME SALAD, AT LEAST, DREAM.
I did not come here seeking food, my brother.
NO. YOU CAME HERE SEEKING ME.

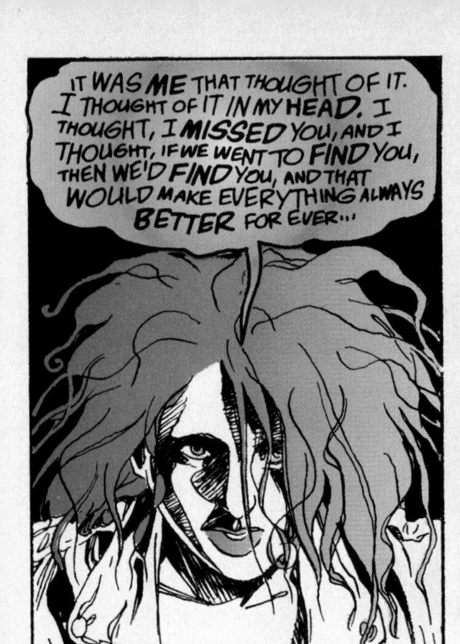
IT WAS ME THAT THOUGHT OF IT. I THOUGHT OF IT IN MY HEAD. I THOUGHT, I MISSED YOU, AND I THOUGHT, IF WE WENT TO FIND YOU, THEN WE'D FIND YOU, AND THAT WOULD MAKE EVERYTHING ALWAYS BETTER FOR EVER...

SO I WENT AND LOOKED FOR YOU AND FIRST OF ALL DESIRE WAS AT THIS PARTY AND SHE SAID SHE WOULDN'T HELP AND THEN DESPAIR SHOWED ME HER RATS AND SHE HAD A SAD MAN IN A MIRROR BUT SHE WOULDN'T COME WITH ME AND I WENT TO SEE DREAM BUT FIRST I WENT HOME AND CRIED A LITTLE BIT.

SO I WENT TO SEE DREAM AND I THOUGHT HE'D SAY NO BUT HE GAVE ME LITTLE CHOCOLATE LOVERS AND HE SAID OKAY. AND WE SAW THIS TRAVELLING MAN AND I MADE LITTLE FROGS AND THIS LADY WANTED MY NAME, AND I WENT ON A AIRPLANE.

I LIKE AIRPLANES. I LIKE ANYWHERE THAT ISN'T A PROPER PLACE. I LIKE IN-BETWEENS.

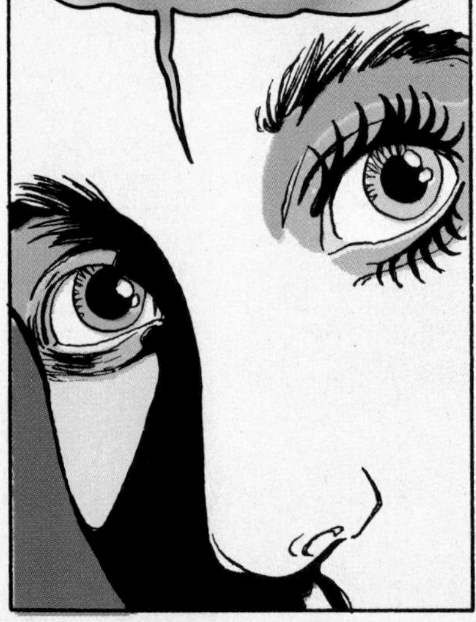
THERE WAS A LADY NAMED RUBY ONLY SHE GOT BURNED ALL UP BUT THAT WAS LATER. AND THERE WAS A LAWYER TOO BUT HE GOT ALL BURNED UP TOO. I MEAN HE GOT SQUASHED.

AND THE ETAIN LADY RAN AWAY BECAUSE HER HOUSE WENT BOOM AND THE ALDER MAN WASN'T IN THE WORLD ANY MORE AND I FOUND TIFFANY AND SHE WAS WITH THE DANCING LADY.

AND THEN I DID DRIVING AND I WAS REALLY GOOD.
THEN WE WENT TO THE DANCING LADY AND DREAM TALKED TO HER AND I MADE THIS MAN GIVE TIFFANY ALL HIS DOLLARS, THEN WE WENT AWAY.

THEN DREAM SAID HE WOULDN'T GO WITH ME ANY MORE AND I WENT HOME AND CRIED A LITTLE BIT, BUT THEN HE SAID HE WAS SORRY AND REALLY HE WOULD COME WITH ME AGAIN, BECAUSE...

I DON'T REMEMBER. SOMETHING. AND THAT HE'D BE NICE TO ME.
FRIENDS.

THEN WE WENT TO NOWHERE AND THEN WE WENT TO THE FAIR AND THEN WE WENT TO DESTINY'S GUARDING. AND THEN DREAM WENT ALL SPOGGLY AND I HAD TO PUT ME ALL...
I...

I HAD TO...
I HAD TO BE...
IT HURT.

AND THEN WE WENT OVER THERE AND I ATE SOME CHERRIES AND THE STONES SAID I WAS GOING TO BE A KANGAROO WHEN I GROW UP AND THEN WE CAME HERE.

SO IT WAS ME.
UM.
THAT'S ALL.

As she says: we have been looking for you for some small time now.

PLEASE EAT SOMETHING. I SPENT MOST OF TODAY COOKING FOR YOU BOTH, AFTER ALL.
SO HOW ARE THE FAMILY? IT MUST BE, WHAT, 300 YEARS?

The family? Little has changed since last we were together.
Destiny is unchanged.
Our older sister is well.

Desire is...well, Desire is Desire. I have seen them all recently.
And when last I saw Despair, she stated that she missed you.

POOR DESPAIR. I REMEMBER WHEN FIRST SHE ASSUMED THE MANTLE OF DESPAIR; WHEN FIRST SHE BECAME DESIRE'S TWIN.
I DON'T THINK IT WAS UM. EASY FOR HER.
It was not easy for any of us. It was the only time one of the Endless had been destroyed, that another aspect of one of us had reassumed the position: we all had much to adjust to.

YES.
THAT WAS WHY I EVENTUALLY CHOSE THE COURSE OF ACTION THAT I DID. AFTER ALL, IT WOULDN'T HAVE DONE FOR ANOTHER VERSION OF ME TO HAVE BEEN DUMPED INTO THE SAME MESS ALL OVER AGAIN...

You abandoned your responsi-bilities.
SO YOU SAID, 300 YEARS AGO.

THEY'RE ALL JUST LIKE THEY WERE. THE FAMILY. NOT CHANGED. BUT IT'S NOT THE SAME. NOT WITHOUT YOU.
I'M SORRY.
IT USED TO BE BETTER. YOU USED TO MAKE EVERYTHING NICE.
I MADE MY DECISION. I CAN LIVE WITH IT.

WELL, IT LOOKS LIKE NEITHER OF YOU IS INTERESTED IN THE DINNER I MADE. IS THERE ANYTHING ELSE YOU WERE AFTER?
BRAINS? A HEART? A RIDE IN A BALLOON?

Mortal food has never held much attraction for me, brother.
I HAD SOME CHERRIES BEFORE I CAME. FROM A TREE. THEY WERE ALL OVER IT.
HAVE YOU REALLY GOT A BALLOON?

I'M AFRAID NOT, LASS. IT WAS BY WAY OF BEING A FIGURE OF SPEECH.
I SUPPOSE WHAT I MEANT WAS, WELL, YOU CAME LOOKING FOR ME. YOU'VE FOUND ME. NOW WHAT?

UM. WELL. NOW WE'VE FOUND YOU, YOU'LL COME ALL BACK, WON'T YOU?
AND EVERYTHING WILL BE ALL RIGHT AND THE FAMILY WILL BE BACK AND ALL TOGETHER AND WE'LL ALL TALK AND LIKE EACH OTHER AGAIN.

I SEE. AND YOU, DREAM, WHY DID YOU COME LOOKING FOR ME?

I came because I wished to. Initially, perhaps, because our sister desired company on the road. I had other reasons.
Later it became a matter of honor. There was a woman named Ruby who died because we looked for you. She knew nothing of our quest.
It was not JUST that she should die...

300 YEARS AGO YOU WOULD HAVE TOLD ME THAT SHE WAS SIMPLY MORTAL, AND WOULD HAVE DIED LATER, HAD SHE NOT DIED THEN.
I doubt I have changed that much.
WHATEVER YOU SAY, MY BROTHER.

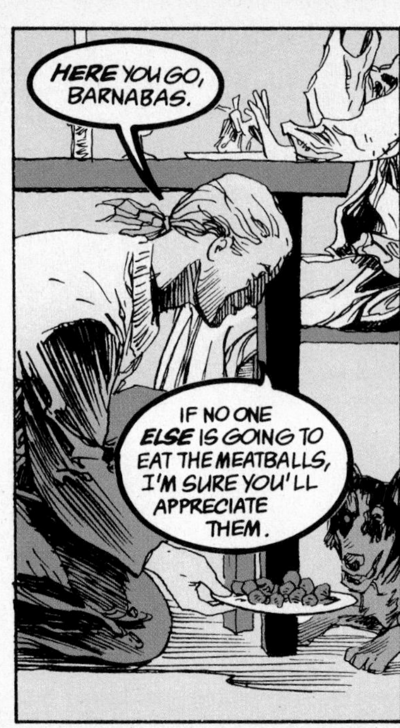
HERE YOU GO, BARNABAS.
IF NO ONE ELSE IS GOING TO EAT THE MEATBALLS, I'M SURE YOU'LL APPRECIATE THEM.

I SUPPOSE I HAD VAGUELY HOPED THAT YOU HAD CHANGED, MY BROTHER. THAT YOU'D NOTICED THAT THERE WERE OTHER PEOPLE IN THE WORLD.
THAT YOU HAD BEGUN TO SEE PEOPLE AS OTHER THAN THINGS THAT DREAM, AS CREATURES OF STORIES.

I have never needed you to instruct me on my duties, brother: now, I would hazard, less than ever. I still perform my responsibilities, after all.
I DON'T. NOT ANY MORE. BUT YOU KNOW THAT.
And what of your realm?

I'M SURE IT'S STILL THERE, IN ITS FASHION. PEOPLE AND THINGS ARE STILL CREATED; STILL EXIST; ARE STILL DESTROYED. THEY TEAR DOWN AND THEY BUILD.
THINGS STILL CHANGE. THE ONLY DIFFERENCE IS THAT NO ONE'S RUNNING IT ANY-MORE.

IT'S NOTHING TO DO WITH ME ANY LONGER. IT'S THEIRS.
THEY CAN MAKE THEIR OWN DESTRUCTION.

IT'S NOT MY RESPONSIBILITY.
AND IT'S NOT MY FAULT.

HAVE YOU BEEN HERE ALL ALONG?
ON THE ISLAND? NO. JUST A FEW YEARS. I'VE BEEN ALL OVER. AS A PRIVATE INDIVIDUAL, SO TO SPEAK.

I HELPED BUILD A CATHEDRAL IN NEW YORK. I'VE FOUGHT FOR PAY IN AFRICA. I'VE WORKED AS A PAVEMENT ARTIST IN LONDON, AND AS A STREET ARTIST IN PARIS.
I SPENT AN ENJOYABLE MONTH FORGING CAVE PAINTINGS FOR A SPANISH TOWN THAT NEEDED TOURISTS, AND A DULL DECADE HELPING DIG THE PANAMA CANAL.

AREN'T EITHER OF YOU GOING TO EAT ANYTHING? I MADE BAKLAVA FOR DESSERT...
AND THERE'S COFFEE.

How did you know we were coming?
HM? OH, I SET UP CERTAIN MECHANISMS, WHEN I LEFT MY REALM FOR THE LAST TIME. NOTHING FANCY.
THERE'S A SCRYING POOL OUT BACK: IT TELLS ME IF ANYONE'S LOOKING FOR ME, IN MY LATE CAPACITY.

THERE ARE ALSO CERTAIN AUTOMATIC FUNCTIONS THAT I SET IN PLACE JUST BEFORE I LEFT TO IMPEDE ANYONE WHO MIGHT ACTUALLY TRY TO COME AFTER ME...
These... functions... you mention--might they have caused damage to those from whom we sought help, on our way here?

I AM AFRAID SO.
THERE WAS NOTHING I COULD DO ABOUT IT. NOTHING I COULD DO TO STOP IT HAPPENING, ONCE YOU BEGAN TO LOOK FOR ME.
NOT WITHOUT RESUMING MY FUNCTION ONCE MORE...

But the people who were hurt...? Some of them had been your friends...
ONE OF THEM WAS ONCE MY LOVER.
OH, BUT YOU DIDN'T KNOW ABOUT HER END, DID YOU?

HERE YOU GO, LITTLE SISTER. GREEK COFFEE.
DON'T DRINK THE SLUDGE AT THE BOTTOM OF THE CUP.
OH. THANK YOU.
AND DON'T DRINK THE CUP, EITHER. JUST THE COFFEE.
OKAY.

HERE. YOUR COFFEE.
HOW DID YOU FIND ME, IN THE END?

In the end?
I...spoke to my son.

YOUNG ORPHEUS? I LIKED HIM.
I'VE THOUGHT ABOUT VISITING HIM, WALKING OVER AND JUST SAYING HELLO. BUT...
NO. HE'S STILL FAMILY, AFTER ALL.

ANYWAY, I THOUGHT YOU TWO WEREN'T TALKING.
We haven't been.
BUT YOU WENT AND SPOKE TO HIM BECAUSE OF ME?
Yes.
I'M FLATTERED. MAYBE SOMETHING CONSTRUCTIVE HAS COME OUT OF THIS LITTLE JAUNT OF YOURS AFTER ALL.

THE LAST TIME I SAW HIM, HE REMINDED ME OF YOU. A ROMANTIC FOOL. SELF-PITYING. BUT WITH A CERTAIN AMOUNT OF PERSONAL CHARM.
THAT WAS SHORTLY AFTER HIS YOUNG LADY HAD MET WITH HER MISFORTUNE, OF COURSE.

u sent to see sister.
IT WAS WHAT HE WANTED.
as a child. He know what he . It is something since had time regret.
My brother? How could you leave?
HOW? OR WHY?
It makes no difference.
YEEUCHH.
BECAUSE THERE'S NO SUCH THING AS A ONE-SIDED COIN. BECAUSE THERE ARE TWO SIDES TO EVERY SKY.
CTION DID NOT CEASE WITH DONMENT OF MY REALM, NO IAN PEOPLE WOULD CEASE SHOULD YOU ABANDON YOURS.
PERHAPS IT'S MORE UNCONTROLLED, WILDER. PERHAPS NOT. BUT IT'S NO LONGER ANYONE'S RESPONSIBILITY.
I TOOK MY SIGIL WITH ME: I DID NOT PASS IT ON.
AS THIS UNIVERSE CAME INTO BEING, DESTINY CAME WITH IT, ALONE IN THE DARKNESS.
BEFORE THE FIRST LIVING THING CAME INTO EXISTENCE, OUR SISTER WAS THERE, WAITING.
And when the first living thing awoke to life, I was also there. You tell me nothing new.
I'M TRYING, MY BROTHER. IT WAS GETTING YOU TO LISTEN TO ANYTHING NEW THAT I ALWAYS HAD PROBLEMS WITH.
LET'S GO OUTSIDE, INTO THE GARDEN. IT'S A WARM NIGHT, AFTER ALL.

I LIKE THE STARS. IT'S THE ILLUSION OF PERMANENCE, I THINK. I MEAN, THEY'RE ALWAYS FLARING UP AND CAVING IN AND GOING OUT.

BUT FROM HERE, I CAN PRETEND...

I CAN PRETEND THAT THINGS LAST. I CAN PRETEND THAT LIVES LAST LONGER THAN MOMENTS.

"SHE SAID WE ALL NOT ONLY COULD KNOW EVERYTHING.
"WE DO.
"WE JUST TELL OURSELVES WE DON'T TO MAKE IT ALL BEARABLE."

It sounds unlikely.

THAT WAS WHAT I SAID TO HER. I SAID, IF THEY DO THAT, WHY DO THEY KEEP WANDERING AROUND AND FALLING DOWN MANHOLES AND TRIPPING ON BANANA SKINS?
WHY DOES IT SEEM LIKE NONE OF US--ENDLESS OR MORTAL, GHOST OR GOD--KNOWS WHAT WE'RE DOING?

And she said?
I TOLD YOU. SHE SAID EVERYONE KNOWS EVERY-THING. WE JUST PRETEND TO OURSELVES WE DON'T.
I NEVER KNEW WHAT TO MAKE OF THAT.

SHE IS. UM. RIGHT. KIND OF.
NOT KNOWING EVERYTHING IS ALL THAT MAKES IT OKAY, SOMETIMES.

Will you return? Will you reassume your role once more?
OF COURSE NOT.
I THOUGHT YOU WOULD.
I'M SORRY, LASSIE.

But you are of the Endless.
We...
We have responsibilities.
You are the embodiment of Destruction. You are of the Endless.

THE ENDLESS? THE ENDLESS ARE MERELY PATTERNS. THE ENDLESS ARE IDEAS. THE ENDLESS ARE WAVE FUNCTIONS. THE ENDLESS ARE REPEATING MOTIFS.
THE ENDLESS ARE ECHOES OF DARKNESS, AND NOTHING MORE. WE HAVE NO RIGHT TO PLAY WITH THEIR LIVES, TO ORDER THEIR DREAMS AND THEIR DESIRES.

AND EVEN OUR EXISTENCES ARE BRIEF AND BOUNDED. NONE OF US WILL LAST LONGER THAN THIS VERSION OF THE UNIVERSE.
EXCEPT OUR SISTER.
So we suppose.

I FILLED MY ROLE MORE THAN ADEQUATELY FOR OVER TEN BILLION YEARS.
A TWO-SIDED COIN: DESTRUCTION IS NEEDED. NOTHING NEW CAN EXIST WITHOUT DESTROYING THE OLD.

THINGS ARE CREATED. THEY LAST FOR SOME LITTLE WHILE, AND THEN THEY ARE GONE. EMPIRES, CITIES, POEMS AND PEOPLE. ATOMS AND WORLDS.
ONE CANNOT BEGIN A NEW DREAM WITHOUT ABANDONING THE LAST, EH, BROTHER?
WHOOMPF

OUR SISTER DEFINES LIFE, JUST AS DESPAIR DEFINES HOPE, OR DESIRE DEFINES HATRED, OR AS DESTINY DEFINES FREEDOM.
And what do I define, by this theory of yours.

REALITY, PERHAPS?

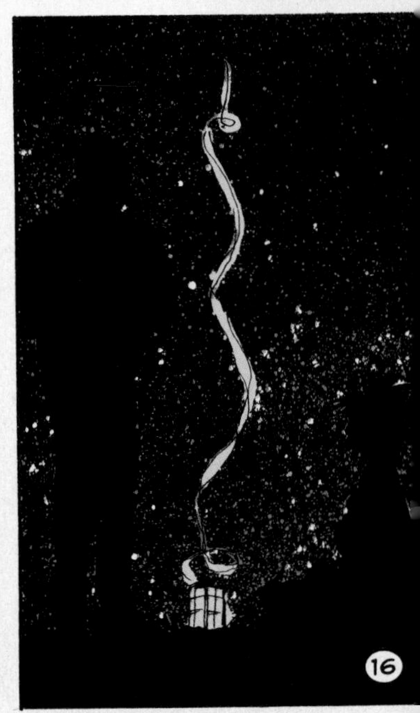

THERE ARE RATHER A LOT OF STARS, AREN'T THERE?
I COULD NEVER LEAVE MY REALM. IT'S GOT ALL MY THINGS IN IT.
YOU KNOW, I WAS REALLY RATHER ENJOYING MY TIME HERE, BEFORE YOU TWO BEGAN LOOKING FOR ME.

LIFE WAS COMFORTABLE AND UNCHANGING. AND YOU'VE RATHER UNDONE THAT.
I SHOULD HAVE SEEN IT COMING.
BUT AT LEAST WE'VE HAD THIS TIME TOGETHER.

MY SISTER. I HAVE ENJOYED SEEING YOU. YOU WERE ALWAYS MY FAVORITE.
I TRUST THAT WHEN YOUR NEXT CHANGE COMES, IT PROVES EASY ON YOU.
CHANGE?

MY BROTHER. THERE IS NO ONE LIKE YOU. YOU ALSO HAVE CHANGED MORE THAN EVEN YOU KNOW, I WOULD SUSPECT.
ONCE YOU ARE DONE HERE, THEN WHERE WILL YOU GO?
There were matters left unfinished with my son.

DREAM, YOU LEFT MATTERS UNFINISHED WITH YOUR SON SOME THOUSANDS OF YEARS AGO.

COME ON IN. THIS IS MY OLD GALLERY. I'VE BEEN DRAGGING IT AROUND WITH ME SINCE I LEFT MY REALM.

I DON'T EVEN KNOW WHY I'VE HELD ONTO IT THIS LONG.
HABIT, I IMAGINE. OR SENTIMENT.

MY BROTHER. THERE IS NOTHING I CAN GIVE YOU, SAVE THIS: MY ADVICE. REMEMBER WHAT I DID. REMEMBER THAT I LEFT.
REMEMBER HOW HARD IT WAS FOR ME TO LEAVE; AND THAT IT WAS NOT YOUR FAULT.

That is your advice?
INDEED IT IS. REMEMBER.
I am not in the habit of forgetting things.

DREAM, MY BROTHER. YOU FORGET NOTHING YOU HAVE INTEREST IN; YOU FORGET, INSTANTLY, THOSE THINGS YOU DO NOT CARE TO KNOW.

DO YOU STILL BLAME YOURSELF?
For what?
BECAUSE I LEFT.
I never blamed myself.
NO?

What will you do now?

I WILL MAKE THE MOST OF WHAT I'VE GOT. I SHALL LIVE OUT MY DAYS DOING WHAT I HAVE TO DO, ONE DAY AT A TIME.

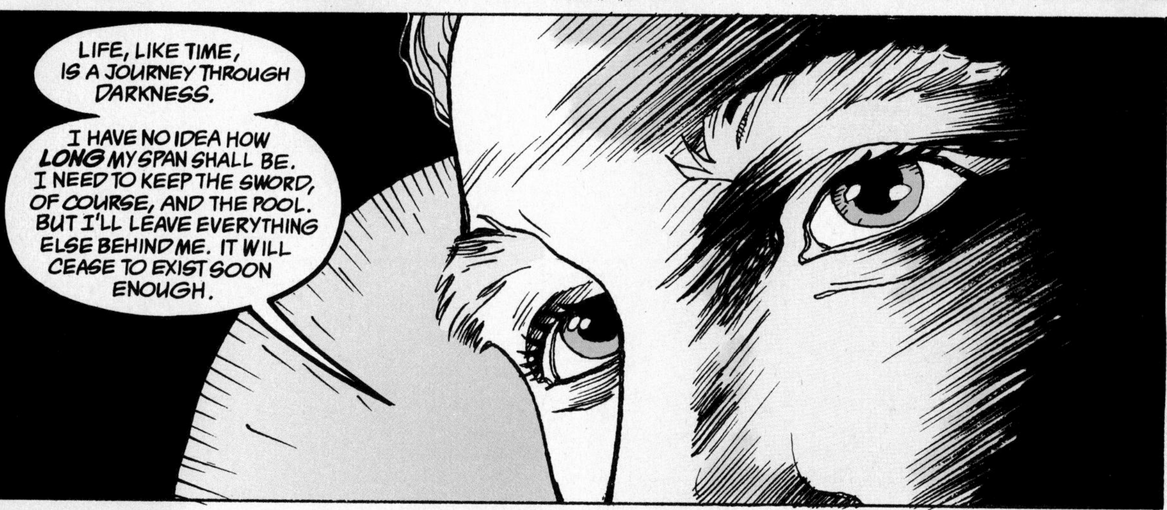
LIFE, LIKE TIME, IS A JOURNEY THROUGH DARKNESS.
I HAVE NO IDEA HOW LONG MY SPAN SHALL BE. I NEED TO KEEP THE SWORD, OF COURSE, AND THE POOL. BUT I'LL LEAVE EVERYTHING ELSE BEHIND ME. IT WILL CEASE TO EXIST SOON ENOUGH.

AND YOU, SISTER. WHAT SHOULD I GIVE YOU?
I DON'T KNOW.
I DIDN'T LIKE THE COFFEE. AND I CAN'T SAY TARAMASALATA OR BAKLAVA OR THOSE THINGS.

MAYBE YOU could COME AND STAY IN MY REALM. YOU CAN LIVE THERE WITH ME, AND YOU CAN MAKE ME LAUGH AND I'LL DO YOU LITTLE DANCES, AND... AND...
YOU WON'T, WILL YOU?
NO.

BUT YOU'VE GIVEN ME AN IDEA.

BARNABAS, MY FRIEND. ANSWER IF YOU WISH.
WILL YOU GO WITH THE LADY DELIRIUM, WALK BESIDE HER, TREAD THE PATH THAT SHE TREADS ALSO? PROTECT AND LEAD AND GUIDE HER?

I CAN'T LOOK AFTER A DOGGIE.

You misheard him. I get to look after you.
OH.
DEL. BARNABAS CAN BE A BIT OF A PAIN, AND HE HAS NO POETRY IN HIS SOUL, BUT HE MEANS WELL.
I resent that remark.
OF COURSE YOU DO.

WELL?
Can't I go with you?
YOU COULD NOT SURVIVE IN THE PLACES I AM TRAVELLING TO.
Oh. I see.
Well, she shouldn't be allowed out off a leash. But I'll do what I can.

HAVE EITHER OF YOU GOT A HANDKERCHIEF? OR A PIECE OF CLOTH?

Here.
THANKS. BLACK, EH? TCH...
HM. STRIPES? OR SPOTS? SPOTS ARE MORE APPROPRIATE.

Desire told me not to come looking for you.
DESIRE WAS RIGHT. ALSO UNTRUSTWORTHY, ACERBIC, DANGEROUS AND CRUEL. BUT RIGHT.
YOU WOULD HAVE BEEN BETTER OFF LEAVING WELL ENOUGH ALONE.

STILL, WHAT'S DONE CAN'T BE UNDONE. OR VERY RARELY. AND DEFINITELY NOT THIS TIME.

You could pass it on.
WHAT? AND DROP SOMEONE ELSE INTO THE SAME OLD MESS?
I'M NO LONGER YOUNG, DREAM. AND I MADE MY DECISION.

IF YOU SEE ISHTAR AGAIN, GIVE HER MY LOVE.
Must I?
YES.

BE GOOD. LOOK AFTER HER.
I'll miss you.
AH YES. YOU'LL MISS THE POETRY READINGS. THE PAINTINGS. THE LATE NIGHT FLAMENCO GUITAR RECITALS.
That's right. Go on. Try to make me feel better.

You are going now?
YES.

Where?
OH, OUT THERE, SOMEWHERE. UP. OUT.

To Be Concluded

chapter 9

Things unlooked-for - Answered prayers - The flowers of romance - Journey's end - The gates of horn -

Brief lives

NINE: FAREWELLS—ANSWERED PRAYERS—THE FLOWERS OF ROMANCE—JOURNEY'S END—THE GATES OF HORN—THINGS UNLOOKED FOR—BRIEF LIVES.

HE HAS HARDLY SLEPT THIS NIGHT.

AT ONE POINT HE DRIFTED OFF INTO A DREAM, IN WHICH HE WAS TEACHING HIS GRANDCHILDREN TO SING A SONG HIS CHILDREN HAD LOVED. HIS WIFE STOOD BEHIND THEM, AND SMILED INDULGENTLY.

COLD TEARS ON HIS FACE WOKE HIM; THE POSITION OF THE STARS TOLD HIM THAT ONLY MINUTES HAD PASSED.
HE WATCHED THE LIGHTS IN THE HOUSE ACROSS THE BAY FOR SEVERAL HOURS.

LATER THERE WERE TINY FIGURES MOVING IN THE GARDEN. AND LATER STILL, A SHOOTING STAR.
THEN HE WAITED.

NOW HE HEARS VOICES OUTSIDE HIS TEMPLE.
I WANT TO COME INSIDE. I WANT TO SAY HELLO. OR GOODBYE. OR SOMETHING.
I COULD SHOW HIM MY DOGGIE.
I am sorry, my sister, but no.

PLEASE? I WENT TO HIS WEDDING.
...very well. But the dog remains outside.

ORPHEUS?
HELLO, MY AUNT.

YOU LOOK. UM. LIKE YOU USED TO ONLY DIFFERENT.
WELL, I JUST CAME TO SAY.
AND NOW I'M GOING AWAY AGAIN NOW.

Orpheus.
HELLO, FATHER.

I must apologize for that intrusion. I did not intend for her to...
IT DOESN'T MATTER.

THANK YOU FOR COMING BACK.
Did you doubt that I would? I gave my word.
I KNOW.
HOW WAS MY UNCLE?
He was... I do not know, my son. He has gone from that place, and from this world.
He was much the same, I suppose.
We do not always accomplish what we set out to do.
NO.
FATHER? MOTHER CAME TO ME, LAST YEAR. SHE SAID THAT SHE HAD BEEN IMPRISONED.
She had.
AND THAT YOU HAD FREED HER.
Yes.
YOU HAVE CHANGED, SINCE THE OLD DAYS.
I doubt it.
FATHER? I AM VERY SCARED.
You asked for a boon, Orpheus. I can grant it.
3

I AM SO SCARED.
IT'S STRANGE. FOR MANY THOUSAND YEARS I HAVE PRAYED FOR DEATH. I HAVE PRAYED TO ALL THE GODS FOR PEACE AND RELIEF AND...
I HAVE PRAYED FOR AN ENDING.

I DID NOT THINK THAT YOU WOULD BE THE ONE TO GRANT IT. DO YOU REMEMBER WHAT YOU SAID TO ME THEN, FATHER?
"YOUR LIFE IS YOUR OWN. YOUR DEATH, LIKEWISE. ALWAYS, AND FOREVER, YOUR OWN. FARE WELL."
"WE SHALL NOT MEET AGAIN."

I believe I said something like that, yes.
THOSE WERE YOUR EXACT WORDS. I HAVE HAD PLENTY OF TIME TO THINK ON THEM.
I SHOULD HAVE DIED LONG AGO.
Perhaps.

FATHER?
Yes.
I WISH THAT THINGS HAD BEEN OTHERWISE.
FATHER, I AM READY.

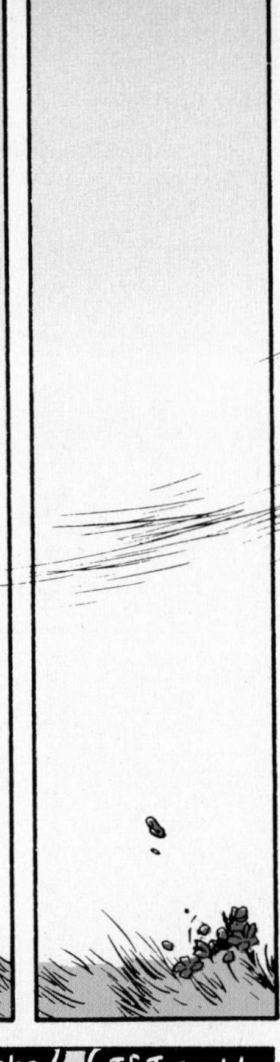

YOU DID IT DIDN'T YOU?

It was... what he wanted. His life... and death... were always his own.
If I could have... lived his life for him, my sister... what then?
I told him many things, when he was young. If he had listened...
but he did not listen.

YOU KILLED HIM.
No. He died long ago, when the Sisters of the Frenzy tore his body to shreds, and threw his head into the Hebrus.

HE DIED BEFORE THAT. ON THE NIGHT OF HIS WEDDING, PERHAPS. OR WHEN DESTRUCTION SENT HIM TO SEE OUR SISTER. OR IN THE UNDERWORLD.

HELLO, DESPAIR.
BARNABAS, THIS IS DESPAIR. SHE'S MY SISTER.
YOU SAW OUR BROTHER, DIDN'T YOU?
YES.
HOW WAS HE?

I THINK HE WAS HAPPY. I'M NOT WORRIED ABOUT HIM ANY MORE. HE GAVE ME THIS DOGGIE.
NOW I'M WORRIED ABOUT... DEE ARR EE, UM AY, UM, EM EM.
That's one em, no ums. But good try.

You are worried about me, my sister?
YES.
NO.
YES.
MAYBE.
You need not worry for me. Our journey is over. All debts are paid.
Good day to you, also, sister.

OUR BROTHER. DID HE... MENTION ME?
He spoke fondly of you, Sister.
OH. GOOD.
HE WASN'T WEARING HIS BEARD ANY MORE EITHER.
I... LIKED THE BEARD.

My sisters. Messire Barnabas. I will take my leave of you all now.

DREAM? THANK YOU FOR COMING WITH ME.
I DON'T THINK I COULD HAVE DONE IT ON MY OWN.

MAYBE I SHOULD HAVE COME WITH YOU. WHEN YOU CAME TO ME, WHEN YOU ASKED... I WOULD HAVE GONE WITH YOU, LITTLE SISTER. THEN I WOULD HAVE BEEN WITH YOU WHEN YOU SAW HIM.
I ALSO WOULD HAVE SEEN HIM ONCE MORE.
I THINK I COULD HAVE BORNE THE CONSEQUENCES. BUT IT IS TOO LATE, NOW.

YOU SAID, "SO?" WHEN I ASKED YOU. YOU SAID, "SO?"
I THINK I'M GOING TO GO HOME NOW.

COME ON DOGGIE. WE'RE GOING TO MY PLACE. IT'S VERY INTERESTING. YOU'LL LIKE IT, UNLESS MAYBE YOU DON'T.

SOON THE PRIESTS OF ORPHEUS WILL WAKE, WILL COME UP HERE TO SEE THEIR CHARGE. FOR THOUSANDS OF YEARS, FOR HUNDREDS OF GENERATIONS, THEY HAVE TENDED HIM, GUARDED HIM, HIDDEN HIM...
SOON THEY WILL WAKE, AND SEE HIM.

GOODBYE, DELIRIUM.

I *THOUGHT* YOU'D STILL BE HERE.
I PICKED YOU A *FLOWER*.
HERE. TAKE IT.
9

SO. THE CHILD IS DEAD?
YES.
AND DESTRUCTION HAS GONE FOR GOOD?
...YES.
AND DREAM?
I DON'T KNOW.

IT COULD HAVE BEEN WORSE. THEY COULD HAVE DRAGGED OUR SISTER AND DESTINY INTO THE MESS.
IT'S STRANGE, MY TWIN. I THOUGHT I'D BE DELIGHTED TO SEE THIS DAY.

HE'S HUMILIATED ME. HE'S BEEN RUDE AND BOORISH. HE'S STUFFY AND STUPID AND THINKS HE KNOWS EVERYTHING. AND THERE'S JUST SOMETHING ABOUT HIM THAT GETS ON MY NERVES.
BUT I CAN'T HELP FEELING SORRY FOR HIM.

HE WAS LIKE A DISASTER, WAITING TO HAPPEN.
YOU CANNOT SEEK DESTRUCTION AND RETURN UNSCATHED.
DELIRIUM HAS.
DELIRIUM HAS BEEN SCATHED ENOUGH IN HER TIME.

HM. THE FIRST ENTIRELY NEW FLOWER IN QUITE SOME TIME. IT SMELLS WONDERFUL.
YOU KNOW, I SWORE AN OATH ONCE. I SWORE I WOULD MAKE HIM SPILL FAMILY BLOOD. AND NOW HE HAS. I SHOULD BE TRIUMPHANT.

IT WAS NOT OF YOUR DOING.
TRUE. BUT IT WAS WHAT I WANTED.
SO. YOU'RE HAPPY?
NO. I'M SCARED.

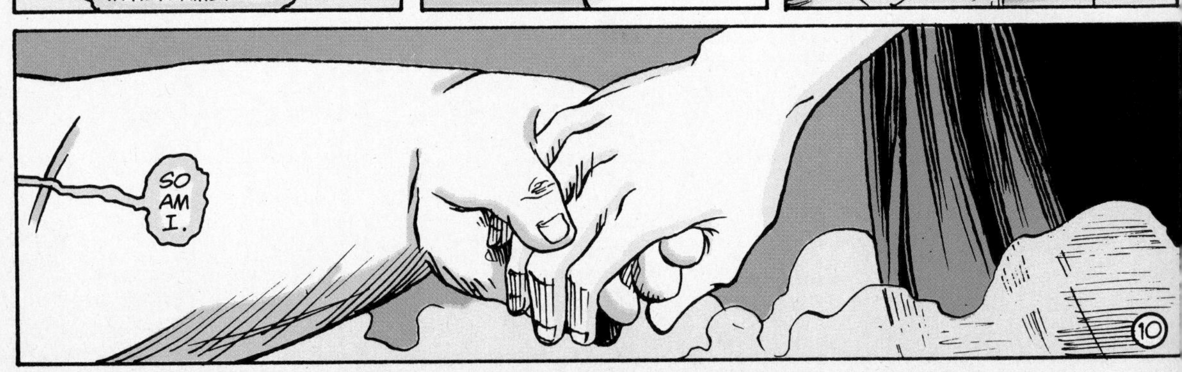
SO AM I.

THERE ARE TWO GATES AT THE ENTRANCE TO THE TRUE DREAMING. THE LORD OF DREAMS SET THEM THERE HIMSELF, A LONG TIME AGO.
THERE WERE THREE GODS, OR SO THE TALE WENT, WHO WISHED TO RULE IN DREAM'S DOMAIN; WHO PLANNED TO FEED ON DREAMS AND TAKE ALL THE POWER OF DREAMS FOR THEIR OWN.

FROM THE SKULL AND FROM THE SPINE OF THE OLDEST, DREAM CREATED HIS HELM.
FROM THE TUSKS OF THE MIDDLE GOD, HE CARVED A GATE THROUGH WHICH THE COMMONALTY OF DREAMS COULD TRAVEL; ALL THE FALSEHOODS AND HOPES AND FEARS.

AND FROM THE HORNS OF THE YOUNGEST, HE CARVED A GATE THAT HE RESERVED FOR TRUE DREAMS.
THIS BECAUSE HE HAD SOME LITTLE REGARD FOR HER, AND HAD, PERHAPS, IN SOME SMALL MEASURE, REGRETTED THE COURSE OF ACTION HE HAD FOUND NECESSARY.

BUT ALL THIS WAS LONG AGO; AND THE TRUTH OF IT ALL HAS NOT EVER BEEN TOLD ON THIS WORLD.
Andros?

Andros? Listen to me, then you may all wake.

Some time ago, I created your priesthood, to tend my son. To guard him from all harm.
Now your responsibilities are at an end.

I have only one thing more to ask of you.
Bury his head, Andros. Bury it safely. But erect no marker.

When that is done your task will be over; your duties will be at an end.
If you wish, you may stay at the temple. Or do... do whatever you may wish.

MY LORD? IS THAT YOU?
A strange question to ask, my servant.
Am I not your creator?
I AM SORRY, LORD. IT WAS JUST THAT... FOR A MOMENT...
Do not trouble yourself, Gryphon.
You three have served me well in the past; as you shall serve me well in the future.
Have I ever told you how much I appreciate your service? That I value you all most highly?
SIRE...?
No matter.
Carry on.
IS HE ALL RIGHT?

Good day, young lady.

You are well?
I... I--I... MY, I...
I trust there is nothing wrong.
WRONG? NO. SIR. NOTHING.
Very good.

Hm. Walk with me. Nuala, isn't it?
YES. YES IT IS.
The faerie gift. I was taught never to trust faerie gifts; they disappear at inconvenient times, and one may find unlooked-for things in their place.

I CANNOT HELP WHAT I AM.
No?
HAVE YOUR JOURNEYINGS GONE WELL, SIR?
They are over. That is, I think, all that can be said for them.

Nuala?
YES.
That pendant, around your neck. I have seen it before, have I not?

YES.

Ah, well. Keep it. Wear it. It is no matter.
Perhaps my journeyings have indeed accomplished one thing.
SIR?

Do not trouble yourself, little one. Go in peace.

Lucien.
I am back.
It is at an end.
VERY GOOD, SIRE.

For the rest of today I will be retiring to my quarters.
I do not wish to be disturbed.

Tomorrow, I shall return to my duties. I have neglected them long enough. And I have responsibilities here, after all.
I have many responsibilities.
YES, MY LORD.

Lucien? The lady Ishtar is presently in the Dreaming, on her way Beyond.
Find her for me. I have a message for her, from my brother.

There are some who have aided me on my journey: Faramond, The Lady Bast, a dead human named Ruby, and others...
They must be suitably rewarded.
OF COURSE, MY LORD.

And there are some whom we sought who had already fled.
The Alder Man is probably being a bear; Etain is almost undoubtedly in hiding in one of the far realms.
No matter; they both dream, and may both eventually be found.

We should send messengers to inform them that they may, if they wish, return.
That it is now safe.
And I am certain that there is much else that needs my attention.

But not today. These things can wait.
Tomorrow, I shall work. But not today...

HEY, LOOSH. WHERE D'YA WANT THIS STUFF? IT'S MOSTLY GUIDEBOOKS TO COUNTRIES AN' CITIES THAT NEVER EXISTED, JUNK LIKE THAT.
OUSLAND CITY FROM TOP TO BOTTOM
POICTESME
KADATH
THE NIGHT LAND
ONE NIGHT IN BAGHDAD
PUDDLEBY
SARDATHRION
SAFFRON PARK
FLORA OF NEVERLAND

AH, YES, THE CRYPTOGEOGRAPHICA. I THOUGHT IT ABOUT TIME IT HAD ITS OWN ROOM. LET'S TAKE IT OVER TO THE SOUTHWESTERN ANNEX.
HY BRASIL BY NIGHT
LOS ANGELES UNDERGROUND RAILWAY MAP
RIGHT. I'VE ONLY SCHLEPPED THEM ALL THE WAY UP FROM THE CELLAR, SO HEY, WHY SHOULD I MIND SCHLEPPING THEM ANOTHER FEW MILES TO THE SOUTHWESTERN ANNEX?
GREAT HOTELS ON THE MOON
ALLEYS AND BRADSTREETS
CAMP CUSACK
AMPERSAND
ROAD TRIPS TO

HEY, IT'S ONLY OLD MERV PUMPKINHEAD, RIGHT? IT'S NOT AS IF HE'S GOT ANYTHING BETTER TA DO.
IF YOU SAY SO, MERVYN.
SO, HE'S BACK.
YES.

HOW'S HE LOOK? MORE RAIN ON THE WAY?
I DON'T THINK SO. NO.
THAT'S GOOD.
DID HE FIND THE BROAD WHO DUMPED HIM?
NO.
YEAH, WELL. IT FIGGERS. ONLY TO BE EXPECTED.

HE... HE'S NOT AROUND, IS HE?
HE'S GONE UP TO HIS ROOMS.
WELL, Y'KNOW. HE'S A GOOD GUY, BUT HE, Y'KNOW, OVERREACTS.
ONE LITTLE THING GOES WRONG, AND HE ACTS LIKE THE SKY IS FALLING.

LIKE YOU ACCIDENTALLY PUT UP ONE LITTLE FOREST WHERE HE WAS MAYBE EXPECTING A LAUNDRY ROOM AND ALL OF A SUDDEN HE'S ACTING LIKE IT'S A MATTER OF LIFE AND DEATH.
REAL LIFE. THAT'S WHAT GUYS LIKE HIM NEVER HAVE TO FACE UP TO.
REAL LIFE.

You should have gone to her funeral.
WHY?
To say good-bye.

I HAVE NOT YET SAID GOOD-BYE TO EURYDICE.
You should. You are mortal: it is the mortal way.
You attend the funeral, you bid the dead farewell. You grieve. Then you continue with your life.

And at times the fact of her absence will hit you like a blow to the chest, and you will weep. But this will happen less and less as time goes on.
She is dead. You are alive.

So live.

So live...

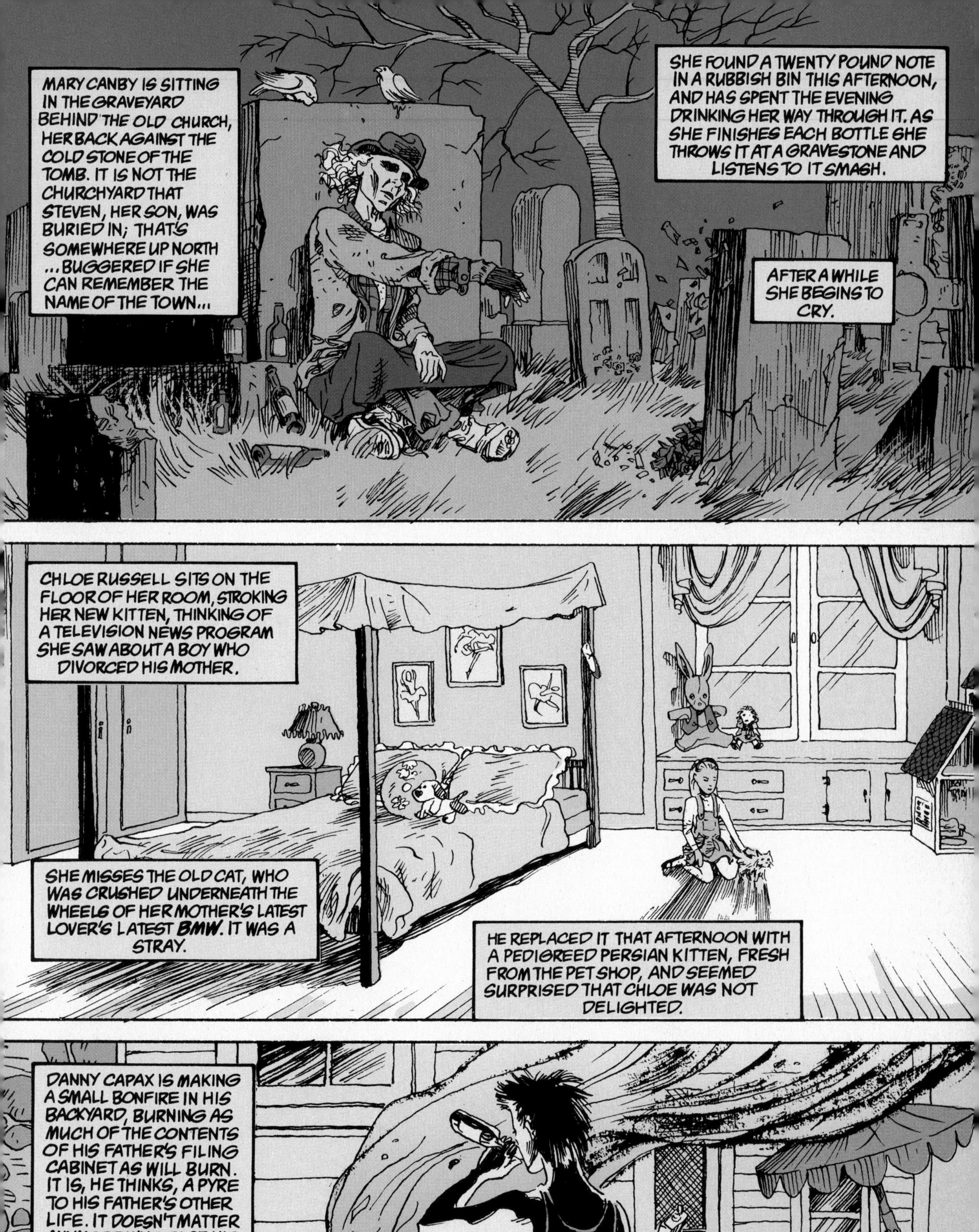
MARY CANBY IS SITTING IN THE GRAVEYARD BEHIND THE OLD CHURCH, HER BACK AGAINST THE COLD STONE OF THE TOMB. IT IS NOT THE CHURCHYARD THAT STEVEN, HER SON, WAS BURIED IN; THAT'S SOMEWHERE UP NORTH ...BUGGERED IF SHE CAN REMEMBER THE NAME OF THE TOWN...
SHE FOUND A TWENTY POUND NOTE IN A RUBBISH BIN THIS AFTERNOON, AND HAS SPENT THE EVENING DRINKING HER WAY THROUGH IT. AS SHE FINISHES EACH BOTTLE SHE THROWS IT AT A GRAVESTONE AND LISTENS TO IT SMASH.
AFTER A WHILE SHE BEGINS TO CRY.
CHLOE RUSSELL SITS ON THE FLOOR OF HER ROOM, STROKING HER NEW KITTEN, THINKING OF A TELEVISION NEWS PROGRAM SHE SAW ABOUT A BOY WHO DIVORCED HIS MOTHER.
SHE MISSES THE OLD CAT, WHO WAS CRUSHED UNDERNEATH THE WHEELS OF HER MOTHER'S LATEST LOVER'S LATEST BMW. IT WAS A STRAY.
HE REPLACED IT THAT AFTERNOON WITH A PEDIGREED PERSIAN KITTEN, FRESH FROM THE PET SHOP, AND SEEMED SURPRISED THAT CHLOE WAS NOT DELIGHTED.

DANNY CAPAX IS MAKING A SMALL BONFIRE IN HIS BACKYARD, BURNING AS MUCH OF THE CONTENTS OF HIS FATHER'S FILING CABINET AS WILL BURN. IT IS, HE THINKS, A PYRE TO HIS FATHER'S OTHER LIFE. IT DOESN'T MATTER ANYMORE WHO ELSE HIS FATHER WAS...
HE ISN'T BURNING EVERYTHING. DANNY SLID A COUPLE OF BLANK PASSPORTS INTO HIS BACK POCKET. YOU NEVER KNOW WHEN YOU'LL NEED TO BE SOMEONE ELSE.

FLAHERTY FEELS A SPIDER STEPPING TENTATIVELY OVER HIS EYEBALL. A MAGGOT SQUIRMS BETWEEN HIS TOES. AN ARMY OF ANTS MARCHES UP ONE ARM.
HE WOULD SCRATCH AT THEM, BUT HIS ARMS ARE BOUND TO THE BED BY LEATHERN STRAPS. HE DOES NOT DARE TO OPEN HIS MOUTH TO SCREAM: THERE ARE FLIES AND THINGS LIKE FLIES SWARMING OVER HIS LIPS, PROBING AND BUZZING AND KISSING...
TIFFANY SITS IN THE LEATHER CHAIR AND TELLS THE STUDIO AUDIENCE HOW SHE FOUND HER NEW LIFE; HOW THE PALACE OF SIN WAS DESTROYED (KINDA LIKE SODOM AND GOMORRAH, INTERJECTS THE SHOW'S HOST) AND OF THE ANGEL WHO APPEARED TO HER, AND GAVE HER AN ARMANI JACKET TO COVER HER NAKEDNESS, AND TOLD HER THAT SHE WAS SAVED.
EVERYBODY CLAPS.
TIFFANY GLOWS.

AT REST IN THE TEMPLE OF ITS BODY, DESIRE, WHO WOULD BE DARKLY AMUSED TO HEAR ITSELF DESCRIBED AS AN ANGEL, FLOATS IN AN EYEBALL LARGER THAN A CATHEDRAL, AND REMEMBERS ITS LOST BROTHER, IN ITS OWN WAY.
DESIRE'S THOUGHTS ARE PRIVATE.
IT HOLDS A SMALL RED FLOWER, VERY TIGHTLY.
AND ON THE ISLAND, ANDROS LEANS ON HIS SPADE. HIS CHEST HURTS, AND HE FINDS IT HARD TO CATCH HIS BREATH.
DO YOU *THINK* THAT IS *DEEP* ENOUGH?
IT'S DEEP ENOUGH, ANDROS.

MAYBE IT SHOULD BE DEEPER.
IT IS DEEP ENOUGH, GRANDFATHER.
IF YOU SAY SO.

ANDROS TAKES THE LINEN-WRAPPED BUNDLE FROM HIS SON.
WE WILL PUT HIM TO REST, THINKS ANDROS RHODOCANAKIS, BENEATH THE CHERRY TREE. AND PERHAPS HIS SPIRIT IS IN ELYSIUM, WITH HIS BELOVED EURYDICE. AND PERHAPS HIS SPIRIT HAS RETURNED TO DARKNESS, OR TO NOTHING...
AND PERHAPS HE IS AT REST.

GRANDFATHER? ARE YOU ALL RIGHT?
I AM FINE, BOY. JUST OLD BONES.
AND PERHAPS HIS SPIRIT WILL MOVE INTO THE CHERRY TREE, AND IN SPRING THE NEW BLOSSOMS WILL BE HIS, AND IN SUMMER THE CHERRIES WILL TASTE OF TRUE POETRY AND SONG...

AND WHEN ANDROS TASTES THEM HE WILL FEEL YOUNG AGAIN...
NO.
ANDROS KNOWS HE WILL NOT LIVE TO SEE THE TREE BLOSSOM AGAIN.

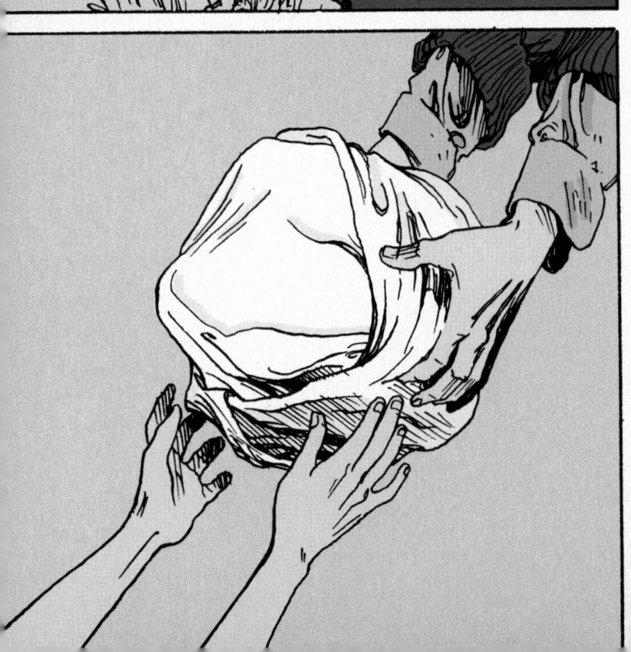

IT IS GOING TO BE A BEAUTIFUL DAY.

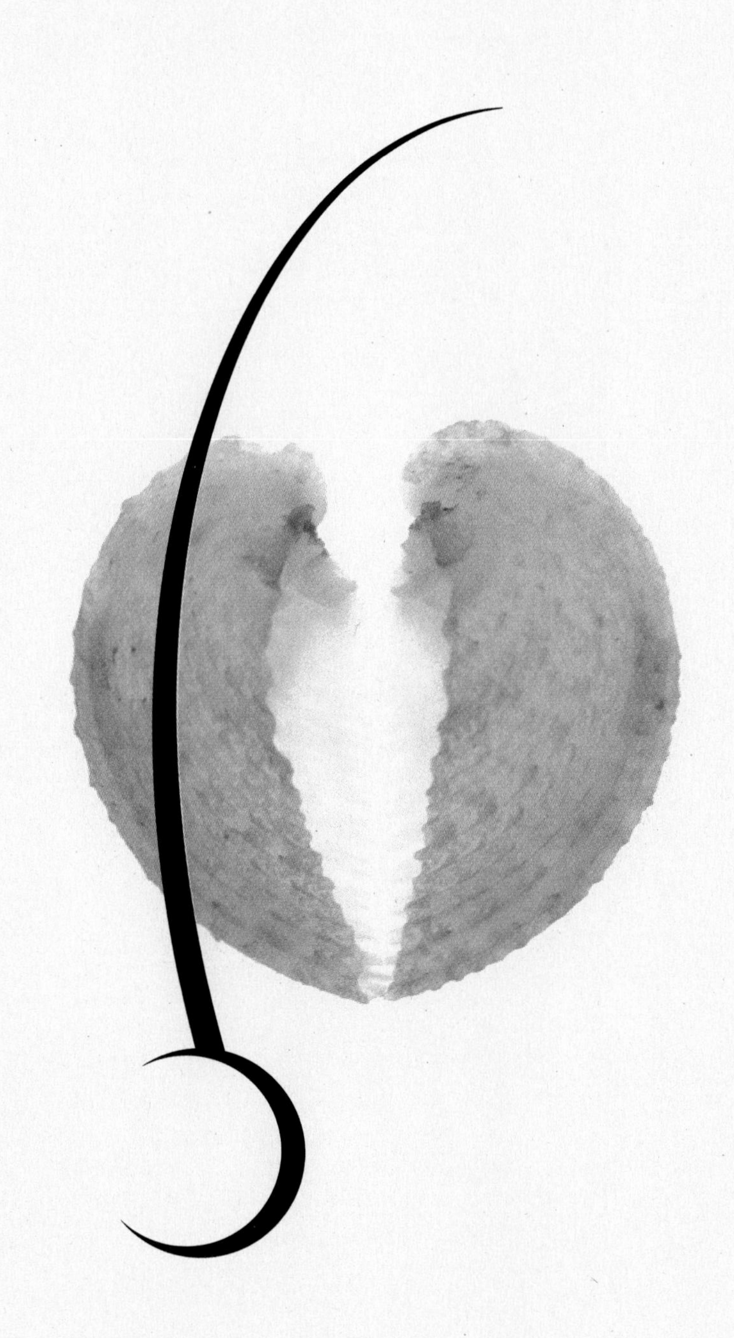

after(word)

on mortality and change

(peter straub) briefs

lives indeed.

The Endless, the clan to which Neil Gaiman and his many gifted collaborators introduced us in the first issues of SANDMAN, who may roam through any realm terrestrial or eternal in search of amusement, employment, diversion, romance, wickedness, or fresh material, are at least hypothetically immortal. And not only are the Endless endless, many thousands of men and women walking around on the earth at this moment are more or less immortal, too. Gaiman tells us that something less than ten thousand "humanoid individuals" remember the saber-toothed tiger, less than five hundred can remember the dinosaurs, and about seventy people still among us were present before the formation of the earth. His point is that not too many of these interesting folk are left, which is why we get the elegiac repetition of "less than," but we might respond that we wouldn't mind lives in which brevity is defined on such a scale.

on mortality and change

In this volume, a lawyer named Bernie Capax, formerly an acquaintance of both the Marquis de Sade and Sigmund Freud, is killed by a collapsing brick wall moments after savoring the memory of the particular and distinctive way mammoths smelled. When he finally understands that he has, after all this time, come to the end of his life, he turns in search of approbation to the attractive, black-clad, slightly punky and slightly slovenly figure before him, one of Gaiman's most inspired notions being that Death looks something like the young Chrissie Hynde. I did okay, didn't I? he asks. Fifteen thousand years – that's not so bad. As ever, Death is sensible, matter-of-fact, and frank, and replies: Bernie, old man, you just got the ordinary deal - you got a lifetime.

So every life, being no more or less than a lifetime, is brief; every life, being brief, is equal. Attorney Bernie's last words are the disappointed protest *"Not yet. . . ,"* are a wail of disappointment. What is of brief duration (and any duration is brief) is to be embraced, valued, reluctantly surrendered. Only the mad and the stupid throw their lives away. The story in which this Bernie's protest is embedded is one of Gaiman's most manifold and inventive, and also one of his most linear. It is the story of a search. All search stories deal at bottom with the gaining of wisdom, and those involving a journey, like *Brief Lives*, tend to focus on the changes and losses suffered along the way.

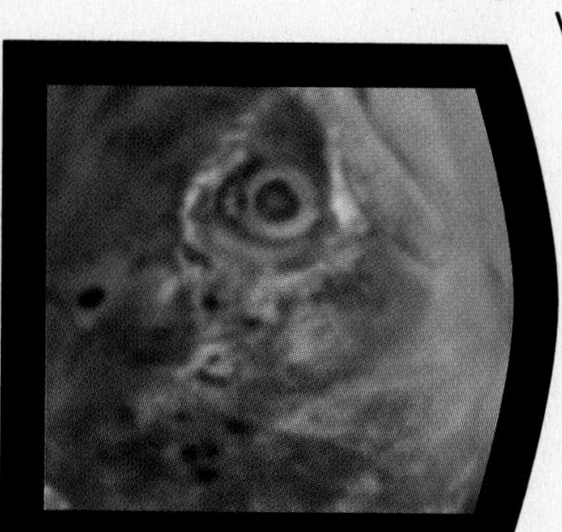

Wisdom is a matter of recognizing that nothing stands still, that everything is hurtling toward its own conclusion. Wisdom is in the celebration and memorialization of the temporal. (So wisdom consists of the ability to observe, "This is a beautiful day.") The concept of change, of drastic change to come and unalterable changes that have already occurred, haunts *Brief Lives*. Of course, the truth is that no one likes change. People in hell not only refuse to leave it, they invite you in, too. Even people who have blasted the other lives that touched their own blasted lives proudly declare in old age that they would not change a thing – all that cursing and screaming was their life, by God, and it is not possible to imagine any other. Change introduces unpredictability, uncertainty, a universe of disorder. Right before an amoeba splits in two, it says to itself, *uh uh, no way, I ain't gonna do that, nope.* Morpheus and his brothers and sisters of the Endless, Despair, Desire, Delirium, Death, Destiny, and Destruction, are moving through millennial upheavals they do not, with one exception, recognize or desire and which predict their own eventual extinction. Even eternity, it seems, is brief.

Morpheus (or Dream) is always at the center of these stories, but here he shares most of the narrative space not with Death, as is usually the case, but with childlike Delirium, represented by Jill Thompson and Vince Locke as bearing an occasional happy resemblance to the avant-garde novelist Kathy Acker, an old friend of Gaiman's. Death speaks straight smart common sense, which the Hamlet-like Dream often requires; Delirium vaults over common sense to land on a kind of giddy profundity. She speaks in little puffs of color as well as words, and she asks a lot of questions. Her first, the answer to which is "vitreous humour," leads directly to an encounter with Desire, who resides, we learn a few panels from the ending, within an eyeball larger than a cathedral. (Gaiman excels at this kind of structural play.) She asks Dream about the existence of three words, the first being the word for the moment when you realize you have forgotten the name of a former love, the second the word for forgetting the names of both parties in an introduction. These would be useful words, but as Dream points out, we do not have them. Her third question is, "What's the name for things not being the same always...the thing that lets you know time is happening." The word, Dream tells her, is Change.

In search of a change, Delirium has polled several of her siblings to see if they will assist her in locating their brother Destruction, who walked away from his job and cut all ties to his family three hundred years earlier. In seventeenth-century London, Destruction had observed that mankind's new concentration on reason, together with its scientific progress, had already begun the questioning of the boundary between light and matter which will ultimately lead to Einsteinian physics and nuclear fission. (In a perfect counterpoint, as Destruction is alluding to the inevitability of these undesirable discoveries, the panel displays the face of Gaiman's best walking nightmare, the Corinthian. He is just about to feast on the vitreous humour within a nice pair of ape's eyes.) Unwilling to direct the changes science will cause, he concealed himself for centuries as an ordinary mortal before finally going to earth on a tiny Greek island (located a short distance from Lesbos, where the severed head of Orpheus, Dream's son, is guarded within a temple).

After being turned down by Despair and Desire, Delirium is finally joined by moping Dream, who feels like getting away from home for a while. Everything that follows takes its character from Delirium. She is the object of universal condescension. Even Destruction's talking dog patronizes her, for, being delirious, she is almost always incapable of following the thread of an ordinary conversation, much less an argument, she speaks in a series of non sequiturs; and her behavior is as giddy and unmediated as a four-year-old's. And like a child, Delirium cherishes excess, spontaneity, grand gestures, color, eccentricity, and excitement. So although it is the search for Destruction that drives the story, it is Delirium who drives the search and in doing so brings these qualities into the story.

In other words, *Brief Lives* is a wild ride, the high point of which takes place in a shabby strip club called Suffragette City as dancing Ishtar turns on the heat to an Iggy Pop record and gives a few louts the opportunity to sample the power of sacred, undebased sexuality before bringing the roof down on them. Before this moment of glorious and insightful power comes an artful skein of characters and incidents, but I will leave the reader to recall them wide-eyed and wondering, and return to my theme.

on mortality and change

Delirium's faithfulness and affection, not to mention her willpower, eventually lead the search to a successful conclusion, and Destruction is discovered in his island redoubt. People have been killed, buildings destroyed, lives ruined (poor nasty Officer Flaherty!) and called into question (poor ignorant Danny Capax!) that Delirium and Dream reach their destination. Ordinarily, our traveling pair would be sublimely indifferent to the confusion and suffering they have brought about, and Delirium clearly is unaffected – her own considerable confusion and suffering are quite enough. But Dream confesses that he felt compelled to continue the search in order to honor the death of a specific innocent (poor calculating Ruby!). Destruction points out that his brother's morality seems to have evolved, and Dream coldly denies this suggestion. It would amount to an acknowledgment of change, and he resists change.

The entire search has been conducted in resistance to change. Delirium does not merely want her brother back because she misses him, she wishes to restore the old order. She wants things back the way they used to be. Dream, less naive, merely wants things to remain as they are and assumes that they will do so. He sees Destruction's defection as no more than a shameful abdication of family responsibility. Destruction's response to this charge is a summary of the book's attitude toward change and a challenge to Dream's central attitudes.

In effect, Destruction says that the Endless do not exist. They are merely mythic patterns, and as such do not have the authority to interfere in human lives. The only one of them to survive this epoch in the ongoing story of the universe will be Death, who existed before life began. In time, mortals will cease to honor or accept the idea-patterns represented by the Endless, and another great change will overtake them. Gaiman is preparing us for the end of the Sandman tales, perhaps even for the end of the Sandman mythos itself – for a kind of death.

on mortality and change

Then, as if inadvertently, Destruction remembers a night – long ago and far away – when Death told him something that he still does not comprehend, that we all, Endless and human beings both, know everything that can be known. All knowledge – it must be assumed, I think, that knowledge is other than fact – exists within us. When he asked her why, then, did people, the Endless, and gods all keep on making ridiculous and painful mistakes, she answered: in order to make the knowledge bearable, we pretend not to possess it.

Dream just ignores this, it doesn't penetrate at all, but Delirium, who has perfectly understood Destruction's first point – that there is no such thing as a one-sided coin, that the believed requires the believer, that beginnings imply endings – understands this one, too. "Not knowing everything is all that makes it okay, sometimes," she says. This is true, it's wise and sad, but it depends for its truth on the coin's other side. Mortal humans possess the secrets known to gods, and these secrets are often painful. To negate the pain, men and gods forget, pretend to forget, then forget to pretend, but the great secret knowledge remains within, ready to be gained again, however partially. We share more than the brevity of life with the Endless.

on mortality and change

Finished with what he has to say, Destruction sails off into unknown alien realms, leaving Dream to acknowledge its accuracy by bringing about a great change precisely of the sort described. He must grant to his son, Orpheus, the literal death he had promised him long ago. When that has been accomplished he may return to his realm, so altered by heartache the Gryphon attendant on his door does not recognize him.

All of this action, emotion, and revelation is contained within a frame which contains in haikulike form the values and insights of the larger story.

This frame introduces and concludes the Orpheus story by focusing on his aged attendant, Andros, whose father held the same position, as did his grandfather, and so on, back for thousands of years. These mortals coexist with the divine, in full recognition of what that means. The first and last sentences of Brief Lives are Andros's – that is, they are the words of a man in close proximity to death. Andros begins this long, energetic, brilliant story by saying, "It is, of course, a miracle." The oxymoronic of course is pure Gaiman, anchoring the miraculous in dailiness. He concludes the story by saying the same thing in another way: "It is going to be a beautiful day." The sacred severed head has been buried, deep. All change is change for the worse. All change is change for the better. It's going to be, like every day, a beautiful day.

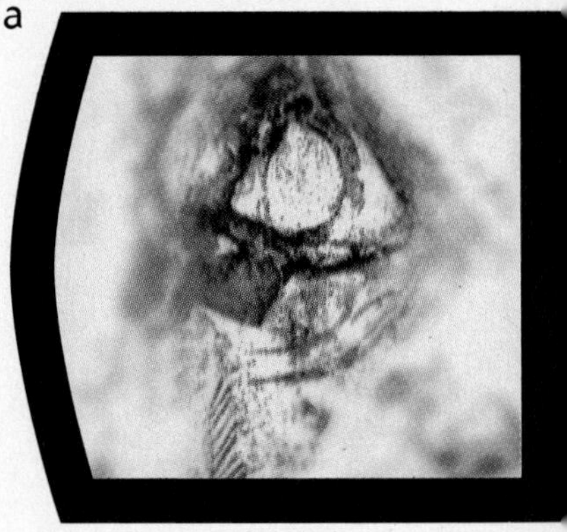

on mortality and change

Neil Gaiman is on a plane all his own. Nobody in his field is better than this. No one has as much range, depth, and command of narrative. Gaiman is a master, and his vast, roomy stories, filled with every possible shade of feeling, are unlike anyone else's.

If

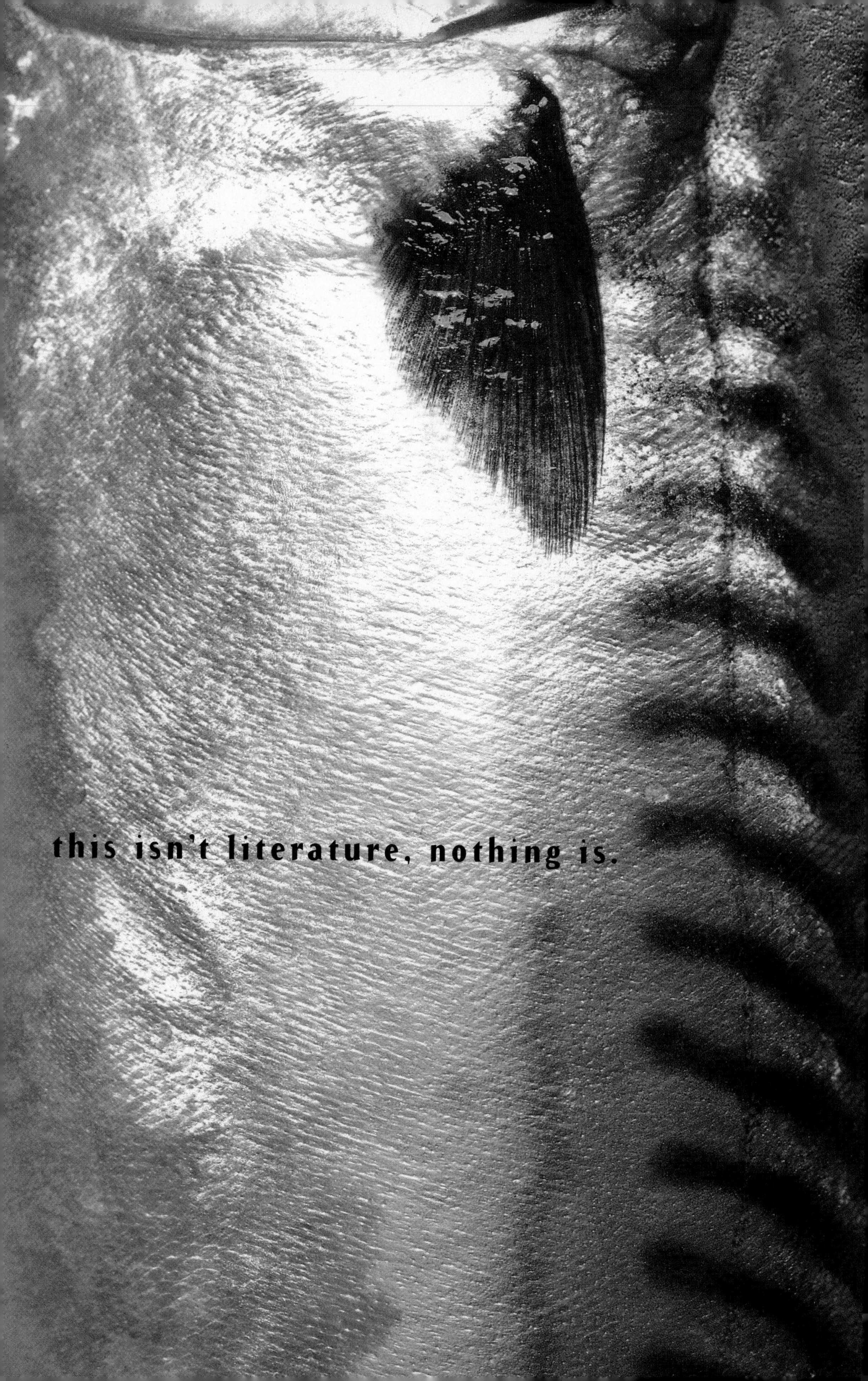
this isn't literature, nothing is.

bio GRAPHIES

RODNEY SPANDREL (b. 1911) -
Looked for love in all the wrong places.
Eventually found it where he'd left it.

NEIL GAIMAN (b. 1960) -
his dreams come only true

FISGARD ROSEMARSH (b. 1913) -
Drank too much, but gave freely to those less fortunate than himself.

RORY CHESS (b. 1912) -
Would obliquely refer, from time to tim[e] to the single sexual relationship in whi[ch] he had indulged, in Calcutta, during th[e] winter of 1929, but with whom, and what occurred, he would never say.

Biographies researched and written by Neil Gaiman. Photographic research by Dave McKean.

BUTTON NELSON (b.1949) -
Wrote a short book about his childhood, to be remembered forever. You have not read it, and you do not know anyone who has.

PETER STRAUB (b. 1943) -
Writes fine, fine novels.

DICK GIORDANO (b. 1932) -
Has retired in order to work more and harder.

VICTORIA SUNSHINE (b. 1947) - Died in 1963 with the reputation of having saved no fewer than twenty-eight lives from water and fire.

JILL THOMPSON (b. 1966) - Is a one-woman episode of *Talk Soup*.

SHELLY ROEBERG (b. 1966) - If only Snow White could tap-dance, she would want to be Shelly Roeberg (currently available in brunette, auburn, platinum, and honey-blonde.)

MANDY THURIBLE (b. 1601) - Terribly afraid of kittens.

KAREN BERGER (b. 1958) - Ever so slowly her jurisdiction will spread. She will eventually dominate the entire universe, whether she wishes it or not.

DAVE McKEAN (b. 1963) - Spawned a goblin and is wary of sheep.

VINCE LOCKE (b. 1966) - Is getting married, but still speaks little and listens much.

DAEDALUS HOOPER (b. 1914) - Sang sweet, sad songs of quiet lust and madness.

BOB KAHAN (b. 1954) - Makes fine galleries and strange books.

FRANK L. PRIVETT (b. 84 A.D.) - There are too many places to which he will now never return, but there are a number of places he has yet to visit.

S. HOTTES (b. 1951) - s still alive, but no longer nswers his telephone.

TODD KLEIN (b. 1951) - Sends calligraphed letters and hunts for certain old books, written for dead children.

DANNY VOZZO (b. 1963) - His future wife phoned him to ask if he was behind all the colors. That was how they met.

WOOLMER WHITE (b. 1950) - Not his real name.

JEREMIAH JOHN MAHONEY (b. 1952) - Collects butterflies.

The man in the mask swings a sword of bright stars
The cloud of his breath is the shroud of the earth.
But the man in the robe from a book reads our fears,
And ticks off the minutes from death until birth.

The woman in white is the mother of hope,
And the twin doves of peace rest on her twin breasts.
But the woman in black, with a knife and a rope,
Is the watcher at gateway, the guardian of ghosts.

Copyright © 1946 for The Estate of Henry Treece from

The Collected Poems of Henry Treece.

Reprinted by permission of John Johnson Ltd., London.